Exploring Matter AND Energy

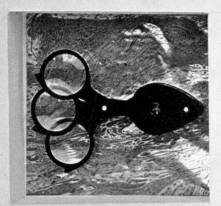

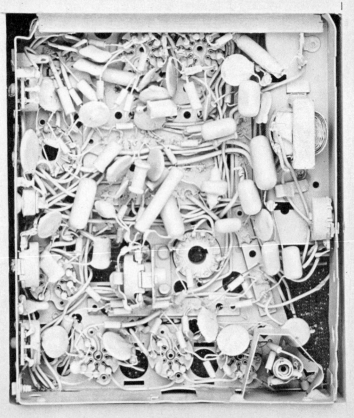

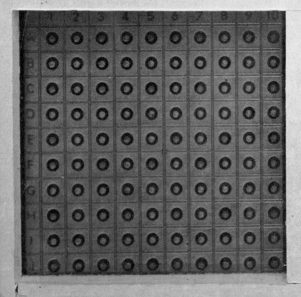

Exploring Matter AND Energy

MILO K. BLECHA
Professor of
Science Education
College of Education
University of Arizona

FRANKLIN G. FISK
Associate Professor of Science
and Teacher Education
Western Michigan University

JOYCE C. HOLLY
Science Coordinator/
Programmer
Jackson Public School System
Jackson, Mississippi

LAIDLAW BROTHERS • PUBLISHERS

A Division of Doubleday & Company, Inc.

RIVER FOREST, ILLINOIS

Irvine, California   Atlanta, Georgia   Dallas, Texas   Toronto, Canada

The Laidlaw Exploring Science Program

Exploring Science ORANGE   Exploring Science BROWN

Exploring Science GOLD   Exploring Science GREEN

Exploring Science BLUE   Exploring Science RED

Exploring Matter and Energy

Exploring Living Things

Project Director David W. Appenbrink / *Production Director* LaVergne G. Niequist / *Art Director* Gloria J. Muczynski / *Photo Researcher* William A. Cassin / *Staff Editors* Ronald A. Cwiak, Judith E. DeMichaels, J. David Johnson / *Production Supervisor* Marilyn Scheda / *Production Associates* Kathleen Kasper, Therese Reuteler / *Production Assistant* Jo Ann Hines / *Artists* John D. Firestone & Associates, Donald C. Meighan, Paul Hazelrigg / *Cover Design* Donald C. Meighan

ISBN 0-8445-5529-0

345678910111213 14 15   432109876   PRINTED IN THE UNITED STATES OF AMERICA

CONTENTS

UNIT **1**

ZEFA

SCIENCE

Something People Do

Some people think that science is just a lot of facts to learn and understand. But science is more than that. Science is a way of learning about the world around us.

Until the seventeenth century, thinking was believed to be the best way to learn about the world. Great thinkers, called philosophers [fuh-LAHS-(uh-)furz], *thought out explanations for questions such as, Why do things fall to the earth? and What is matter? The thinkers did not see any need to test their ideas by experimenting. Then in the seventeenth century, science had its real beginning. People began to learn about the world by doing things such as observing, measuring, explaining, and testing their ideas. Today, doing these things is believed to be the best way to learn about the world.*

Chapters

1. Observing
2. Measuring
3. Explaining
4. Testing

CHAPTER 1

Observing

"Look how thick it is."
"Can you hear it sizzle?"
"Wow, it really smells good."
"Wait'll you taste it!"
"Ouch! Be careful. It's really hot."

If you heard people saying things like this, would you think they were in a science class? Probably not. They would more likely be at a cookout. But at a cookout, in a science class, or anywhere else, people use their senses to find out about the things around them. This is called *observing* [uhb-ZURV-ihng].

This chapter is about observing and about the importance of observing in science. As you read the chapter, you will find out some things about your senses and about science. How do the senses help you learn about the world around you? Can you always trust your senses? You will have a chance to do some things that will make you a better observer. And you might find out that describing what you observe is not as easy as it sounds.

People use their senses all the time—even in school. What senses could these students use to find out what is inside the test tube?

De Wys, Inc.

USING YOUR SENSES

*What senses do people use to find out what's
   happening around them?*
What is the scientific method?
How are the senses fooled?

What's the sense?

Use your imagination for a minute. Picture in your mind some people doing the following things:

A cook is making soup. She wonders if it needs more salt. What is an easy way for the cook to find out?

A girl is walking to a friend's house. It is cool outside and she wishes she had worn a sweater. How does she know it's cool?

A mechanic is telling the owner of a car, "Your car's running fine now. But it needs a new muffler." How does the mechanic know?

A girl is saying to her friend, "I wish you hadn't gotten an extra slice of onion on your hamburger." Why, do you suppose, did she say that?

A man is admiring his wife's new dress. "That color really looks good on you," he says. How does he know?

Each person is doing something different. But in a way, they are all doing the same thing. They are using their senses to help them know what is going on in the world around them. That is, they are observing their environment.

All the senses are used in finding out about the world. However, the sense most used is seeing. People seem to rely more on their sense of seeing than on any other sense. That's why observing is often thought of as being the same as seeing. But, observing does not necessarily mean seeing. In a general way, to observe is to use any of the senses in getting information. You can observe that sugar tastes sweet or that a radio is playing in another room.

★ **Is seeing the sense used most by other animals?**

11

DO IT YOURSELF

Make an observation

Drop a seltzer tablet into a glass of water. Try to use all your senses in observing the changes that occur. Write on a sheet of paper what changes each sense observed, then answer the following questions: What kinds of changes took place? Did the tablet dissolve? Did the water change in temperature, taste, or color? Was any sound produced? When you finish, compare your list of observations with someone else's list.

Use your senses

How important are the senses? Just think, all that you know about the world around you comes to you through your senses. You, like the people in the examples, are always getting information through your senses of seeing, hearing, tasting, smelling, and feeling.

Look around. Your eyes help you see things that are all around you. Now close your eyes, and listen carefully. Your ears help you hear things. Your nose helps you smell things that are around you. Every time you eat, your tongue helps you taste the food in your mouth. When someone touches you, you are able to feel where you have been touched because of the nerves in your skin. The nerves in your skin can even warn you if something is very hot.

Some of your senses are "on duty" all the time. Even when you sleep, you can sometimes hear thunder or smell something cooking in the kitchen. So every day, every second of your life, you are finding out about the world around you through your senses.

But people do more than just see, hear, smell, taste, and feel. People also think, wonder, and imagine. Thinking, wondering, and imagining are different from using the senses. A person can do these things without using the senses.

Find Out More

Suppose some people told you that they had a sixth sense, or ESP. They might claim to be able to see another person's thoughts, or see objects or events at a distance too great to be seen, or even see into the future. Using different reference materials, find out more about ESP and how scientists try to test people who claim to have ESP powers.

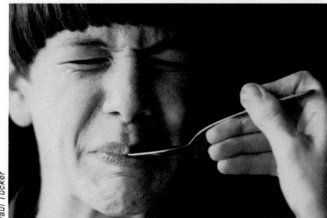

Figure 1–1. How are the people pictured here getting information about the world around them? What do you suppose they are learning about the world?

Barbara Van Cleve/Van Cleve Photography

The scientific method

All people use their senses, and all people think, wonder, and imagine. Of course, the term "all people" includes scientists. How, then, is what scientists do different from what other people do?

The main difference is in what scientists do after they observe something. They may try to observe the same event again to be sure they observed it correctly. They may check with other people to see if others observed the same thing. They may try to explain what they observed. Then they may test their explanation by setting

Figure 1–2. In the seventeenth century, Francis Bacon studied the way scientific knowledge is gained. He described four steps that scientists use in thinking about a problem. What is this way of thinking about a problem called?

up an experiment. They may use their explanation to predict what will happen in certain situations. So science is more than just observing, thinking, and wondering. Science is doing all these things and more.

The way scientists do their work is often called the *scientific method* [sy-uhn-TIHF-ihk MEHTH-uhd]. Trying to define the scientific method is not easy. It is easier to say what the scientific method is not. For one thing, the scientific method is not a formal procedure. It is not a detailed plan to explore the world around us. It does not promise that important discoveries will be made. Instead, the scientific method is a way of thinking about a problem or a question. This way of thinking helps guide scientists. It allows scientists to sort out all the information they get from their senses. The sorting-out of information helps scientists understand whatever problems or questions they are studying.

In the seventeenth century, Francis Bacon outlined four steps for learning. These steps were a way to describe the scientific method. This description included these steps:

1. Observe
2. Measure
3. Explain
4. Verify

Other people changed the steps. By the nineteenth century the scientific method was commonly described as having these six steps:

1. Ask a question or discover a problem.
2. Collect information by observing and measuring.
3. Present an explanation.
4. Predict new information by using the explanation.
5. Test the new information predicted.
6. Accept, reject, or change the explanation on the basis of the results of the test.

Describing the scientific method as a series of steps may be of some help in understanding the scientific method. But remember that the steps are only guides. Not every scientist follows these steps in perfect order. There are no rules about the kinds of questions that can be asked, or about how to observe, or about how an explanation is to be worded.

In other words, the scientific method alone cannot create scientific knowledge any more than a manual on how to paint pictures can create a work of art. The minds and talents of people are the real keys to learning about the world around us.

★ **The scientific method is the way scientists do their work. Can the scientific method be used by people other than scientists to do their work? Could you use the scientific method to repair your bicycle? Explain.**

Fooling the senses

A great deal of the work that scientists do depends on observing. Many scientists would say that seeing is one of the best ways to make observations. However, although the eyes may be the best senses to use for observing, the eyes can be fooled.

Did you know that you can look at something and not see everything that is there? Read the sentence inside the triangle in Figure 1–3 to yourself. Did you read, "She saw the birds sitting on the birdhouse"? Look at the triangle again, but this time read the sentence aloud. Point to each word as you say it. Did you notice some words the second time that you did not notice the first time?

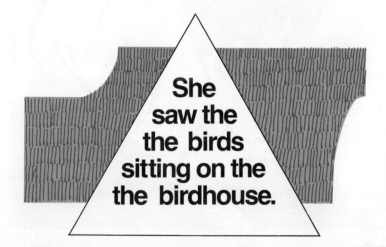

Figure 1–3. Sometimes you can understand the meaning of a sentence by reading the sentence quickly. How might reading quickly affect what you read inside the triangle?

Sometimes when you look at something, what you see is not really there. Have you ever looked down a long, straight road in the summer? If you have, you may have seen what looked like a puddle of water on the road. If you were to walk to the place where you thought the water was, it would not be there. Your sense of sight was fooled. The appearance of water would be what is called a *mirage* [muh-RAHZH]. A mirage is caused by hot air near the surface of the earth.

Now and then you might see something one way, then suddenly it appears to be another way. Look at Figure 1–4. Do you see a young girl with a feather in her hat? Or do you see an old woman? This picture shows that even when you look at one certain thing, you do not always see the same thing each time you look. Now

Figure 1–4. When looking at this picture, some people see an old woman. Others see a young woman. Which do you see? Can you see them both?

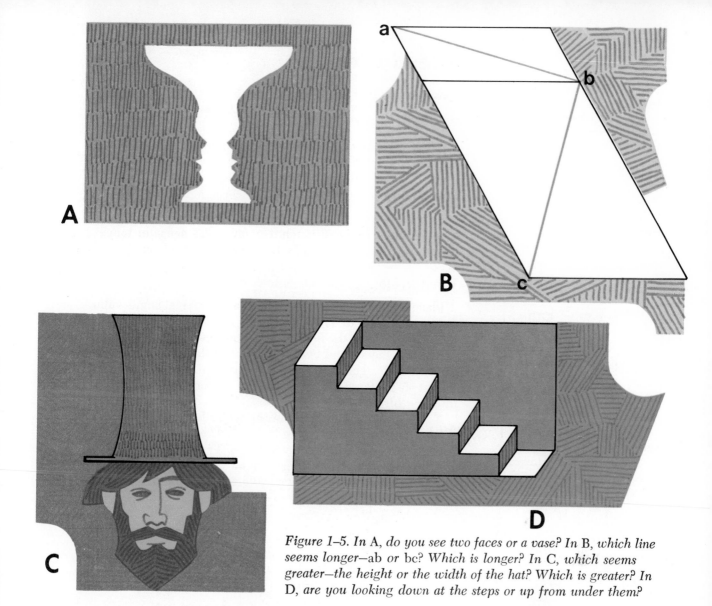

Figure 1–5. In A, do you see two faces or a vase? In B, which line seems longer—ab or bc? Which is longer? In C, which seems greater—the height or the width of the hat? Which is greater? In D, are you looking down at the steps or up from under them?

look at the diagrams in Figure 1–5. These are examples of diagrams that can fool your sense of seeing. Such diagrams are called *optical illusions* [AHP-tih-kuhl ihl-OO-zhuhnz]. These diagrams are only a few of the ways in which your sense of seeing can be fooled.

Is your sense of seeing the only sense that can be fooled? If not, what other senses do you think can be fooled? What are some ways to fool the other senses? How can you keep your senses from being fooled?

Investigate

How can you fool your sense of touch?

You Will Need

Celsius thermometer, burner, ring stand, ring clamp, wire gauze, 3 large beakers or bowls

Background

People are usually able to tell if something is hot or cold by using their sense of touch. However, the sense of touch is not always accurate. In fact, sometimes it fools us.

What to Do

Place 3 large beakers or bowls on a table. Heat some water to a temperature of 45°C (about 115°F). Pour some of the heated water into the first beaker. Pour some of the heated water into the second beaker. Add room-temperature water to the second beaker until the temperature of the water is 35°C (about 95°F). Pour room-temperature water (25°C or 75°F) into the third beaker.

Now, put your right hand in the water having a temperature of 45°C. Place your left hand in the 25°C water. Leave your hands in the water for thirty seconds. Then put both hands in the water having a temperature of 35°C. Observe and record whether the water feels hot or cold for each hand.

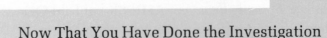

Now That You Have Done the Investigation

—Did the 35°C water feel hot or cold to your right hand after your hand had been in the 45°C water?
—Did the 35°C water feel hot or cold to your left hand after your hand had been in the 25°C water?
—How would you explain the results?

WHAT MAKES YOU CURIOUS?

*What is one reason why people want to learn
  about things?*
What made Joseph Black curious about snow?
*How might a woman's curiosity about wrinkles
  help doctors?*

Are you curious?

When was the last time you took some ice cubes from
the freezer to use in an iced drink? You probably have
done this many times. Did you ever wonder what happens when you put the ice in the drink? Why do the
ice cubes cool the drink? Why do the ice cubes melt so
slowly? How long does it take the cubes to melt? How
cold is the drink when the ice has melted?

If you wonder about what happens to ice after it is
put into a drink, you could say you are *curious* [KYUR-
ee-uhs]. Being curious simply means that you would like
to know more about something that you have seen or
done. You do not expect to gain anything by learning
more; you just want to know more to satisfy your
curiosity.

Being curious, or wanting to learn more, about the
world is the way scientists are. Many important discoveries in science have been made because a scientist
was curious about something that was observed. Being
a careful observer and being curious are important in
doing scientific work.

Of course, not every person is curious about the same
things. Often many people see the same thing, but not
everyone is curious about what they see.

★ **What things have you observed that made you
  curious?**

Curious about snow

The following story is about a person who observed
something that many other people also observed. This
person, however, became curious. About 200 years ago,

Joseph Black was walking along the street. The day was warm for a spring day, but there was still a lot of snow on the ground. Black thought it was odd that there was so much snow when the weather was very warm. No one else seemed to wonder about this. Everyone else seemed to think, "That is just the way it is with snow. Snow takes a while to melt." But Black was curious. He knew that snow melted at a temperature much lower than the temperature of the air that day.

Black's curiosity caused him to do some things. First he measured the temperature of the snow. The snow was cold. It was at the temperature at which snow normally melts—0°C (32°F). That temperature was low compared to that of the air—possibly 20°C (68°F). Now a new question needed answering. Why did the snow stay cold even though the air was warm and the snow was slowly melting?

Black's being curious about the snow led to a lot of experiments. During these experiments, Black discovered many new facts about heat and temperature. You might learn more about these facts in other science classes. For now, though, the facts are not important. For now, the important idea is that the facts were discovered because one person was curious about something that many people had observed but had not questioned.

★ **When a pot of water is put on a stove and the heat is turned on, does the water begin to boil right away? Is this similar to the observation made by Joseph Black? Explain.**

Wrinkles return

Another example of someone observing and being curious may turn out to be important in the field of medicine. You have probably observed that your skin becomes wrinkled when you have been in water for a long time. This story is about this kind of wrinkling.

A small child fell on a broken bottle, cutting one hand very badly. Some nerves in two fingers were cut. The child had little, if any, feeling in these fingers. The

(*Text continues on page 22.*)

Investigate

How does heat affect the temperature of ice and water?

You Will Need

large beaker, Celsius thermometer, ring stand, ring clamp, wire gauze, burner, ice cubes

Background

Adding heat to water will cause the water to become warmer. Adding heat to ice will cause the ice to melt. However, you might be surprised by the rate of temperature change for a mixture of water and ice as heat is added to the mixture.

What to Do

Place some ice cubes in a large beaker. Add a little water to the beaker. Stir the water and ice so they become well mixed. Use the thermometer to find the temperature of the mixture of ice and water. Now use the burner to add heat slowly to the ice water. Record the temperature at 1-minute intervals. Three minutes after the ice melts, stop adding heat.

Make a graph of your results. Use the sample of a graph shown below. Record the temperature on the vertical scale and time on the horizontal scale.

Now That You Have Done the Investigation

—For every minute that heat was added to the ice water, how did the temperature change?

—According to your graph, when did the temperature of the ice water increase? How would you explain the result?

—Was the result you observed for the change in temperature the result you expected? Why or why not?

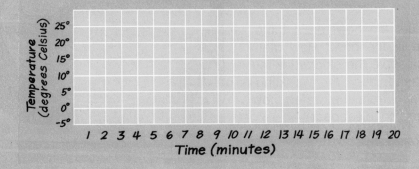

21

child's mother noticed that when the child bathed, the skin on the two fingers stayed smooth. It did not wrinkle as the other skin did.

As time passed, feeling began to return to the cut fingers. The mother noticed that the skin began to wrinkle on these fingers as well. She was curious and told her doctor of her observation. The doctor was curious, too, so he tested some other patients with similar damaged nerves. These patients had the same results. Their skin remained smooth after being in water. As the nerves healed, the wrinkling slowly returned.

The doctor wrote a report which stated that the simple test of soaking in water could turn out to be very important. Someday, doctors might be able to tell by the wrinkles (or by the lack of wrinkles) which nerves were damaged and how well the nerves were healing.

The two examples—melting snow and wrinkling skin—show some important things about being curious. Being curious starts with an observation. Being curious causes people to want to find out more about the world.

Not all people who are curious are scientists. But being curious is a characteristic most scientists have. Scientists see the same things that others see. But because scientists are curious, they ask important questions about the things they observe. In trying to answer these questions, scientists often discover new facts about our environment.

DO IT YOURSELF

Observe the wrinkles that form when your hand is placed in warm water

Fill a bowl with warm water. Set the bowl on a table or a counter, and put your hand in the bowl. How many minutes does it take before you observe the skin wrinkling on your hand? Where, on your hand, does the wrinkling occur? After you remove your hand from the water, how long does it take for the wrinkling to disappear?

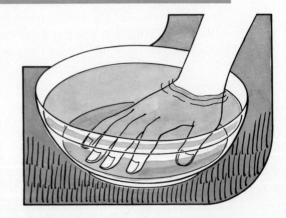

WATCH WHAT YOU SAY

Why is it important to describe observations carefully?

What is an inference?

What may be used to help the senses in making good observations?

Making an observation

Do you remember the story of Henny-Penny? You might be surprised to hear about that kind of story in a science book. But that story has an important message for people who are learning about what scientists do.

In the story, Henny-Penny told everyone that the sky was falling. She "knew" it was happening because she felt a "piece of the sky" hit her head. Henny-Penny would not have been a good scientist. For one thing, she was not a good observer. If she had been, she would have noticed that the "piece of the sky" looked very much like an acorn.

Henny-Penny jumped to a conclusion. That is, she did not check out the information she had gotten through her senses. Scientists try to follow certain rules in checking out such information. Some of these rules are as follows:

1. Whenever you can, make a second observation. What you sensed the first time might seem different the second time.
2. If possible, have someone else observe with you.
3. If you can, make the observation from more than one place. Sometimes you can be too far away to make a good observation. Or, you may be too close. Or, perhaps you could observe better from a different direction.

> ★ How would the story of Henny-Penny be different if Henny-Penny had used the rules for observing listed above? Do you think science would be as far advanced as it is if scientists jumped to conclusions the way Henny-Penny did?

Investigate

What can you learn about a familiar object by a careful observation of the object?

You Will Need

flowering plant, wristwatch, ball-point pen

Background

Like everyone else, scientists use their senses to learn about the world. Because scientists want information that is accurate, they try to make very careful observations. One way in which scientists make their observations more useful is by paying close attention to all important details. Some of the details that could be noticed are: size, shape, amount, color, sound, temperature, and weight.

What to Do

Choose a familiar object from those needed for this investigation. Observe the object carefully, and write down all the details you can. Try to look for details you have not noticed before.

If you have been observing the flowering plant, there are certain things to observe: Are all parts of the plant alike? What is the shape of the plant's leaves? Is the stem smooth or hairy?

If you have been observing the wristwatch, there are certain things to observe: Are numerals or marks used for the hours? How is the watch connected to the bracelet? How thick is the watch?

If you have been observing the ball-point pen, there are certain things to observe: What kind of material is used for each part of the pen? How long is the pen?

Now That You Have Done the Investigation

—From the list of details you wrote down for each familiar object, which are details that you had never noticed before?

—Why do you think you did not notice these details before?

—What could you do to help yourself notice important details from now on?

Making inferences

Henny-Penny did not make a good observation. And she did some things that made the situation worse. She reached a conclusion using a bad observation. That is, she made an *inference* [IHN-f(uh-)ruhn(t)s] using her observation. And, she stated her inference as a fact. Making an inference about an observation is not necessarily wrong. But a person should be sure that he or she knows the difference between an observation and an inference. Also, the person should be reasonably sure that the observation is good. Look at the drawings in Figure 1–6. In each case the people observe the same thing. But each makes a different inference.

Figure 1–6. What observation did each person make in the drawing on the left? In the drawing on the right? What inferences were made by each person? Do you know which inferences were correct? Explain.

Knowing the difference between an observation and an inference can help you be a careful thinker. If you are careful, you will not state any inference as a fact, the way Henny-Penny did. (Look at all the trouble she got herself and her friends into by stating her inference as a fact.) More important, you will be able to recognize the difference between observations and inferences in what you see and hear in your daily life.

DO IT YOURSELF

Observing and inferring

Look at the picture. Then tell whether each sentence below is something that is observed or that is inferred.
1. There are three plants shown.
2. It doesn't rain much here.
3. There are no water puddles on the ground.
4. The air is very hot.
5. A man is wiping his face with a rag.
6. The burro will need water soon.

Many times people make inferences without even realizing it. Have you ever heard of a UFO? The letters stand for *U*nidentified *F*lying *O*bject. UFO is a term that is often used for any observation of something in the sky that cannot easily be explained.

Many books and articles have been written about UFO's. Some people believe they are spaceships with beings from other planets. Some people think that most of the sightings of UFO's can be explained in terms of well-known events.

No matter what people believe or think about UFO's, using the name UFO is an inference. Suppose that a person sees strange lights in the sky and reports seeing a UFO. This infers that what was observed was unidentified, was flying, and was an object. Maybe what was seen was simply light reflecting off some low clouds.

Because the name UFO infers "flying" and "object," some scientists who are studying UFO's want to stop using the letters UFO. They would rather just use the letter U for unidentified. Calling an observation in the sky a U would not be inferring that the U was flying and was an object.

★ **What is the difference between an observation and an inference?**

Helping the senses

Good observations are important to scientists. In fact, good observations are so important that scientists often use instruments to aid the senses. Instruments are used to extend the senses, to keep the senses from being fooled, and to detect observations that cannot be detected by the senses. After all, there are limits to a person's senses. Some instruments change these limits. A telescope, for example, helps a person see farther. A microscope helps a person see tiny objects.

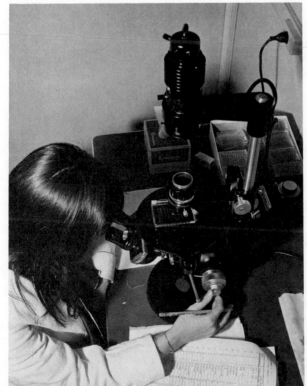

Figure 1–7. What are the names of the instruments shown here? How do these instruments help scientists make observations?

Photo Research International

Daniel Brody

M. Nissen/ZEFA

Figure 1–8. Why is a thermometer better than the sense of feeling for finding temperature? Can any person's senses detect the radio waves that the antennas detect? Why does a scientist use an electron microscope?

Find Out More

Scientists have developed many instruments to help them measure accurately such details as temperature, brightness, loudness, and weight. Use reference materials to find out more about the many different kinds of science instruments and how they are used.

Other instruments help keep our senses from being fooled. A thermometer is a way to find out temperature. A thermometer is not "fooled" by going from hot water to cold water as your sense of touch was in the "Investigate" on page 18.

Another use of instruments is to detect things that the human senses do not detect. We are surrounded by radio waves all the time. But we cannot detect them with our senses. We use an instrument called a radio receiver, or simply a radio, to detect these waves.

Good instruments can be a big help to scientists. But remember, instruments only help make observations. Instruments do not explain what is observed. People must explain and make inferences about what they observe. Making observations, explanations, and inferences are important parts of what scientists do.

Observations—Important in Many Jobs

Many people have to make careful observations as part of their job. In fact, observing is part of every job. But observations must be made with greater care in some jobs than in others.

The job of Air Traffic Controller requires very careful observations. The safety of many people depends on Air Traffic Controllers. Using equipment such as radio, radar, and computers, controllers watch the flight of each plane flying in their assigned area. They notify pilots if changes in course are needed to avoid accidents.

Weather forecasting also requires careful observations. The weather is often very changeable. Observing, recording, and analyzing these changes can be important to the safety of many people. When hurricanes and other violent storms begin to develop, for example, the National Weather Service sends out warnings so that people can find protection. Careful observations are needed so that accurate predictions and warnings may be made.

Farmers also make many careful observations in growing crops and raising livestock. They need to observe the weather, the soil, the growth of new plants, and the condition of their animals. For example, for plants to grow well, they must be cultivated. They must be sprayed to protect them from insects and weeds. Farmers can tell when these things must be done by observing the condition of the soil and of the plants.

Some day you will make observations as part of your job. What kind of a job would you like? What kinds of observations do you think you will have to make in the job you like?

Grant Heilman

What kinds of observations do you think are important in growing crops? What jobs do you know of that require no observations?

29

Reviewing and Extending

SUMMING UP

1. People use their senses to help them know what is going on in the world around them. This is called observing.
2. You get information through your senses of seeing, hearing, tasting, smelling, and feeling.
3. The way scientists do their work is often called the scientific method.
4. Although the eyes may be the best senses to use for observing, the eyes can be fooled.
5. Being curious simply means that you would like to know more about something that you have seen or done.
6. Scientists try to follow certain rules in describing observations.
7. An inference is a conclusion a person may reach about an observation.
8. Scientists often use instruments to aid the senses.

CHECKING UP

Vocabulary   Write the numerals *1–5* on your paper. Each numbered phrase describes a term from the following list. On your paper, write the term next to the numeral of the phrase that describes it.

observing	scientific method	mirage
curious	explanation	inferring

1. caused by hot air
2. wanting to know more about something
3. reaching a conclusion
4. way scientists do their work
5. using the senses to find out things

Knowledge and Understanding   Write the numerals *6–10* on your paper. Beside each numeral, write the word or words that best complete the sentence having that numeral.

6. Most people seem to rely more on their sense of (*seeing, tasting, smelling*) than on any other sense.
7. Observing is often thought of as being the same as (*inferring, seeing, being curious*).
8. The appearance of water on a road in summer is called (*a mirage, an optical illusion, an inference*).
9. Good observations are so important that scientists often use (*inferences, instruments, questions*) to aid the senses.
10. The first step of the scientific method is to (*infer, explain, observe*).

Concepts Beside each of the numerals *11–14* on your paper, write the word or words that best complete the sentence having that numeral.

11. To observe is to use (*only the eyes, none of the senses, any of the senses*) in getting information.
12. The scientific method is a (*way of thinking about a problem, formal procedure, detailed plan to explore the world*).
13. Being curious means that you (*want to learn more to make money, would like to know about some things, make inferences about things you observe*).
14. An inference (*should always be stated as a fact, is a conclusion based on observations, is a way to collect information*).

Application and Critical Thinking Answer the following questions as briefly as you can without leaving out any important ideas.

15. Suppose you are eating breakfast. Make a list of five senses, and tell at least one way each sense might be used as you eat your breakfast.
16. Look at the picture. Then determine whether each sentence is an observation or an inference.

   a. The spaceship is going to the moon.
   b. The spaceship is in space.
   c. The spaceship is going very fast.
   d. There are stars in space.
   e. There are three planets visible.

DOING MORE

1. Place an object in a small box. Seal the box with tape so the box cannot easily be opened. Have classmates try to describe the object in the box without opening the box. Have them record their descriptions. Also have them tell what information they used as a basis for their description and what senses they used to obtain the information.
2. Make a bulletin-board display that would show one or more of the following topics: (1) the five senses, (2) steps used in the scientific method, (3) mirages and optical illusions, (4) things that many people are curious about, or (5) different kinds of instruments that are used to help the senses.

CHAPTER 2

Measuring

"Look at that! Collins must have hit the ball a mile."

"Chris! Aren't you ready to leave? Do you need all day to comb your hair?"

How often have you heard sentences like these? Probably many times. In one sentence an amount of distance is used to describe something. In the other an amount of time is used. Because of the amounts used, you get the idea that the ball went a long way and that some people take a long time to comb their hair. Each sentence is a general way of describing something that happened.

To a scientist, such a general description is often not good enough. A scientist wants to know more accurately, How far? or How much time? Answers to these questions are found by comparing the unknown amounts with known amounts. This is called *measuring* [MEHZH-(uh-)rihng]. The known amounts used in comparing are called *units* [YOO-nuhts] of measure.

This chapter is about measuring and units used in measuring. You will get a chance to learn about some units that are easy to use. And you might also learn how to make certain kinds of measurements.

© 1974 United Feature Syndicate, Inc.

At first, using unfamiliar units for measuring seems confusing. What units that these girls are talking about are unfamiliar to you?

WHAT IS MEASURING?

Why is measuring important?
Can you tell how tall a person is by comparing
that person with another person?
How are units used in measuring things?
Why must units used in measuring things be
familiar to all people?

Measuring is important

Measuring is something people have been doing for a long time. Even in early civilizations, people had to measure. In some ways, their reasons for measuring were much like our reasons today. Measuring has always been needed for buying, selling, and trading. Without some way of measuring, how could a person be sure of getting a fair deal?

There is one use of measuring today that was not important to early civilizations. Today, measuring is important in science. In fact, measuring is essential in science. Measuring is one of the most important things scientists do in learning about the world. The more you study science, the more you will understand why measuring is important in science.

★ **What are some things that are bought or sold by the pound, the gallon, or the yard?**

Making comparisons

Every day, almost every person does some kind of measuring. For example, you might measure the amount of time you are in school. You might measure the amount of food you give your pet. You might measure the air pressure in a bicycle tire. These kinds of measuring do not seem very hard to do. You may think you already know all you need to know about measuring. But, as you study about measuring, you may learn some things you did not know before. You will find out, for example, that making comparisons is a kind of measuring.

Find Out More

In early civilizations, people bought, sold, and traded all kinds of things. Buying, selling, and trading made measuring necessary. Use reference materials, such as encyclopedias, school books, and library books, to help you find out what some of these things were and how they were measured.

33

Larry P. Trone

Figure 2–1. By looking at these pictures, what can you tell about the height of each of these people?

Look at the people in Figure 2–1. You can find out a little about each person by looking at the pictures. Two persons have dark hair. The other one has light hair. Two are boys. One is a girl. These are just some of the observations you can make about each person.

Just from these pictures, however, can you tell anything about the height of the people? Can you tell which is the tallest? Which is the shortest? Are they all the same size? Just by looking at the pictures, there is no way to know the answers to these questions.

34

Now look at the people in Figure 2–2. The same three people are all together. In this picture, you can compare their heights. Now you can see that the girl is taller than the boys. The light-haired boy is the shortest. When you compare like this, you can see which person is tallest and which is shortest. In a way, this is measuring. But you still do not know just how tall any of the people are. You have only compared the heights of three people.

Figure 2–2. When you see the three people from Figure 2–1 standing together, you can easily tell which is tallest and which is shortest. But how tall is each person?

Larry P. Trone

165 cm
155 cm
145 cm

65 in
63 in
61 in
59 in
57 in
55 in

Larry P. Trone

Figure 2–3. In order to tell how tall a person is, you compare that person's height with a known amount of distance. How tall are the people pictured here?

Look at Figure 2–3. Behind the people you can see lines showing measured distances above the ground. From this picture you can compare each person's height with a known amount of distance. You could now tell someone just how tall the girl is. Other people wouldn't know much about the girl's height if you said, "She's taller than Mike," unless they knew Mike. But if you said, "She's 165 centimetres tall," or "She's about 65 inches tall," they could use a ruler or a tape measure to find just how tall 165 centimetres, or 65 inches, is.

Measuring, then, is comparing some observed property, such as height, with a certain known amount, such as a centimetre or an inch. The known amount is called a unit. In order for measuring to have any meaning, the units have to be the same for everybody.

★ **What are some examples of things people generally do not measure, but instead compare to other things?**

Using units to measure

When you use units to measure, you are finding out how many times the unit will "fit into" whatever it is you are measuring. The girl in the picture is 165 centimetres (about 65 inches) tall. That is, 165 one-centimetre-long (or 65 one-inch-long) units placed end to end would equal a distance that was the same as the distance from the ground to the top of her head.

Sometimes you do put unit amounts end to end to measure distance. If you wanted to find how long a room is, for example, you might use a ruler. You could lay the ruler down, mark where the end is, then move the ruler and continue marking and moving the ruler until you have gone all the way across the room. By doing this, you would see how many ruler lengths "fit into" the length of the room.

Of course, most of the time, measuring is not done in such a bothersome way. An easier way would be to use a long tape measure. On the tape measure, the units are already marked. But whether you measure with a ruler or a tape measure, you are doing the same thing. You are finding out how many unit lengths can fit into the length you are measuring.

In measuring amounts other than length, the same idea is used. A runner finishes a race, for example, in 11.5 seconds. When the timer uses a watch to measure the time, the timer is really seeing how many seconds fit into the time it takes the runner to finish the race.

Two important points to remember about measuring are these: (1) Measuring is finding out how many times a known amount (called a unit) will fit into the unknown amount you are measuring. (2) In order for one person to tell another about the results of measuring, the units used must be familiar to both people.

For You to Think About

What units would you use to measure the distance from the point of a pencil to the end of the pencil, the distance across a room, and the distance from one city to another? Would the units you use be the same size, or would they be different? For what reason would the units used be the same size? For what reason would they be different?

DO IT YOURSELF

Using units in measuring

Using your shoe as a unit, measure the distance across the room. This may be done by standing against the wall with the heel of your right shoe against the wall. The heel of your left shoe is placed against the right shoe's toe. Then move the right shoe in front of the left. Count each time one shoe is placed in front of the other. Record the number of shoes that "fit into" the distance across the room. Now have a classmate measure the distance across the room in the same way. Was the measure of the distance across the room you made the same as that made by your classmate? Is a shoe useful to use in measuring distances? Explain.

SYSTEMS OF UNITS

What two systems of units are in use in the United States?
What are some units of the English system?
What are some SI units?
Why is SI preferred to the English system?

Measurement today

In measuring, the units to be used are very important. Most people in the United States use units commonly called English units. Some English units you know for measuring length are inch, foot, yard, and mile.

Units for measuring length are only part of a larger group of units. Other units in the group can be used for measuring other amounts, such as time. The whole group of units that are related to each other is called a *system* [SIHS-tuhm] of units. The system most used in the United States now is commonly called the English system.

The English system got its name because it was started in England. When the British Empire was worldwide, the

Figure 2–4. Today, many items that you can buy in a store are marked in English units and in SI units. How would you use packages like these to tell how a gram is related to an ounce?

English system was used in many places, including the United States. As years passed, most countries—including England—stopped using the English system because a new and better system had been developed. However, the English system is still used by most people in the United States.

Using two different systems causes some confusion in trading between countries. Because the system used by most other countries has many advantages, plans are being made to change to this system in the United States. Even now, many cans and boxes in stores have their weight or capacity recorded in units of both systems.

The other system is called the International System of Units. It is abbreviated SI in all languages. SI, sometimes called the metric system, is used by scientists everywhere. It is also used for business and industry in nearly every country except the United States. In fact, SI is used throughout the world, including England. It is simpler to use and easier to remember than the English system.

★ **Why do some cans and boxes in grocery stores have their weight or capacity recorded in units of both systems?**

For You to Think About

If the metric system is easier to use than the English system, why hasn't the United States completely converted to the metric system?

39

Units of the English system

Some units of length in the English system are the inch, the foot, the yard, and the mile. The following list shows how these units are related:

$$12 \text{ inches} = 1 \text{ foot}$$
$$3 \text{ feet } (36 \text{ inches}) = 1 \text{ yard}$$
$$1{,}760 \text{ yards } (5{,}280 \text{ feet}) = 1 \text{ mile}$$

The *volume* [VAHL-yuhm] of an object, or piece of matter, is the amount of space the matter takes up. Volume is usually represented by cubic units of length. For example, a truckload of sand might be described in cubic yards.

The amount of space inside a container is its *capacity* [kuh-PAS-uht-ee]. Some units of capacity in the English system are the fluidounce, the pint, the quart, and the gallon. The following list shows how these units are related:

$$16 \text{ fluidounces} = 1 \text{ pint}$$
$$2 \text{ pints } (32 \text{ fluidounces}) = 1 \text{ quart}$$
$$4 \text{ quarts} = 1 \text{ gallon}$$

Other units of capacity are also used. One measure of liquids is the barrel, and one measure of solids is the bushel.

Some units of weight in the English system are the ounce, the pound, and the ton. (Note that the term "ounce" is very much like the term "fluidounce," a unit of capacity.) Ounces, pounds, and tons are related in the following way:

$$16 \text{ ounces} = 1 \text{ pound}$$
$$2{,}000 \text{ pounds} = 1 \text{ ton}$$

★ **What numerical relationship, if any, can you see in the way basic units in the English system are related?**

SI units

In SI, the unit of length is the *metre* [MEET-ur]. The symbol for metre is m. This unit of length was adopted

Figure 2–5. In the coming years, you will see more and more signs that give distances in kilometres. How is a kilometre related to a mile?

by the National Assembly of France in 1795. Later, the amount of length called one metre was marked off on a metal bar. The bar was then placed in a container in a town near Paris, France. This length was declared to be the standard unit of length. Copies of this bar were sent to governments all over the world.

Prefixes are used to extend the use of the metre for lengths that are much greater or much smaller than a metre. For lengths much greater than a metre, the term *kilometre* [KIHL-uh-MEET-ur] is used. The symbol for kilometre is km. The prefix "kilo-" means 1 000. So a kilometre is 1 000 metres. For lengths very much less than a metre, the terms *decimetre* [DEHS-uh-MEET-ur] (symbol dm), *centimetre* [SEHNT-uh-MEET-ur] (symbol cm), and *millimetre* [MIHL-uh-MEET-ur] (symbol mm) may be used. "Deci-" means 1/10, or 0.1. So a decimetre is 0.1 metre. "Centi-" means 1/100, or 0.01. So a centimetre is 0.01 metre. "Milli-" means 1/1 000, or 0.001. So a millimetre is 0.001 metre. Although the term "decimetre" is described here, it is not used very often.

41

Figure 2–6. *A litre is 1 000 cubic centimetres.*
Is a litre more than a quart or less than a quart?
How can you tell?

Volume of cube is 1 cm³

Find Out More

The standard metre was not adopted until 1795. Use reference materials, such as encyclopedias, library books, and school books, to find out more about who established the standard metre, where it was first established, and what was used to represent the length of the standard metre.

As shown below, all SI units of length are related by some power of ten. That is, you can change from one unit to another by multiplying or dividing by ten. Sometimes you need to multiply or divide more than once.

$$10 \text{ millimetres} = 1 \text{ centimetre}$$
$$10 \text{ centimetres} = 1 \text{ decimetre}$$
$$10 \text{ decimetres} = 1 \text{ metre}$$
$$100 \ (10 \times 10) \text{ centimetres} = 1 \text{ metre}$$
$$1\,000 \ (10 \times 10 \times 10) \text{ millimetres} = 1 \text{ metre}$$
$$1\,000 \ (10 \times 10 \times 10) \text{ metres} = 1 \text{ kilometre}$$

Volume may also be given in SI units. One way of stating volume is in cubic metres, with the symbol m³. For small volumes, such as doses of medicine, cubic centimetres, with the symbol cm³, may be used.

A unit of capacity that you will probably use in the future is the *litre* [LEET-ur]. The symbol for litre is l. The same prefixes used with metre may also be used with litre. See Figure 2–6 for examples that show about how big these units of volume and capacity are.

Advantages of SI

Using SI has certain advantages over using the English system. People often make mistakes when changing from one unit to another in the English system. One reason for some mistakes is that you must divide or multiply by numbers other than ten. For example, you must multiply by 12 to change from feet to inches. In SI, changing from one unit to another is done by multiplying or dividing by a power of ten. Multiplying or dividing by ten may be done by simply moving the decimal point.

Suppose that the length of a pencil is 14 centimetres. This amount could also be written as 0.14 metre or as 140 millimetres. The amount may be written either way because units of length in SI are related by powers of ten.

Another advantage of SI is that the same prefixes are used with all kinds of units. The prefix milli- always means 1/1 000, or 0.001. A millimetre is 0.001 metre and a millilitre (ml) is 0.001 litre. Kilo- always means 1 000. A kilometre is 1 000 metres and a kilolitre (kl) is 1 000 litres. These prefixes and others are used with all units in SI. With a little practice, you should be able to use SI units quite easily. Throughout this book, SI units will be used so you will become more familiar with them.

★ **Which is easier—changing kilometres to metres or miles to yards? Why do you think so?**

DO IT YOURSELF

Use SI

Measure distance by using a metre stick. Practice using the metre stick by measuring the width of a tabletop. List your measurement in metres, centimetres, and millimetres. Area is found by multiplying the length by the width. What is the area of the tabletop?

Measure volume by using a graduated cylinder. Practice using the graduated cylinder by measuring the volume of a marble. To do this, place some water in a graduated cylinder. The volume of the water is indicated by the level of the water in the cylinder. Record this volume. Then, place the marble in the water. The level of the water changes. The new level indicates the volume of the water plus the volume of the marble. Record this new volume. If you subtract the original volume of the water from the new volume of the water plus the marble, you will obtain the volume of the marble. Write the volume of the marble in millilitres and litres.

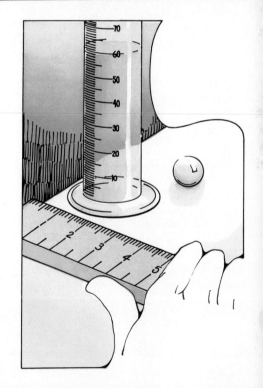

MEASURING MASS AND DENSITY

Why is volume not a measure of the amount of matter in an object?

What is used to measure mass?

What can be used to explain why objects sink in water? Why objects float in water?

Measuring mass

Scientists are often interested in finding out just how much matter is present in a certain object. But how can an amount of matter be measured? Volume is not a good measure of the amount of matter in an object. The space that a certain amount of matter takes up can change. For example, a large volume of air can be squeezed into a small space. Also, solids expand and contract when they are heated and cooled. In these examples, the volume, or size, changes, although the amount of matter does not change.

As long as 7,000 years ago, people must have known that volume was not a good way to measure an amount of matter. At that time they had found a way to measure amounts of matter that did not depend on volume. In an ancient Egyptian tomb—possibly 7,000 years old—scientists found a small *equal-arm balance* [BAL-uhn(t)s]. See Figure 2–7. The balance is a bar carved of stone. With the bar are several small, carefully made stones. Scientists think that this balance was used for carefully measuring amounts of gold dust or gold nuggets. Even then, goldsmiths knew that the balance was the best way to find out how much gold was in a pile of gold dust or in an odd-shaped nugget.

The balance works like this. The bar is hung from a loop at the middle of the bar. The bar then has "arms" of equal length on each side. When nothing is hanging on either arm, the bar is level. Hanging an object on one arm causes the bar to slant. The bar could be made level again, or be balanced, by hanging other pieces of matter from the other arm.

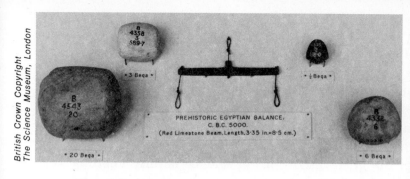

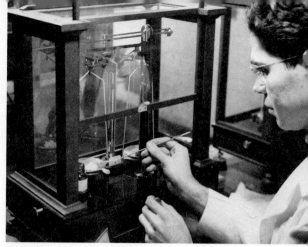

Figure 2–7. One of the earliest balances known is shown next to a modern balance. How are they alike? How are they different?

The balance is not affected by the shape or by the size of the object hung on it. The balance responds to something quite different than shape or size. What the balance responds to is called *mass,* or amount of matter.

Suppose a certain amount of gold just balances a piece of wood, which in turn just balances a piece of iron. We say that each piece of matter has the same mass. An equal-arm balance is a way of comparing masses of matter. The shape or size of the matter is not important.

Today, scientists use balances that are more accurate than the one found in the Egyptian tomb. But the principles on which many of today's balances work are the same. That is, masses are compared with each other.

Comparing masses with each other is not exactly the same as measuring masses. Remember, comparing is measuring only if an unknown amount is compared with some known amount, or unit. As with the unit for length, the unit for mass is decided on by people. Any mass can be chosen. But the unit must be agreed upon. An agreed-upon SI unit of mass is the *gram* (g).

As with other SI units, prefixes are used for amounts that are greater and smaller than the gram. For example, a kilogram (kg) is 1 000 grams, and a milligram (mg) is 0.001 gram.

Weight

The terms "mass" and "weight" are sometimes used incorrectly. In science, remembering that mass and weight are not the same is important. But what is the difference between them? You know that the mass of an object is the amount of matter in that object. The next paragraph describes what weight is. When you know what mass is and what weight is, you will be able to describe the difference between them.

One of the great discoveries in science is this: There is a force of attraction between all pieces of matter. The force is called *gravitational attraction* [GRAV-uh-TAY-shnuhl uh-TRAK-shuhn]. The force of attraction between two objects depends on their masses. The greater their masses, the greater the force of attraction between them. The earth has a very large mass. So the force of attraction between the earth and another object on or near the earth is easily noticed. This force is called the *weight* of the object.

It is true that on the earth, the more mass an object has, the more weight it has. But mass and weight are not the same. If you could take an object far away from the earth—say, out in space—the attraction between the object and the earth (the object's weight) would be less. But the amount of matter in the object (its mass) would be the same.

In the United States, people have used the units pounds and ounces to measure weight. Now that SI is coming into use, people will become familiar with other units. For example, they will become familiar with a unit of force called the *newton* [N(Y)OOT-uhn]. A pound is an amount of force that is about 4.45 newtons. If your weight is 80.0 pounds, in SI units you would weigh 356 newtons.

$$80.0 \text{ pounds} \times 4.45 \text{ newtons/pound} = 356 \text{ newtons}$$

Explaining density

Suppose you are holding two closed boxes of equal size, one in your right hand and one in your left hand. Suppose that one box is full of rocks and the other is full of feathers. It is very easy to tell which box has rocks in it and which has feathers. The box of rocks feels heavier.

But now suppose that each box is not full. Suppose, too, that one box has one kilogram of rocks in it. The other has one kilogram of feathers. The masses of the two boxes are the same. Is the weight of the rocks more than the weight of the feathers? If you say that they are equal in weight, you are correct. If the boxes are closed and the rocks and feathers are spread out evenly, you may not be able to tell which box has rocks in it and which has feathers. But, if you could see inside the boxes, you would see that a kilogram of rocks takes up a lot less space than a kilogram of feathers.

As the example shows, mass alone is not enough to tell one kind of matter from another. However, by comparing the mass to volume ratio (mass/volume) of one kind of matter with that of another, you can tell one kind of matter from the other. Some examples for which this comparing has been made are shown in Figure 2–8.

Notice that mass/volume ratio of water is 1.0 gram per cubic centimetre. Notice, also, that some ratios are greater than 1.0 and some are less than 1.0. The mass/volume ratio of gold is 19.3 times that of water. Dry pine wood has a mass/volume ratio only half that of water. The mass/volume ratio is called *density* [DEHN(T)-suht-ee].

★ **What other substances have a density less than that of water? How could you find out?**

For You to Think About

Solid matter that has a density greater than that of water sinks in water. Matter with a density less than that of water floats in water. Ice floats in water. What does this tell you about the density of ice as compared with that of water? A glass marble sinks. How does the density of glass compare with that of water?

MASS AND MASS/VOLUME RATIO OF VARIOUS SUBSTANCES AT 15°C

Substance	Mass (g)	Volume (cm³)	Mass/Volume Ratio (g/cm³)
Water (pure)	10	10	1.0
Water (sea)	10.3	10	1.03
Gold	193	10	19.3
Gasoline	6.6	10	0.66
Cooking oil	9.2	10	0.92
Lead	114	10	11.4
Iron	78	10	7.8
Limestone (rock)	27	10	2.7
Aluminum	27	10	2.7
Dry pine wood	5	10	0.5

Figure 2–8. The mass/volume ratio of a number of substances is given here. Which of the substances on this list would float on water? How do you know?

47

Determining density

All matter has density. Each kind of matter has a certain density. To find the density of any matter, the volume and the mass of the matter must be known. Once the mass and the volume are known, the density can be found by dividing the measure of the matter's mass by the measure of its volume. The following formula shows you how to find the density of any matter:

$$\text{Density} = \text{Mass} \div \text{Volume} \ (\text{Mass}/\text{Volume})$$

The mass of any piece of matter can be found by using a balance. The method used for finding volume depends on the shape of the piece of matter. If a piece of matter, such as a piece of wood, has a boxlike shape, its volume can be found by measuring the length, width, and height

Figure 2–9. To find the density of an object, you must know the mass and the volume of the object. One kind of instrument—a balance—can be used to find the mass of any fairly small piece of matter. However, a single way of finding volume cannot be used for all kinds of matter. Why is displacement of water not a good way to find the volume of a seltzer tablet?

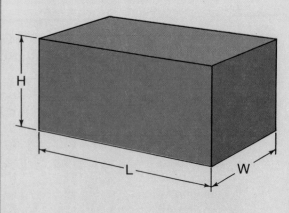

FINDING VOLUME

Solid: Regular Shape

1. Measure the dimensions directly.
2. Use the correct formula.
   (For this shape, Volume = Length × Width × Height)

FINDING MASS

1. Put the unknown mass on the left platform.
2. Add known masses on the right until the platforms are level.

48

of the piece of wood. Then the measurements are multiplied in the following way:

$$\text{Volume} = \text{Length} \times \text{Width} \times \text{Height}$$

The volume of an odd-shaped piece of matter may be found by *displacement* [dihs-PLAY-smuhnt]. When the matter is placed in water, the water is pushed aside, or displaced. The displacement causes the level of the water to rise. The amount of water that rises is equal to the volume of the matter.

The density of a liquid may be found by using a graduated cylinder and a balance. First, use the graduated cylinder to find the volume of the liquid. Then use the balance to find the mass of the liquid. Finally, divide the mass by the volume to find the density.

Find Out More

The volumes of objects that have shapes such as spheres and cones may be found by using certain formulas. Use encyclopedias, science books, mathematics books, and other reference materials to find out the names of various shapes and the formulas that are used to determine the volume of each kind of shape.

Solid: Irregular Shape
(by Displacement)

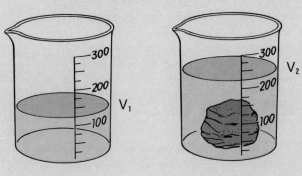

Liquid

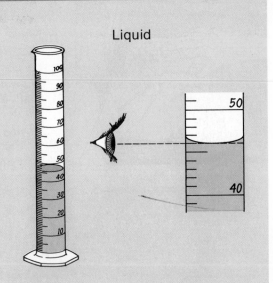

1. Put a known volume of water (V_1) in a container.
2. Place the object in the water, raising the water level.
3. Determine the volume of the object plus the water (V_2).
4. The volume of the object equals V_2 minus V_1.

1. Put the liquid in a graduated cylinder.
2. Keep your eye level with the liquid in the cylinder.
3. Read the mark nearest the bottom of the curved surface.

49

Investigate

How can you find the densities of various objects?

You Will Need

small wood block, large nail, textbook, balance, metric ruler, graduated cylinder

Background

The density of an object is found by dividing the measure of the object's mass by the measure of its volume. A balance is used to find the mass. If an object has a boxlike shape, its volume can be found by measuring its dimensions and then using these dimensions in the following formula: Volume = Length × Width × Height. The volume of an irregularly shaped object may be found by displacement.

What to Do

On your paper, make a table such as the one shown. Use the balance to measure the mass of each object. Record the masses in your table. The volume of the wood block and the textbook may be found by measuring the dimensions of these objects. Then, use these measurements with the formula for volume. Record their volumes in the table.

The volume of the nail may be found by placing the nail in a graduated cylinder that has enough water in it to cover the nail. The volume of the nail is the same as the apparent increase in the volume of the water that occurs when the nail is placed in the graduated cylinder.

Use the measurements recorded in your table to determine the density of each object.

OBJECT	MASS	VOLUME	DENSITY
Block			
Textbook			
Nail			

Now That You Have Done the Investigation

—Could the volume of the textbook be computed accurately? Explain.

—Would finding the volume of the textbook by water displacement be desirable? Explain.

—Which object had the greatest density? Which had the least?

Why objects float or sink

Water seems to push upward on any matter that is put into the water. This upward push is called *buoyancy* [BOY-uhn-see]. Buoyancy depends on the amount of water displaced by an object put in water.

Suppose you place a piece of dry wood in water. The weight of the wood is a downward force. The wood's weight causes it to sink into the water. As the wood sinks into the water, water is displaced. An upward force (buoyancy), equal to the weight of the water displaced, tends to keep the wood from sinking into the water. When the upward force (buoyancy) of the water is equal to the downward force (weight) of the wood, the wood does not sink any further into the water. In other words, the wood floats. See Figure 2–10.

Figure 2–10. Why does the object shown here float? Do all objects float? Why or why not?

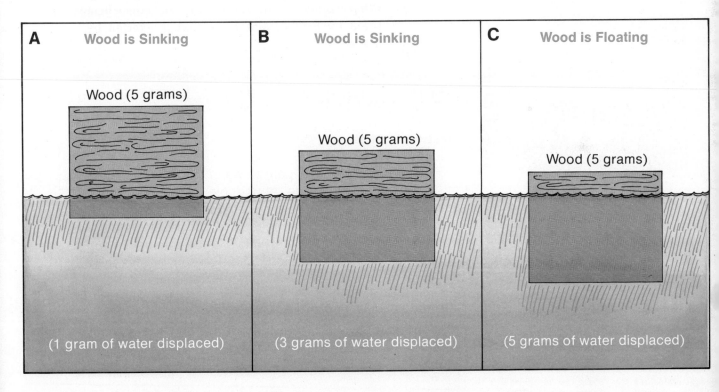

A Wood is Sinking	B Wood is Sinking	C Wood is Floating
Wood (5 grams)	Wood (5 grams)	Wood (5 grams)
(1 gram of water displaced)	(3 grams of water displaced)	(5 grams of water displaced)

Figure 2–11. When fully loaded, a ship will displace more water than when it is empty. Thus, it will sink farther into the water. Of the two ships pictured here, which do you think is more fully loaded? Why do you think so?

What about an object that has a density greater than that of water? The most water that the object can displace is an amount equal to its own volume. This happens only when the object is submerged. Even then, the amount of water displaced is not enough to cause an upward force equal to the weight of the object. The object sinks.

In the examples given, water was displaced. However, the rules of buoyancy can be used with any liquid. They can also be used with gases.

★ **What examples can you give of an object being lifted by the buoyant force that is exerted by a gas?**

DO IT YOURSELF

Float a pie plate

Float a pie plate in a pan of water. Observe the level of the water on the side of the pie plate. Now pour some sand into the pie plate, being careful not to tip over the pie plate. What happens to the level of the water on the side of the pie plate? Is the amount of water displaced by the pie plate and sand greater or less than the amount of water displaced by the pie plate alone? Is the buoyant force greater on the pie plate and sand or on the pie plate alone? How would you explain the relationship between the buoyant force and the amount of water displaced?

Measurement—Important Everywhere

Almost everyone makes various measurements every day. We look at our watches to measure time. We read the thermometer to measure temperature. Sometimes we use a ruler to measure the length of some object. And once in a while we step on a scale to measure our weight. These measurements do not have to be very precise, and usually nothing happens if the measurement is not exactly right.

Some people, besides making the kinds of measurements mentioned above, have jobs in which accurate measurements are very important. For example, a *carpenter* [KAHR-puhn-tur] must make many careful measurements. A carpenter must be able to understand blueprints, or scale drawings. Using information from the blueprint, a carpenter measures, cuts, and assembles the pieces of whatever is being built—perhaps a home, a boat, or a cabinet.

The job of a *surveyor* [sur-VAY-ur] also involves accurate measuring. In general, surveyors measure distances on the surface of the earth. Some reasons for making such measurements are for making maps, for planning the route of a highway, and for preparing sites for buildings and bridges.

There are many other jobs in which accurate measurements are important. Most jobs that require accurate measuring also involve the use of special measuring tools and instruments. Have you thought about the kind of job or career you would like to have? If so, what kinds of measuring would be involved in this job?

What kinds of measurements are the people shown here making? What jobs do you know about that require accurate measuring?

Reviewing and Extending

SUMMING UP

1. Measuring is finding out how many times some known amount, or unit, will "fit into" the unknown amount you are measuring.
2. Using SI is easy because one unit may be changed to another by using powers of ten and because the same prefixes are used with all units.
3. The mass, or amount of matter, of an object may be found by using a balance.
4. The force of gravitational attraction between an object and the earth is called the weight of the object.
5. The ratio of the mass of a piece of matter to its volume is called density.
6. When an object is placed in water, an upward, or buoyant, force acts on the object. The buoyant force is equal to the weight of water displaced by the object.

CHECKING UP

Vocabulary   Write the numerals *1–7* on your paper. Each numbered phrase describes a term from the following list. On your paper, write the term next to the numeral of the phrase that describes it.

measuring	SI	capacity	displacement
metre	mass	density	buoyancy

1. amount of space inside a container
2. amount of matter
3. comparing unknown amounts with familiar amounts
4. metric system of units
5. basic SI unit of length
6. upward force exerted by water on an object in the water
7. mass/volume ratio

Knowledge and Understanding   Write the numerals *8–13* on your paper. Beside each numeral, write the word or words that best complete the sentence having that numeral.

8. In SI, the length of an airplane would most likely be expressed in (*grams, litres, metres*).
9. In SI, the capacity of a container would most likely be expressed in (*grams, litres, metres*).
10. In SI, the mass of a small object, such as a wristwatch, would most likely be expressed in (*grams, litres, metres*).
11. A balance responds to an object's (*capacity, mass, volume*).

12. A newton is an SI unit of (*force, density, capacity*).
13. Another word that is used for the mass/volume ratio is (*capacity, force, density*).

Concepts Beside each of the numerals *14–17* on your paper, write the word or words that best complete the sentence having that numeral.

14. To measure is to find out how many times a (*power of ten, unit, system*) will "fit into" the unknown amount being measured.
15. The mass of an object may be found by using (*an equal-arm balance, a graduated cylinder, a system of units*).
16. The ounce, the pound, and the ton are units of (*weight, length, time*) in the English system of units.
17. The gravitational attraction between an object and the earth is called the (*weight, displacement, mass*) of that object.

Application and Critical Thinking Answer the following questions as briefly as you can without leaving out any important ideas.

18. Suppose a small wooden box is 25.0 centimetres long, 13.0 centimetres wide, and 6.00 centimetres high. Use the formula for volume to find the volume of the box.
19. A metal ball has a mass of 81 grams and a volume of 30.0 cubic centimetres. Find the density of the ball. The formula for density is: Density = Mass ÷ Volume. What kind of metal is the ball made of? (Hint: Use the table on page 47.)

DOING MORE

1. Find the mass of a litre of water, a nickel, and a pencil. Find the volume of each of these items in cubic centimetres. Then, find the density of each item. Which item has the greatest density? Which has the least density? How could you check your answers?
2. Find and record the weight of a small block of wood. Then, place an overflow can on a dial scale. Fill the can with water so that any rise in water level will cause the can to overflow. Add a few drops of liquid detergent. Record the weight of the can and water. Now float the small block of wood in the overflow can. Catch any water that overflows from the can. Do not let this water fall on the scale. Does placing the wooden block in the can cause the reading of the scale to change? Find the weight of the water that overflowed. How does its weight compare with the weight of the wooden block? How would you explain the results of this activity?

CHAPTER 3

Explaining

In Chapters 1 and 2, two important things that scientists do were described. These are observing and measuring. But scientists do more than that. They also try to explain what they have observed and measured.

Trying to explain can be thought of as trying to tell how something happened. But knowing exactly what happened comes before telling how it happened. So, scientists observe carefully. They record what has been observed. And they try to measure all the different aspects of what has been observed.

Why is explaining important? Why do people want to explain how things happen in the environment? The main reason is that knowing how things happen helps us to better understand the world we live in. Such an understanding also helps us control what will happen. Knowing how things happen might even help us predict what will happen in the future. As you study Chapter 3, you will have a chance to find out why explaining is one of the important things that scientists do.

Explaining is an important part of science, but do you think scientists are the only people who try to explain what they observe? What do you think this teacher is explaining? What things have you tried to explain?

Carol Ann Bales/Van Cleve Photography

OBSERVING AIR AND WATER

What are some ways in which you have observed
  water drying up?
What are some ways to observe air?
How does heat affect water?

Two common kinds of matter

Is there anyone in your class who has not heard of air and water? Certainly not. Air and water are very common forms of matter. You may not be able to give a scientific definition of these kinds of matter, but you do have a good idea of what air and water are.

As you study this section, you will not be expected to learn a lot of technical data about air and water. Because air and water are so common, you have observed them many times. Even without making a scientific study, you have learned some of the ways in which air and water behave.

Where did it go?

You might be surprised how much you already know about water. For example, you know that water "dries up." Puddles of rainwater on a street dry up after the rain stops. Sometimes they dry up very quickly. Sometimes they remain for a long time. Have you ever wondered what might cause puddles to dry up quickly one day and slowly the next? And where does the water go when it dries up?

You could make a long list of examples of water drying up. (A scientist would probably use the term *evaporate* [ih-VAP-uh-RAYT] rather than dry up.) If you made such a list, you would probably begin to realize that there are several different things that affect how fast water dries up.

You have observed water drying up many times. One example of a situation in which you have observed this happening is the drying of wet clothes. When you get out of a swimming pool, does your suit dry faster on a windy day or on a calm day? Does a wet towel dry faster when

Figure 3–1. Sometimes a lot of rain falls in a short time. What happens to the puddles of water left by the rain?

(Text continues on page 59.)

Investigate

What changes the rate at which water dries up?

You Will Need

electric fan, eyedropper, source of heat, ring stand and ring, 2 aluminum pans (such as frozen-dinner trays)

Background

At certain times water dries up faster than at other times. Several different factors can change the rate at which the water dries up. Finding out what some of these factors are can be done by using various tests.

What to Do

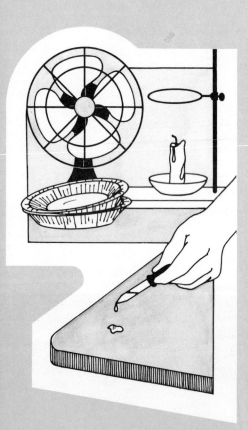

Fill the eyedropper with water. Near one end of a table, use 5 drops of water to make a small puddle. At the other end, use 5 drops of water to make a second puddle. Then use the edge of a ruler to spread the second puddle over a large area of the table. Observe both areas of water to determine which dries up sooner. When you finish your observation, wipe up all the water left on the table.

Fill the eyedropper again. Use about 5 drops of water to make a small puddle near one end of the table. Do the same at the other end. Then set up the electric fan so that the moving air blows on the second puddle. Observe both puddles to determine which dries up sooner.

Place about 5 drops of water in each aluminum pan. Place one pan on the ring of the ring stand. Place the source of heat under that pan. Do not heat the second pan. Observe the water in each pie pan to determine which dries up sooner.

Now That You Have Done the Investigation

—In the first part, which puddle dried up faster: the one that was spread out or the one that was left as a puddle?
—In the second part, which puddle dried up faster: the one with air moving against it or the one that had no air moving against it?
—In the third part, which puddle dried up faster: the one that was heated or the one that was not heated?
—What things other than area, moving air, and heat might change the rate at which water dries up?

58

it is hung up or when it is left lying in a pile? What is there about a clothes dryer that gets clothes dry in a short time? If you think about these examples, you will begin to get some ideas about what causes water to dry up faster at one time than at another.

★ **Where might you be able to observe some water drying up?**

How to observe air

Air is not as easy to observe as water is. One reason is that you cannot see air. But air is all around you. You can feel air when air is moving. For example, if you hold your hand up to your mouth and breathe out, you can feel the air against your hand.

You can see and feel the effects of moving air. But can you observe the air itself? In most situations air is invisible. But air is matter, and matter takes up space. So air can be observed in certain ways.

One good way to observe air is to put it into a container such as a plastic bag. Do not use the kind that

For You to Think About

What are some examples of liquids other than water that dry up? What liquids can you think of that dry up very fast? That dry up very slowly, if at all?

A. Devaney, Inc.

Figure 3–2. Although you cannot see air, it can be observed. Can you observe air in the picture at the left? Explain.

holds onions or potatoes, because these bags have holes. First fill the bag with ice cubes. You can see that the bag bulges out. The ice cubes cause the bulges. Now empty the bag, and fill it with water. Again the bag bulges, this time because of the water. Empty the bag again. This time hold the bag up to your mouth and blow into the bag. When the bag fills up, hold it tightly at the neck so that the air will not escape. Notice that the bag bulges out just as it did with the ice cubes and the water. What does the bulging of the bag tell you about air?

Air sometimes changes in certain ways. Suppose you leave an air-filled ball, say a football or a volleyball, outside overnight. Suppose, too, that it gets very cold that night. The next morning you might notice that the ball feels softer than it did the day before. The ball has no leaks, so you are pretty sure that no air was lost. The air inside the ball changed in some way so that the ball now feels soft. The way the ball changed helped you observe how air changes.

★ **How could a balloon and a freezer be used to show that air changes with changes in temperature?**

DO IT YOURSELF

Observing air

Observe air by pouring some air from one glass to another Obtain two glasses of the same size. Put one glass into an aquarium that is almost full of water. Let the glass fill up with water. Then hold the glass, mouth downward. Now lower the second glass into the aquarium with its mouth facing down. Water will not go into this glass. The glass stays full of air. Move the edge of the glass of air under the edge of the glass full of water. Then slowly tip the glass of air so that the bubbles of air move up into the glass of water. The bubbles of air push the water out of the glass of water. With a little practice, you can fill the glass of water with air. What else might you do to observe air?

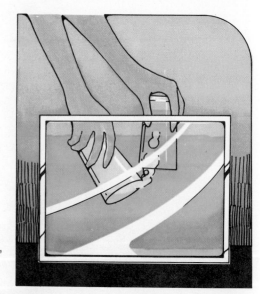

Temperature and water

In the situation with the ball, the temperature of the air had something to do with the way air behaved. Do you think temperature has any effect on the way water behaves? To find out, you could set up some equipment as shown in Figure 3–3. Push a fifty-centimetre-long (twenty-inch-long) glass tube partway into a rubber stopper. Fill a flask with water. Then push the rubber stopper into the flask. Some water will be forced up into the tube. (Putting some food coloring in the water will make it easier to observe the water inside the glass tube.) Place the flask on a wire screen which is supported by a ring stand. Place a source of heat under the wire screen. As the water warms up, what happens to the water in the flask? What happens to the water in the tube?

★ **What do you think would happen if the water in the flask were cooled instead of warmed?**

For You to Think About

How did the glass tube help you observe the effect of changes in temperature on water? How are the glass tube and flask in Figure 3–3 like a thermometer? How could you use a glass tube and a flask like those in Figure 3–3 to measure temperature?

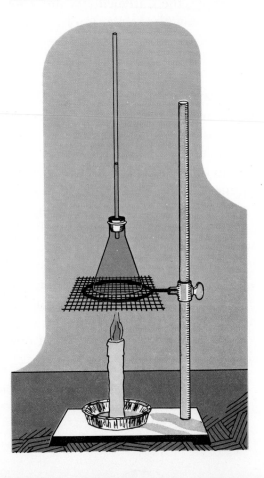

Figure 3–3. How does the equipment you see here show that temperature has an effect on the way water behaves? What is the effect?

61

HYPOTHESES, THEORIES, AND MODELS

What is a hypothesis?
How are models and theories related?
*What theory could be used to explain how air
   and water behave?*

Hypothesis

You have made many observations about air and water. Perhaps many of these observations have made you wonder. Maybe you have even asked yourself questions like, What caused the water to dry up? What caused the ball to become softer when cooled? What caused the water to rise in the tube?

A statement made to answer a question about the cause of some happening is called a *hypothesis* [hy-PAHTH-uh-suhs]. For example, the statement—Water dries up because pieces of water mix with the air—is a hypothesis that might be used to answer the first question. Hypotheses (plural of hypothesis) can also be made for the other two questions. A hypothesis for the ball might be—The ball felt soft because the cold air in the ball took up less space. A hypothesis for the water might be—The water rose in the tube because heat made the water expand.

These statements are hypotheses because they are possible answers to questions. You might say that a hypothesis is a kind of guess. But it should not be just a "wild" guess. It should be an "educated" guess. Before making a hypothesis, a person should think carefully about the question being answered.

Hypotheses are very helpful to scientists. They use hypotheses a lot. Scientists must remember, though, that a hypothesis is not a fact. It is only a possible answer to a question about the cause of some observation. If the hypothesis is found to be wrong, however, a new hypothesis is worked out.

★ **What is the difference between an "educated" guess and a "wild" guess?**

For You to Think About

If a hypothesis is not a fact, what is the purpose of making a hypothesis about an observation?

DO IT YOURSELF

Make a hypothesis

Fill a large beaker or jar with cold water. Allow the water to become calm. Place one or two drops of food coloring in the water. Do not stir the water. Observe the coloring in the water. Note the amount of time it takes for the color to spread to the sides of the beaker.

Repeat the test, using hot water instead of cold water. Remember to allow the water to become calm. Again note the amount of time it takes for the color to spread.

Try to write a hypothesis that explains why the color used in the two tests took different amounts of time to spread.

Other explanations

A hypothesis is a possible answer to a question about the cause of some happening. There are other ways of explaining the cause of some happening. One of these other ways is with a *model* [MAHD-uhl]. Another is with a *theory* [THEE-uh-ree]. Models and theories are related. Sometimes a model is part of a theory. Models and theories can be used to explain observations.

Here is an example of how you might make up a model. Suppose someone places a common object, say a tennis ball, in a box. Then the box is sealed. This is done without letting you know what was put in the box. Your job is to find out what is in the box without opening it. You can get ideas by holding the box, by shaking it, by listening, or by any other way except looking inside.

You might tip the box and notice that the "thing" rolls to the lowest part of the box. So the thing must be round. Maybe it is a baby-food jar. But then you notice that the thing rolls no matter which way the box is tipped. The thing must be more like a ball than a baby-food jar. What kind of ball might it be? It's not heavy enough to be a shot put. It's too heavy to be a table-tennis ball. It doesn't make a sharp sound when it hits the side of the box. So it must not be hard like a golf ball.

In trying to decide what the thing is, you observe how it behaves. It rolls. It is not very heavy. It doesn't seem to be hard. What must the thing be like to fit all these observations? To answer this question, you form a model of what the thing is like. Your model helps you explain what you hear and feel the thing do inside the box. The more correct your model is, the more likely you are to guess that the thing is a tennis ball.

How is a theory different from a model? A theory is a model or a set of models that can be used to explain a lot of things. Your model of what is in the sealed box could be a theory. Your model could be a theory if it could be used to tell what happens in many different sealed boxes.

★ **How might a square thing behave in a sealed box? How might you describe your observation of a square thing's behavior?**

A scientific theory

Scientists use models and theories to explain their observations. For example, scientists have observed air and water in much the same way you have. They have noticed that water dries up. They have also noticed that air-filled balls become soft when cold.

Scientists have asked the question, What is it about air and water that causes them to behave the way they do? To answer this question, scientists have formed a model of what air and water are like. Because the same model explains many different observations, the model is often called a theory. This theory is called the *kinetic-molecular* [kuh-NEHT-ihk muh-LEHK-yuh-lur] *theory*. (Sometimes this theory is called the kinetic theory of matter.) The word "kinetic" is used to mean moving. The word "molecular" refers to tiny pieces of matter. The theory, then, is based on a model in which matter is believed to be made of tiny, fast-moving particles.

64

Some ideas of the kinetic-molecular theory are listed in the table below.

KINETIC-MOLECULAR THEORY

1. Each liquid or gas is made of tiny particles called molecules.
2. Molecules are always moving.
3. When molecules hit each other (or if they bump into any other matter) they bounce away without slowing down.
4. At a given time, some molecules of a substance are moving faster than others.
5. The average speed of the molecules of a substance depends on temperature. The higher the temperature, the greater the average speed of molecules.

There is no need to memorize the ideas of this theory. The ideas are listed here only so that you can see how a theory or a model is used to explain observations.

★ **Why is the word "kinetic" used in naming the kinetic-molecular theory?**

USING THEORIES TO EXPLAIN

How can the kinetic-molecular theory be used to explain why the air pressure inside objects changes?

How can the kinetic-molecular theory be used to explain why water dries up?

What is one example of a scientific law?

Explaining observations of air

One reason for having a hypothesis, a model, or a theory is to explain observations. On the next page is an example of using the kinetic-molecular theory to explain some observations of air.

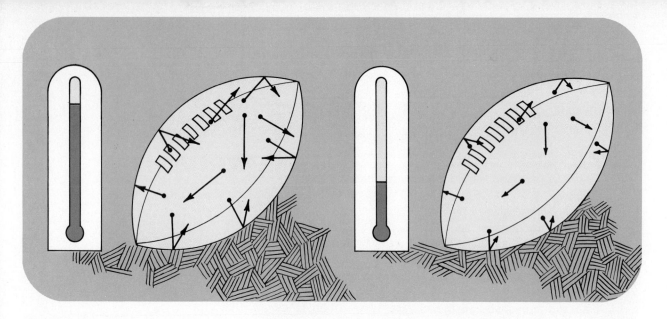

Figure 3–4. The black dots represent molecules. The length of the arrows indicates their speed. In which ball—warm or cold—do the molecules hit harder against the inside of the ball? Which ball will feel harder?

Observation: Air inside a closed container has a lower pressure when the air is cold than when it is warm. (You observed this when you left the air-filled ball outside on a cold night and it felt softer the next morning.)

Explanation: According to the theory, air molecules move faster at high temperatures than at low temperatures. The faster the molecules move, the harder they bump into the sides of a container. The harder they bump, the higher the pressure. (Inside the ball, the harder they bump into its sides, the more pressure inside the ball. The ball, then, feels hard.)

Does this explanation sound reasonable? Are you bothered by the fact that you cannot see the air molecules? Think about the sealed box that was described earlier. You couldn't see inside the box, either. But you could be pretty sure that there was some ball-like object in the box. Your idea that the object was ball-like was the model for that thing inside the sealed box. In much the same way, the idea that tiny, moving particles called molecules make up air is also a model.

In the situation with the ball that was left outside on a cold night, you observed a change in the air pressure inside the ball. So, you made up a model of what the molecules

(*Text continues on page 68.*)

Investigate

How can you use the kinetic-molecular theory to explain the way air behaves?

You Will Need

   soda bottle, aluminum pan (such as a frozen-dinner tray), source of heat, balloon, beaker, hot pads, ring stand and ring

Background

   Since air is invisible, it is often studied while it is inside a container so that the air can be observed better. One way to study air is to find out what effect heat has on air in a container. Then, the kinetic-molecular theory can be used to explain any changes you might observe.

What to Do

   Stretch the neck of a balloon over the top of an empty soda bottle as shown. Now heat the bottle. Heat the bottle by standing it in water in the aluminum pan. The pan should be placed on the ring stand and ring. Observe the balloon. Record what happens to the balloon while the bottle is being warmed. Allow the bottle to cool, and record what happens to the balloon.

   Now remove the balloon and fill the bottle with hot water. Using the hot pads to hold the bottle, pour out the hot water and quickly place the mouth of the bottle in a pan of cool water. Observe what happens near the mouth of the bottle. Record what happens to the level of water inside the mouth of the bottle.

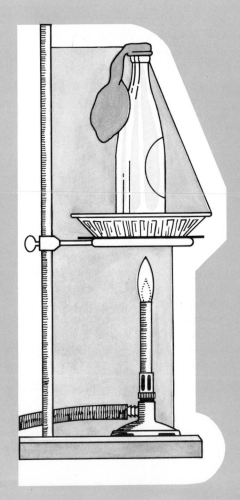

Now That You Have Done the Investigation

—What happened to the balloon while the bottle was being warmed? While the bottle was cooling?

—How could the kinetic-molecular theory be used to explain what happened to the air inside the bottle while it was being heated?

—What must have happened to the air that entered the bottle as the hot water was poured out of the bottle? How do you know?

—What must have happened to the air inside the bottle as the bottle cooled? How do you know?

—How could the kinetic-molecular theory be used to explain what happened to the air inside the bottle as it was warmed and then cooled?

must be doing in order to explain what you observed. You might say that the colder air molecules did not bump as hard inside the ball as they did when they were warm. So, the ball felt soft. The kinetic-molecular theory can be used to explain other ways that air behaves.

★ **How would you use the kinetic-molecular theory to explain what happens to the air inside a car's tires during a drive through a hot desert?**

Explaining observations of water

In the previous section, the kinetic-molecular theory was used to explain differences in pressure that happen because of differences in temperature. Perhaps the theory can be used to explain some other observations that were described earlier. Try using the theory on the following observation:

Observation: Water in a dish seems to disappear over a period of time.

Explanation: Molecules of water are moving all the time. The molecules of air above the water are moving too. Some water molecules near the surface move up through the surface. They actually leave the water. They get mixed in with the moving air molecules and do not come back to the water. As more and more water molecules leave, the water seems to disappear.

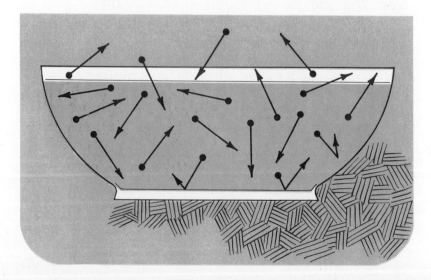

Figure 3–5. The black dots represent molecules of water. The arrows indicate that the molecules are moving. What happens to the amount of water as more and more water molecules leave? Where do the water molecules go?

In this explanation, the same model that was used to explain air pressure is also used to explain why water dries up. Since this model explains several different kinds of observations, the model can be called a theory.

You have already used the kinetic-molecular theory to explain two different observations. There are many other observations that can be explained by this theory. The theory, then, is a very useful one for explaining observations about air and water.

DO IT YOURSELF

Use the kinetic-molecular theory

You have probably observed that hot water evaporates faster than cold water. Perhaps you have wondered why it does. Try to use the features of the kinetic-molecular theory listed on page 65 to explain this observation.

There are many theories. Theories are an important part of science. In fact, there would not be any science if there were no theories. Theories are ways of explaining why things happen as they do. Therefore, theories must be based on accurate observations and measurements. As you study science, you'll be reminded over and over that observing, measuring, and explaining are very important to scientists.

★ **When water dries up, where do the molecules of water go? How can the kinetic-molecular theory be used to explain where they go?**

Scientific laws

One other term—in addition to model, theory, and hypothesis—that you often hear about in science is the term "law." Sometimes such a law is called a *scientific law*. You may also have heard these laws called laws of nature. What is a scientific law? Can a scientific law be broken?

A scientific law is a statement about the way things happen in the world. An example of a scientific law is the law of freely falling bodies. The law says that all freely falling bodies fall with the same speed. The words "freely falling" mean that an object is falling so that nothing, including air resistance, is interfering with the falling of the object.

You might be thinking that if you drop a feather and a coin, the coin would fall faster. Does this mean the law is broken? No. It is the resistance of the air that holds the feather back. If you could remove all the air from the room and then drop the feather and the coin, both would fall together.

A similar test that uses a feather and a coin has been done. Only instead of removing the air from the room, the test is done in another way. A feather and a coin are put in a large glass tube. When the tube is turned over, the coin falls faster than the feather. Then the air is pumped out of the tube. Now when the tube is turned over, both the feather and the coin fall at the same speed.

Figure 3–6. Almost all the air has been removed from the glass tube shown here. Inside the tube, the coin and the feather fall at the same speed and hit bottom at the same time. How does air resistance affect the coin and the feather falling outside the tube?

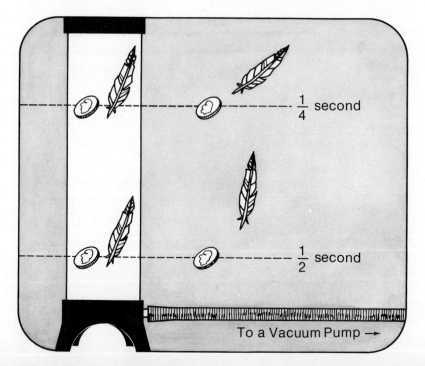

$\frac{1}{4}$ second

$\frac{1}{2}$ second

To a Vacuum Pump →

Figure 3–7. In this picture, an astronaut is shown dropping a hammer and a feather at the same time. Astronaut David Scott did this experiment on the moon to see which would fall faster. Which do you think fell faster? Why was the surface of the moon a good place to do this experiment?

Scientific laws, then, are statements in which scientists try to tell how things happen in the world. There are several such laws. For example, one law is called Boyle's law. This law tells what happens to the amount of space a gas takes up when the pressure on the gas is increased. Another law, called Ohm's law, tells something about what happens when electricity goes through a wire.

Before such laws are accepted by scientists, each law is tested in many ways. You'll read more about the testing of ideas in the next chapter. For now, the important points to remember are the following: (1) Laws are statements about what happens in the world, and (2) These statements have been tested many times.

Figure 3–8. Are the people in these pictures "breaking" the law of freely falling bodies? Why aren't they falling rapidly toward the earth, as a rock or a baseball would?

You can ignore a scientific law, but you cannot change it. For instance, you can step off a cliff if you want to. But you'll fall if you do. Of course, you might use a parachute to keep from falling too fast. Does using a parachute to slow your fall mean you are breaking the law of gravity? Not at all. What it does mean is that you probably know about the law. You also know that if you have enough air resistance you won't fall fast. And you know the parachute gives you that air resistance.

One of the results of studying science is learning about the laws of nature. We would like to know enough about the world to explain why things happen as they do. Then we could use the laws of nature to help make life more enjoyable for everyone.

★ **On the moon, which would fall faster: a large rock, a small stone, or a grain of sand?**

Find Out More

There are many other scientific laws besides those you have just read about. For example, the laws of motion are scientific laws. Use reference materials, such as encyclopedias, school books, and library books, to help you find out more about the laws of motion.

Explaining Ideas

When you try to explain an idea to someone, you probably use words to say what you mean. However, some people use pictures. That is, they use diagrams and drawings in their work to explain ideas.

Men and women who design machines or structures such as buildings or bridges use drawings to explain their ideas to other people. The drawings they use show different views of the object being described. The views have dimensions next to them in order to show the exact size and shape of each part. The drawing, along with the dimensions, helps to explain just what the finished structure or machine will look like.

Illustrators use diagrams and drawings to explain ideas too. Illustrators are artists. They use paintings, drawings, or photographs to explain and add interest to the written part of a book. An illustration may serve to decorate or to draw attention to a story. A good illustration helps the reader understand what is written.

There are other kinds of jobs in which diagrams and drawings are important ways of explaining things. Using diagrams or drawings with your classwork can even help you in school. If you like to draw, perhaps you would like a job or career that involves using pictures to explain ideas. What kind of a job or career that uses pictures to explain ideas might you like?

Alfa Studio

Zimmerman/Alpha

What kinds of diagrams and drawings are being used by the people in these pictures? Why are diagrams and drawings used in explaining ideas?

Reviewing and Extending

SUMMING UP

1. Explaining is trying to tell how something happened.
2. Water and air are common forms of matter, and they may be observed in many ways.
3. Changes in temperature cause changes in the way air and water behave.
4. A statement that tries to answer a question about the cause of some happening is called a hypothesis. It is important to remember that a hypothesis is not a fact.
5. Models and theories can be used to explain observations.
6. The kinetic-molecular theory is based on a model in which matter is believed to be made of tiny, fast-moving particles called molecules.
7. A scientific law is a statement about the way things happen.

CHECKING UP

Vocabulary Write the numerals *1–6* on your paper. Each numbered phrase describes a term from the following list. On your paper, write the term next to the numeral of the phrase that describes it.

evaporate	hypothesis	kinetic	scientific law
molecule	observation	theory	measurement

1. possible answer to a question
2. term that means "moving"
3. model or a set of models that can be used to explain many things
4. statement about the way things happen
5. term that means "dry up"
6. tiny, fast-moving piece of matter

Knowledge and Understanding Write the numerals *7–11* on your paper. Beside each numeral, write the word or words that best complete the sentence having that numeral.

7. (*Observing, Explaining, Measuring*) can be thought of as trying to tell how something happened.
8. There (*are several things, is nothing, are only two things*) that can affect how fast water dries up.
9. According to the kinetic-molecular theory, air (*cannot be observed, is made of tiny particles, keeps water from drying up*).
10. A statement made to answer a question about the cause of some happening is called (*an observation, a hypothesis, a law*).
11. When it comes to scientific laws, you (*can ignore them and change them, cannot ignore them even though you can change them, can ignore them although you cannot change them*).

Concepts   Beside each of the numerals *12–16* on your paper, write the word or words that best complete the sentence having that numeral.

12. The "thing" in the box was a good example of how we know that (*models help us understand things, molecules are like a tennis ball, water expands when heated*).
13. The behavior of water and air sometimes changes because of changes in (*temperature, theory, a model*).
14. A hypothesis is used to explain (*where, how, when*) something happened.
15. The pressure of the air inside a ball can change with changes in (*the kinds of containers used, the kinds of observations made, temperature*).
16. Laws are statements about the way things happen. These statements (*have been tested many times, have been tested only once, do not need to be tested*).

Application and Critical Thinking   Answer the following questions as briefly as you can without leaving out any important ideas.

17. Use the kinetic-molecular theory to explain what happens in the following situation: An inflated balloon that has been placed in a freezer for a few minutes becomes soft.
18. What is one way you can observe the presence of air, even though air itself is invisible?

DOING MORE

1. Add about 1¾ cups of sugar to 1 cup of boiling water. Stir until the sugar dissolves and let the solution cool a little. When cool, pour the solution into a glass jar and hang a piece of cotton thread or string in it. The string may be held in position by tying it to a pencil laid across the top of the beaker. In a few hours small crystals will start forming on the string. If left alone for a few days, the crystals will grow large. Explain to the class how the growth of the crystals might be explained by the kinetic-molecular theory.
2. Make a bulletin-board display of all the different scientific laws you can find. In your display try to show a picture or drawing of the scientist who discovered the law. Also use pictures to show what the law describes.

CHAPTER 4

Testing

Suppose you observe something and figure out a way to explain what you have observed. How can you be sure your explanation, or theory, is correct? There is no way to be perfectly sure. However, to test an explanation, you can use it to try to *predict* [prih-DIHKT] what will happen in a new situation. For example, you might think, "If my explanation is correct, and if I do this, then a certain result should occur."

The "if-then" parts of the sentence above tell that you are going to test your explanation by predicting what will happen. Then you plan to set up a certain set of conditions and observe the results. The process of setting up a situation and making observations is called *experimenting* [ihk-SPEHR-uh-mehnt-ihng].

Testing by doing experiments is a very important part of science. This chapter is about experimenting and about how the results of experiments are useful—even if they are not the expected results.

Testing is important in science. Do you think testing is important in areas other than science?

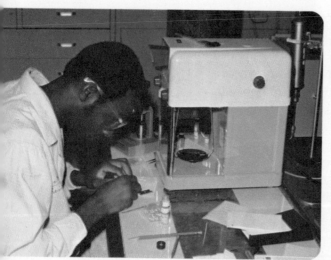

Dr. E. R. Degginger

Photo Research International

WHY TEST IDEAS?

Who was one well-known philosopher?
Who is called the founder of modern
  experimental science?
What is a superstition?
Why would you try to control an experiment?

Early ideas

Today, the testing of ideas and hypotheses seems very natural. But such testing has not always been done. Testing was not done by people thousands of years ago. Even though testing was not part of their way of doing things, the early "scientists" did learn a lot about the world. They had many correct ideas. But they also had some wrong ideas. And because no one tested the ideas, wrong ideas were believed to be correct for many years.

Notice that quotation marks are used with the word "scientists." The reason the marks are used is that in those days, the words "science" and "scientist" were not used. Instead, those who tried to describe the natural world were called philosophers. Philosophers spent a lot of time talking about the things they observed around them.

One philosopher, *Aristotle* [AR-uh-STAHT-uhl], was especially well known. His ideas about plants and animals, about the nature of matter, and about how objects fall were in his writings. He wrote about many other ideas as well. Aristotle was a great thinker and teacher, but some of his ideas were wrong. He was so respected that for centuries men and women tried to learn about the world by reading his ideas, instead of by observing the world themselves.

Using tests

Almost 2,000 years after the time of Aristotle, one of his big ideas was shown to be false. Aristotle had taught that a heavy object would fall faster than a light one. But *Galileo* [GAL-uh-LEE-oh] did not agree with this idea.

Find Out More

There are many famous philosophers. Use reference materials like science books and encyclopedias to learn more about some famous philosophers and about their ideas.

According to some accounts, Galileo did more than discuss and argue the point. One story is that he took two objects of different weight up into the Leaning Tower of Pisa. He dropped both objects at the same time from the top of the tower. According to the story, nearly everyone was surprised to see the objects hit the ground at almost the same time.

Galileo often used tests like this to see if ideas and explanations were correct. Such testing is part of the way today's scientists work. Since he was one of the first people to work this way, Galileo is sometimes called the founder of modern experimental science.

Today, testing ideas is pretty much a part of everyday life. We wonder why people did not always try to test their ideas. It seems amazing that in the past, people reached definite conclusions without ever checking them. For example, about 600 years ago the following idea was taught: The blood of a deer, killed under certain conditions, can make diamonds soft. It cannot, of course, but at that time no one ever thought of trying it. The idea was simply accepted.

★ **What ideas do you have that you have not tested but simply accepted?**

DO IT YOURSELF

Test an idea

An idea that was thought to be true for a long time was that a heavy object falls faster than a light object. Obtain two objects having different weights. You might use a glass marble and a steel ball-bearing. Have someone drop both objects from a second-story window at the same time. Observe the objects strike the ground. Be sure you are a safe distance away from where the objects will strike the ground. Repeat the test a number of times. From your observations, what can you conclude about the idea that heavy objects fall faster than light objects?

Reaching conclusions

Don't get the idea that people today never jump to conclusions. Some people do. Suppose a person is kept awake by a dog howling all night. That person tells others about it. Then two days later, some member of the family dies. Three years later, another death happens two days after the howling of a dog was noticed. Some people might decide that if a dog howls at night, someone in the family will die in two days. Of course, the evidence for such a conclusion is nearly zero. Dogs howl many nights and no one dies. But some people still reach such false conclusions from incomplete evidence.

Not only do some people jump to conclusions, but many people still believe in *superstitions* [soo-pur-STIHSH-uhnz]. A superstition is an idea that people believe even though there is no evidence to support it. Here are some superstitions you may have heard about: If you break a mirror, you will have seven years of bad luck. And if a black cat crosses your path, something bad will happen.

How, then, should a person come to a conclusion? How can a person find out if an idea is good or if it is just a superstition? One way to find out is test the idea.

For You to Think About

Some people say that a four-leaf clover and a rabbit-foot can bring good luck. What could you do to find out if a four-leaf clover and a rabbit-foot can bring good luck?

Observing and explaining

If you are like most people, you often observe things that you cannot easily explain. If you are curious, you will make other observations. From your observations, you will get ideas about why things happen as they do.

Think about some thunderstorms you have seen. The flashes of lightning are followed by loud claps of thunder. Sometimes the sound of thunder comes right after the lightning. Sometimes many seconds pass between seeing the lightning and hearing the thunder. Why do you always see lightning before hearing thunder? Why does the sound of thunder sometimes come right away and sometimes come several seconds later?

If you are a good observer, you may have noticed that distance has something to do with the time between seeing lightning and hearing thunder. When the lightning is nearby, the sound of thunder comes quickly. When the lightning is far away, the sound of thunder is heard several seconds after the lightning.

You could explain the time difference by saying that light travels faster than sound. At the place where lightning strikes, the thunder and the lightning happen at the same time. As the sound and the light travel away from that place, the sound falls farther and farther behind the light. The farther you are from the place the lightning strikes, the longer the time between seeing the flash and hearing the thunder.

So far, you have observed the lightning and the thunder. You have an idea that explains why the time interval between seeing the flash and hearing the thunder is different for different distances. Now you want to test your idea, or explanation.

★ **Is thunder always produced by a flash of lightning? Explain your answer.**

Make a prediction

If your explanation is correct, you can predict that the amount of time between lightning and thunder would be about twice as great for a two-kilometre (1.2-mile) distance than for a one-kilometre (0.6-mile) distance. By measuring both the distance and the time, you can test your explanation. Measuring the distance to a flash of lightning is not easy. You do not know where or when lightning will happen. But if light and sound behave the same in all situations, you do not have to use real lightning. You can use any happening that makes a loud sound and some visible signal at the same time.

When blanks are fired from a gun (like those used to start races at a track meet), there is a loud sound and a visible flash. You could go to a track meet and stand at different distances from the starter who fired the gun. If you did this, you would find the amount of time changes just the way your explanation predicted it would. In this way, you could gather information to make certain your explanation was correct.

De Wys, Inc.

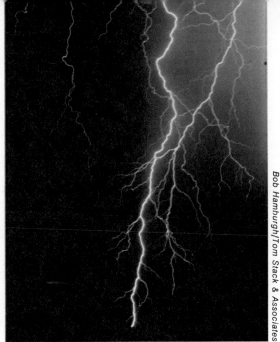

Courtesy of Lockheed Aircraft Corp.

Figure 4–1. What sounds do you think of when you see these pictures? Do you always hear a sound at the same time that the sound is produced? Explain.

Of course, making measurements at a track meet depends on some things you can't control. You have to wait for a track meet to happen. You have to go to where the track meet is taking place. And even if you get there, you may not be allowed to go down on the field to make the measurements you need. Instead of going to a track meet, it would be easier to work with a friend. Together you could measure the distances, measure the times, and fire the gun whenever you are ready. If you could arrange to do these things, you would be doing an experiment in much the same way a scientist does.

Investigate

How does distance affect the time between seeing when a noise is being made and hearing the noise that was made?

You Will Need

binoculars, metal garbage can or lid, metre stick, rubber mallet or plastic bat, stopwatch, string

Background

Distance has something to do with the time between seeing when a noise is being made and hearing the noise that was made. Any happening that makes a loud sound and some visible signal at the same time may be used to investigate what effect distance has on this time.

What to Do

You will need a partner to help you do this investigation. Use the metre stick to measure a piece of string so it is 50 metres long. One person should stand at one end of the string and hold the metal garbage can and the rubber mallet. This person will not move away from that place during the investigation. The other person has the stopwatch and should stand at the other end of the string. For each test, the can should be hit once with the mallet. The person with the stopwatch should measure the difference in time between seeing the can being hit and hearing the noise made by hitting the can. In order to measure the time correctly, you may have to repeat the test a number of times at each distance.

Repeat the test when you and your partner are 100 metres apart, 150 metres apart, and so on. With greater distance, it may be necessary to use the binoculars to see when the can is hit to make the noise. Record the interval of time determined for each distance. Continue testing until the person with the stopwatch cannot hear the noise made by hitting the can.

Now That You Have Done the Investigation

—Did the time recorded for each test seem to increase as the distance between you and your partner increased?

—By what amount did the difference in time increase?

—How would you describe the effect a greater distance had on the difference in time between when a sound was made and when the sound was heard?

Control your experiment

An experiment, then, is an arrangement to help make an observation. In an experiment, you arrange things so you have control over the observation. Instead of waiting for a chance to observe something, you create the chance. Working with someone to fire the gun and to measure distances when and where you want is an example of such an arrangement.

In doing an experiment, you try to control what you observe. You also try to control the time and place in which you make the observation. That way, you are making observations when you are best prepared to make them accurately. You can also repeat the experiment as often as you wish. Therefore, you can check your data and get as much data as you wish.

Remember that the situation just described is an ideal situation. Scientists cannot always do their work in a nice, comfortable laboratory. If you had a hypothesis about the way a glacier moves, for example, you could not bring a glacier into the laboratory. You would have to go to the glacier to test your ideas.

★ **What other experiments can you think of that cannot be done in a laboratory?**

Photo Research International

Figure 4-2. These two scientists are collecting samples of ice and of meltwater from a glacier. Why, do you suppose, did they travel to the glacier to do these things?

TESTING THEORIES

What are two theories that might be used to explain why glasses "sweat"?

What can you do to help decide which theory is more likely to be correct?

What should be done when a theory does not give good results?

Choosing explanations

What happens to the outside of a glass of ice-cold lemonade or soda pop on a hot, humid, summer day? It gets all wet. Sometimes people say the glass is "sweating." Where is the wetness coming from? One explanation might be that there are tiny openings, or pores, in the glass. Tiny drops of the lemonade from inside the glass seep out through these openings. Let's call this explanation the "tiny-opening theory."

The wetness on the outside of the glass might also be explained by the kinetic-molecular theory. This is the same theory used in Chapter 3 to explain evaporation. When water evaporates, molecules of water mix with molecules of air. This theory also says that molecules move faster when hot than when cold.

The kinetic-molecular theory can explain the wetness on the glass by using the following ideas: Water is always evaporating from oceans, lakes, and rivers. Therefore, the air contains many molecules of water. Air that is next to something very cold becomes cool. The molecules in the air slow down. When the water molecules in the air slow down, they tend to stick together. If a lot of water molecules stick together, they may form drops of water on a cold surface.

★ **Besides glass, what other kinds of containers do you suppose might sweat if they contained ice-cold lemonade?**

Predictions based on theories

To decide which theory is most likely to be correct, you could test them. First, make some predictions based on the tiny-opening theory. Do the same for the kinetic-molecular theory. Then, design an experiment to see which predictions come true.

Let's suppose you first predict what should happen according to the tiny-opening theory. (1) If there are drops on the outside of the glass, they are there because liquid on the inside is seeping out. Then the drops on the outside would be the same as the drops on the inside. That is, if there is lemonade in the glass, the drops on the outside will also be lemonade. (2) If the tiny openings are there, they are there all the time. Drops will always seep out, whether the glass is hot or cold.

Now let's make predictions based on the kinetic-molecular theory. (1) The drops on the outside come from water molecules in the air, not from inside the glass. So, the drops on the outside will be water, no matter what is in the glass. (2) The drops form whenever the water molecules move slowly enough to stick together. Therefore, drops will form on the outside of cold glasses, but not on the outside of warm ones.

What kind of experiments would you do to test these predictions? Two experiments you could try are on pages 86 and 87.

Figure 4–3. The drops of water on a cold glass and the tiny drops of water that make up mist may be explained by one of the theories you have read about. Which theory explains them best?

Investigate

Which theory—the tiny-opening theory or the kinetic-molecular theory—best explains predictions about the kind of liquid that forms on the outside of a glass?

You Will Need

ice, salt, soda pop, sugar, vinegar, 4 glasses

Background

The tiny-opening theory may be used to explain where the drops of liquid on the outside of a glass come from. The tiny-opening theory predicts that the liquid on the outside will be the same as the liquid on the inside. The kinetic-molecular theory may also be used to explain where the drops of liquid come from. But the kinetic-molecular theory says that the liquid on the outside will be water, no matter what is inside the glass. To find out which theory best explains where the liquid comes from, you can do an experiment to test the prediction made by each theory.

What to Do

Put water in 2 glasses. The first glass should have salt mixed into the water. The second glass should have sugar mixed into the water. In a third glass put soda pop, and in a fourth glass put vinegar. Add 3 or 4 ice cubes to each of the 4 glasses. Taste the liquid in each glass. Write down a description of each taste.

After a minute or so, drops of liquid will form on the outside of the glasses. When drops form on the outside, taste them. Record the taste for each glass next to the descriptions of the tastes of the liquids in the glasses.

Now That You Have Done the Investigation

—Did the liquid on the outside of a glass taste like the liquid on the inside of that glass?

—If the taste of the liquid on the outside was different from that on the inside, what did the liquid on the outside taste like?

—Did the results support one theory more than the other? If so, which theory was supported?

Investigate

Which theory—the tiny-opening theory or the kinetic-molecular theory—best explains predictions about why the outside of a glass becomes wet?

You Will Need

Celsius thermometer, ice, salt, 4 glasses

Background

The tiny-opening theory may be used to explain why the outside of a glass becomes wet. The kinetic-molecular theory may also be used to explain why a glass becomes wet. But each explanation is different. According to the tiny-opening theory, a glass will get wet no matter how hot or cold it is. The kinetic-molecular theory predicts that only cold glasses will get wet. This is another experiment to test the prediction made by each theory.

What to Do

Put water in 4 glasses. The first glass should have hot water, and the second glass should have water at room temperature. The third glass should have 3 or 4 ice cubes in the water. The fourth glass should also have 3 or 4 ice cubes in the water, and salt should be mixed with the ice and water. (The salt will make the temperature lower than ice alone will.)

Measure and record the temperature of the water in each glass. While you are measuring the temperature of the water, observe the outside of each glass. Look carefully to see if there is any wetness on the outside of the glasses.

Now That You Have Done the Investigation

—Did the same amount of wetness form on the outside of each glass?

—On which glass did the most wetness form?

—On which glass did the least wetness form?

—Did temperature seem to have anything to do with the amount of wetness that formed on each glass?

—Did your results seem to support one theory more than the other? If so, which theory was supported?

Choosing theories

If you did the two experiments on pages 86 and 87, you found out that predictions based on the tiny-opening theory do not work out. There must be something wrong with the theory. Maybe a different theory is needed.

Since the tiny-opening theory does not explain observations about sweating glasses, a different theory is needed. The kinetic-molecular theory works well in explaining some observations about liquids and gases. The kinetic-molecular theory seems to explain all the observations it was used for. This gives us confidence in the theory. Scientists, too, have confidence in the theory, and will continue using it until some experiment shows the theory to be wrong.

We have confidence in the kinetic-molecular theory because the predictions we made seem to work out pretty well. Since they do work out well, this lends support to the theory. But the theory is not proved. At some future time, the results of an experiment may show that the theory is not completely correct.

Changing theories

Whenever a theory does not give good results, the theory has to be changed or thrown out. This has happened many times in the history of science. A good example of such a theory is one that was once used to explain burning. Many years ago, burning was believed to have something to do with a material called *phlogiston* [floh-JIHS-tuhn].

According to the phlogiston theory, whenever something burned, phlogiston flowed out of the burning material. No one ever saw phlogiston. No one could weigh it, or smell it, or feel it. But phlogiston explained some early observations about burning.

As time passed, ways of studying burning improved. Better measurements of mass and temperature could be made. Phlogiston could no longer explain the observations that were being made. So the idea of phlogiston was given up.

★ **If phlogiston could not be seen, weighed, smelled, or felt, why did people believe it existed?**

Find Out More

The idea of phlogiston was an important explanation of burning for many years. Use reference materials such as encyclopedias and science books to find out more about how scientists explain burning today. Also find out how the modern explanation is different from the phlogiston theory.

88

Courtesy of Westinghouse Electric Corp.

Kinds of Scientists

There are many different fields of study in science. You know what some of them are. Biology, chemistry, geology, physics, and meteorology are some familiar fields of science. In all fields of study, however, there are two kinds of scientists. Some scientists are *experimentalists* [ihk-SPEHR-uh-MEHNT-uhl-uhsts]. Others are *theorists* [THEE-uh-ruhsts].

Experimentalists work with things. They design and use different kinds of tools and instruments. They study many different aspects of the world. Some study matter and energy. Some study living things. Some study weather. They observe carefully. They gather and record information about whatever it is they are studying.

Theorists try to explain what has been observed and discovered in the laboratory. Theorists, then, work with facts, data, and ideas. They propose models and theories to explain what has been observed.

In the past, some famous scientists were both experimentalists and theorists. Some were experimentalists only. Others were theorists only. For example, Sir Isaac Newton did both experimental and theoretical work. Marie Curie was an experimentalist. She was a winner of two Nobel prizes for her work. Albert Einstein was an outstanding theorist who had no interest in laboratory work.

Today there is a tremendous amount of scientific knowledge. Perhaps you wish to become a scientist. If so, you will need a college education to prepare for such a career. Perhaps you could help develop a theory or a model to help explain something about how the world works.

R. Ritchie/FPG

New products and new theories must be tested again and again before they are accepted. Would you like a job that involves testing products and ideas?

Reviewing and Extending

SUMMING UP

1. The process of setting up a situation and making observations is called experimenting.
2. Testing ideas was not done by philosophers thousands of years ago, but testing is used by scientists today.
3. In an experiment, you arrange things to try to control what you observe.
4. A theory is tested by finding out if predictions based on the theory are true.
5. Scientists have confidence in a theory when predictions based on the theory work out well.
6. Whenever the results of an experiment are not what the theory predicts, the theory has to be changed or thrown out.

CHECKING UP

Vocabulary   Write the numerals *1–5* on your paper. Each numbered phrase describes a term from the following list. On your paper, write the term next to the numeral of the phrase that describes it.

phlogiston   superstition   kinetic-molecular theory
experimenting   prediction   tiny-opening theory

1. process of setting up a situation and making observations
2. theory that explains evaporation
3. statement made in advance about the outcome of an experiment
4. material believed at one time to have something to do with burning
5. idea that people believe, although there is no evidence for it

Knowledge and Understanding   Write the numerals *6–9* on your paper. Beside each numeral, write the word or words that best complete the sentence having that numeral.

6. The ideas that early "scientists" had were (*never believed, always tested, sometimes false*).
7. In ancient times, philosophers (*spent a lot of time talking about things, used superstitions to test observations, used predictions to test explanations*).
8. Superstitions are often believed (*after they have been tested, even though there is no evidence for them, because they always come true*).
9. The tiny-opening theory is not a good way to explain observations made about sweating glasses because (*cold glasses do not sweat, predictions based on the theory did not work out, observations based on the theory were too easy to make*).

Concepts   Beside each of the numerals *10–13* on your paper, write the word or words that best complete the sentence having that numeral.

10. Today, scientists learn about the world by (*just talking about the things they observe around them; jumping to conclusions; observing, measuring, explaining, and testing their explanations*).
11. An experiment (*must always be done in a laboratory, can only be done by waiting for a chance to observe something, is best done if you can control the time and place in which you make observations*).
12. One advantage of controlling an experiment is that you can (*prove your predictions, control the results, repeat the experiment over and over*).
13. The kinetic-molecular theory explains wetness on the outside of a glass as (*liquid seeping through the glass, water molecules from the air condensing on the glass, an example of phlogiston*).

Application and Critical Thinking   Answer the following questions as briefly as you can without leaving out any important ideas.

14. Predict whether or not tiny drops of water will appear on cold surfaces of materials other than glass. Then describe a procedure that could be used to find out whether or not your prediction is correct.
15. Based on what you learned in this chapter, would you say that a person sweats for the same reason that a glass of cold liquid sweats? Explain.

DOING MORE

1. Remove and discard the core from each of several apples. Then freeze the apples. Try to discover by using your senses what effect freezing has on the apples. For example, compare the taste of a fresh apple with that of a frozen apple. Have the frozen apples changed in color, texture, or juiciness? Examine frozen and fresh apples with a microscope. Can you find an explanation for some of the changes you observed? Use your explanation to predict what might happen if you froze lettuce, potatoes, or other foods. Set up and conduct an experiment to test your predictions.
2. Prepare a report for the class on the life and accomplishments of Galileo. Stress Galileo's accomplishments in science—especially experimental science. But also mention his work in other areas, because he was a person of many talents.

Pros and Cons

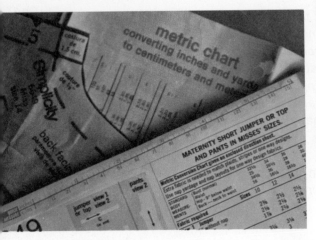

While the changeover to the use of SI units is taking place, you will see many materials intended to help people learn the units. How might what you see pictured here help people learn SI units?

Changing to SI—Will It Be Worth the Trouble?

Before many years pass, the things you buy will be measured in different units than they are now. Milk and gasoline will be measured in litres, not quarts and gallons. Butter and sugar will be measured in kilograms, not pounds. Wood that is now called a "2 by 4" might be referred to as a "5 by 10." The reason for all these differences, of course, is that the United States is changing from the customary system (commonly called the English system) of weights and measures to the International System of Units (*Le Système International d'Unités,* or SI as it is abbreviated in all languages).

There will be some advantages in this change. Many people think these advantages will make the change worthwhile. You might say these advantages are the "pros," or arguments in favor of changing, that make the change worth the trouble. On the other hand, changing to SI will have some disadvantages. These disadvantages are the "cons," or arguments against changing, that tend to make the change not worth the trouble.

One argument in favor of the change to SI is that SI is easier to use than the system we now use. SI is easier because there are fewer kinds of basic units. For example, the SI unit for distance is the metre. All distances are expressed as some multiple or subdivision of the metre. Also, all the multiples and subdivisions are related to the basic unit by some power of ten. Contrast this with

92

our customary system, which includes the inch, the foot, the yard, the rod, the chain, the furlong, and the mile. These customary units are not related to each other in an easy-to-use manner.

Another argument in favor of changing to SI is that practically all other nations use SI. The United States loses many millions of dollars in foreign trade each year because our products cannot be used with the products of other countries. The reason our products cannot be used is because they differ in size.

Those people who argue that changing will not be worthwhile claim that we are getting along very well with the customary system. After all, of all the countries in the world, the United States has one of the highest standards of living. Why bother to change? Furthermore, some people claim that the cost of the changeover will be very great. Many factories will have to retool—that is, put in all new machines—to make their products in the new sizes. The old machines will have to be kept, however, to make replacement parts for products already in use. Shops where machines are repaired will need two sets of tools. One set will be needed to repair machines that use SI sizes. The other will be needed for working on older machines that were made before the changeover. Couldn't the money that would be spent in changing over be better used in building hospitals and taking care of needy people?

Some people claim the change is not worth the trouble because it will cause confusion in many ways. Maps give distances in miles. New maps will give distances

Artstreet

In some cases, SI units are already in use. Where, besides in recipes and in the Olympic Games, have you seen SI units in use?

VEGETABLES, HERBS, AND SALADS   255

541. **Stuffed Tomatoes.** Cooking time 20 minutes

Temperature 400° F. (200° C.) Mark 6.

Quantities for 6 helpings:

6 large tomatoes (about
   1 lb. or 500 g.)
½ oz. fat (1 Tbs.)
½ onion, chopped
1 oz. chopped bacon
   (25 g.)
1 Tbs. grated cheese

1 tsp. chopped parsley
¼ tsp. salt
Pinch of pepper
Pinch of sugar
Pinch of grated nutmeg
½ c. fresh breadcrumbs

Measures level. Cut a slice off the stem end of the tomatoes. Remove the pulp carefully, using a small teaspoon, and rub it through a sieve. Fry the bacon and onion in the fat and mix with the pulp and other ingredients. Stuff the tomatoes with this and sprinkle the tops with crumbs. Bake in a moderate oven for 20 minutes. Serve hot.

Photo Research International

in kilometres. Imagine what might happen if someone got confused using such maps while on a vacation. Building materials are sold in customary units, not SI units. If someone became confused while buying lumber, that person might have problems during the construction of a building. These are only a couple of examples of the confusion that might be caused by the change.

The pros and cons given here are not the only arguments that could be used to decide whether or not changing to SI will be worthwhile. Talk about the change to SI with your teacher, with your friends, and with your family. What do they think about the change—is it going to be worth the trouble? What do you think?

Investigate On Your Own

1. Obtain a sample of the mineral called galena. Determine its density. Obtain a sample of the mineral called quartz. Determine its density. How does the density of galena compare with that of quartz? Break the samples of galena and quartz by covering the samples with a cloth and hitting them with a hammer. Determine the density of one of the larger pieces of galena and one of the larger pieces of quartz. What differences do you note, if any, between the first determination of a mineral's density and the second determination? From this activity, what can you say about the density of materials?

2. Obtain a block of wood having the following dimensions: 10 cm wide, 10 cm high, and 20 cm long (4 inches, 4 inches, 8 inches). Put a screw eye in the center of one end of the wood. Tie one end of the string to the screw eye. Tie the other end of the string to a spring scale. While holding the scale, drag the block of wood across samples of wood, cork, rubber, sandpaper, etc. What materials seem to cause the most drag on the block of wood? What hypothesis can be made from this experiment?

3. Compare barometer readings and weather forecasts for about three weeks. Form a hypothesis about using the barometer readings to forecast weather changes.

Read On Your Own

Adler, Irving, *The Changing Tools of Science: From Yardstick to Cyclotron.* New York: The John Day Company, 1973.

The tools used by scientists, ranging from the simplest measuring devices to complicated machines, are explored in detail.

Asimov, Isaac, *Great Ideas of Science.* Boston: Houghton Mifflin Company, 1969.

In this book, the development of a scientific theory is described step by step. This book also shows how one theory led to many important ideas.

Asimov, Isaac, *More Words of Science.* Boston: Houghton Mifflin Company, 1972.

This book is an informal survey of the language of modern science. Each description goes beyond a narrow definition in providing a great deal of valuable information.

Hirsch, S. Carl, *Meter Means Measure—The Story of the Metric System.* New York: The Viking Press, 1973.

In this book, you can read about the history and the future of the metric system of measurement in this country. You can also read about some experiences famous scientists have had with the metric system.

Klein, Aaron E., *The Hidden Contributors: Black Scientists and Inventors in America.* New York: Doubleday & Company, 1971.

This book is about people whose contributions have added much to our lives. Each story describes personal background as well as important accomplishments.

Soule, Gardner, *Surprising Facts—About Our World and Beyond.* New York: G. P. Putnam's Sons, 1971.

Unusual and surprising ideas about things of science are described in this book.

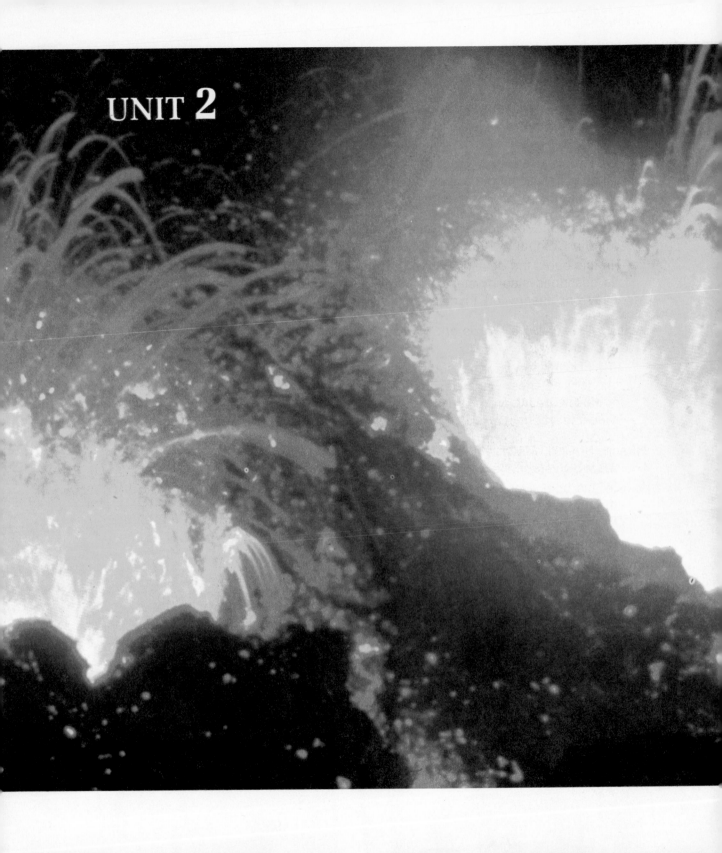

UNIT 2

MATTER

Its Forms and Changes

Just what is matter? Perhaps you think things such as air and water and rocks are matter. If so, you are right. All these things are matter. But if they are all matter, they must be alike in some ways. How are they alike? Some of the ways that kinds of matter differ from one another are easy to see. But does matter differ in ways that are not easily seen? Can matter be changed from one kind into other kinds? And, if so, what causes these changes in matter? These questions and others are discussed in this unit.

Chapters

Photo Research International

CHAPTER 5

Describing Matter

Each kind of matter can differ from other kinds in many ways. Some differences, such as color, are easy to see. Other differences cannot be seen. They must be determined in other ways. For example, gold is a yellow-colored metal. Iron pyrite looks so much like gold that it is often called fool's gold. But these two kinds of matter are very different. Fool's gold can be made to separate into two other kinds of matter, iron and sulfur. Gold, however, cannot be separated into other kinds of matter.

The same kind of matter can occur in different forms. For example, water can occur as ice, as water, or as steam. Ice, water, and steam appear to be quite different from each other. Yet they are all water.

So describing matter is not always easy. Different kinds of matter may look alike. A single kind of matter may occur in several forms that look very different. However, there are ways to describe matter so that each kind can be identified. Chapter 5 is about some of these ways of describing matter.

How many different forms of water can you see in this picture? How are the forms different from each other? How are they alike?

Daniel Brody

IDENTIFYING MATTER

What are some special properties of matter?
What are some general properties of matter?
*What kind of properties can be used to tell one
    kind of matter from another?*
*What property makes wood and oil useful as
    fuels?*

How matter differs

Suppose you are looking at three metal balls. All are the same size. One ball is made of gold, one is made of silver, and the third is made of aluminum. Do you think you can tell which ball is which?

Telling which ball is made of gold is easy. The gold ball has a yellow color. The other two balls have a silvery color. But how can you tell the ball of silver from the ball of aluminum if they both have the same color? If you lift the two balls, you can tell them apart very easily. The silver ball is almost five times as heavy as the aluminum ball. In fact, you can use heaviness as well as color to tell which ball is made of gold. The ball of gold will be almost twice as heavy as the ball of silver and almost ten times as heavy as the ball of aluminum.

Each of the metal balls differs from the others in some way. Characteristics, such as color and heaviness, that can be used to tell one kind of matter from another are called *special properties* [SPEHSH-uhl PRAHP-urt-eez].

Each kind of matter has one or more special properties that no other kind of matter has. These properties make each kind of matter different from all other kinds. But all matter is alike in some ways, too.

Some ways all matter is alike

Have you ever dropped something into a full pail of water? If so, you saw some of the water flow over the edge of the pail. Whatever was dropped into the pail took up some of the space that had been filled with water. As a result, some water was pushed out of the pail.

99

Figure 5–1. The jar was originally filled with water. Now air is bubbling into the jar. What happens to the water in the jar? Does air take up space? How do you know?

Find Out More

The flame test is a special test used to identify some kinds of matter. What is a flame test? How is this test done? What are some kinds of matter that can be identified with this test? How does the test help identify a kind of matter?

Air can also push water out of one place and into another. Look at Figure 5–1. Air is bubbling into an upside-down jar that has been filled with water. As the air enters the jar, some water is pushed out.

In both examples, some matter was made to move because other matter was put into the same space. From the two examples, you should have noticed two facts about matter: (1) Matter takes up space. (2) Two pieces of matter cannot be in the same space at the same time. These are two *general properties* of matter. That is, all matter has these two properties.

The amount of space matter takes up is the *volume* [VAHL-yuhm] of that matter. Of course, a fist-sized rock takes up more space than a tiny stone. The fist-sized rock has a greater volume than the tiny stone. However, any piece of matter, large or small, takes up some space.

Have you ever lifted two objects to find out which one felt heavier? If so, you know something about another general property of matter. All matter has *weight* [WAYT].

When you weigh something, you are measuring the pull of the earth's gravity on that object. But why do some things weigh more than others? The answer is that some things have more matter in them than others do. The amount of matter in an object is called the *mass* [MAS] of that object. For objects on the earth, the more mass an object has, the greater the pull of gravity on it. Therefore, the greater the mass of an object, the more that object will weigh on the earth.

Using properties

The general properties of matter cannot be used to tell one kind of matter from another kind. Every kind of matter has these properties. It is the special properties that are used to tell one kind of matter from other kinds.

For example, you use both sugar and salt on your food. The table salt you use on your food is in the form of small white particles. Sugar often has the same form. So, the properties of color, size, and shape are the same for both sugar and salt. You have to use some other special property to tell sugar from salt. One way is by taste.

(*Text continues on page 102.*)

Investigate

How can you find the volume of an odd-shaped object?

You Will Need

graduated cylinder, water, object such as a small rough rock or a large bolt

Background

Finding the volume of a box is easy. All you have to do is multiply the measures of the length times the height times the width of the box. Some objects have odd shapes that are difficult to measure. You can find the volume of some odd-shaped objects by using one of the general properties of matter. This property is that two amounts of matter cannot be in the same space at the same time.

What to Do

Pour water into a graduated cylinder until the cylinder is about half full. Try to do this in such a way that little or no water splashes onto the inside walls of the cylinder. Notice and record the level of the water. This reading is the volume of the water. You may notice that the surface of the water is curved instead of level. Be sure your reading is at the lowest point of the curved surface.

Now, carefully lower an object, such as a rock, into the water. Record the level of the water with the object in it. This reading is the volume of the water and the object. Find the volume of the object by subtracting the reading of the water level without the object in the water from the reading with the object in the water. If you wish, try to find the volume of other objects by this method.

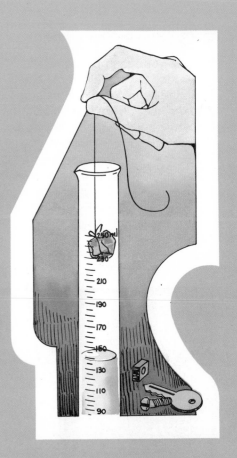

Now That You Have Done the Investigation

—Did the water and object you placed in it take up the same space at the same time? How do you know?

—What was the volume of the object you placed in the water?

—Do you think this method of finding volume could be used for an odd-shaped wooden object that floats? Why or why not?

—Do you think this method of finding volume could be used for salt or sugar? Why or why not?

Taste is useful in telling sugar from salt. But other kinds of matter can also look like sugar and salt. Some of these are poisons. Tasting them is very dangerous. You should never taste anything unless you are sure that tasting it is not dangerous.

★ **What are some things you identify by size or shape? By color? By taste?**

Properties and uses

Once the special properties of a certain kind of matter are known, that kind of matter can be identified wherever it is found. But special properties are important for a reason other than their use in identifying matter. How a kind of matter is used depends on the special properties of that matter.

For example, a furnace made of wood would not be very useful. One of the properties of wood is that wood burns. So a wooden furnace would burn as soon as a fire was started inside. However iron doesn't burn that easily. Iron is very useful for making furnaces.

One of the special properties of coal, oil, and gasoline is that these kinds of matter do burn easily. Because they

H. Armstrong Roberts

Figure 5–2. The fireman is wearing a suit made of asbestos. Why is asbestos used for suits like this? What other things might asbestos be used for?

burn easily, they are useful as fuels. So the property of how easily a kind of matter burns determines whether that matter can be used as a fuel.

★ **What are some properties of a piece of chalk that make the chalk useful for writing and drawing?**

PHASES OF MATTER

What are the three phases of matter?
In what phase of matter is an ice cube?
How is the liquid phase of matter like the solid phase?
How is the gas phase of matter like the liquid phase?

How matter occurs

Do you think one kind of matter can occur in several forms, each very different from the others? Perhaps you had not thought of this before. But think about water. Water can freeze and change into ice. Or it can boil and change into steam. Ice, water, and steam appear to be quite different. Yet each is made up of only water.

Scientists use the term *phase* [FAYZ] to refer to a certain way matter occurs. There are three phases of matter—*solid* [SAHL-uhd], *liquid* [LIHK-wuhd], and *gas*. Ice is the solid phase of water. Water itself is the liquid phase. Steam is the gas phase.

The solid phase

If you were given three jars, each filled with matter in a different phase, you would have no trouble picking out the jar filled with solid objects. But you might have some trouble explaining just what a solid is and how it differs from a liquid or a gas.

If you think about your pencil and this book, you could say that they are both solids, but they are not the same thing. They are alike in some ways and they differ in some ways. In telling how they differ you might say that the pencil is long, thin, and round. The book, however, is thick and somewhat square-shaped.

But how are the pencil and the book alike? Each one has a certain shape. Each one's shape will not change unless something is done to make it change. Besides, the pencil and the book each take up a certain amount of space. As long as nothing is done to change them, they will always take up the same amount of space. In other words, all solids have a *definite* [DEHF-(uh-)nuht] shape and a definite volume.

Another property of solids is that it is hard for other kinds of matter to go through them. If you drop a dish on a solid kitchen floor, the dish will not go through the floor. Instead, it remains on the surface. Liquids and gases usually do not go through solids easily either.

The liquid phase

You know enough about liquids to know that water, soda pop, and milk are liquids. You can pour some water into a glass. Then you can pour the water from the glass into a jar. Whether the water is in the glass or in the jar, the amount of water will be the same. The volume of the water does not change. So liquids are like solids in one way. Both liquids and solids have a definite volume.

However, in being poured from the glass into the jar, the water changes shape. In the glass, the water has the shape of the glass. In the jar, the water has the shape of the jar. So liquids, unlike solids, do not have a definite shape.

Another difference between liquids and solids is that it is easier for other kinds of matter to move through liquids than through solids. When you drop a rock into a pond, the rock moves through the water until it comes to rest on the solid bottom of the pond.

★ **In what way or ways are ice cubes and water different? In what way or ways are they alike?**

The gas phase

You have probably seen many solids and liquids. But because most gases are colorless, you may not have seen

Figure 5–3. Air is being pumped out of the bell jar. What will happen to the balloon? How would you explain what will happen to the balloon?

any gases. Gases are like liquids in one way. For example, you could put air into a balloon. Then you can squeeze the balloon and cause it to have a different shape. The shape of the gas changes as the shape of the balloon changes. Gases, like liquids, have no definite shape.

Gases differ from liquids in that a gas will spread out to fill a space, no matter how large the space is. Look at Figure 5–3. A small amount of air was blown into the balloon and the neck of the balloon was knotted. Then the balloon was put into a bell jar attached to a vacuum pump. As the air is pumped out of the jar, the balloon gets larger. Why? As the air around the balloon is pumped out of the jar, the air in the balloon begins to spread out and fill this space. Another property of gases, then, is that they have no definite volume. They fill any container in which they are placed.

Matter moves through gases more easily than through liquids. A rock moves through air much faster than it moves through water. You can move through air faster than you can through water. In fact every time you move, you are moving through air. You move through air so easily that you do not even notice the air, unless you are moving very fast.

★ **In what way or ways are air and water alike? In what way or ways are they different?**

For You to Think About

Suppose you have an open jar that is about half full of sand and water. Is any of the matter in the jar in the solid phase? In the liquid phase? In the gas phase? Name the kind of matter that represents each phase of matter present in the jar.

Investigate

Can you pour a gas?

You Will Need

small candle, small dish or candle holder, beaker or jar, vinegar, baking soda, matches

Background

Carbon dioxide is a gas that is easy to make by mixing vinegar with baking soda. Besides being easy to make, carbon dioxide is safe to use. But it is invisible. You cannot see whether or not it can be poured. However, a candle will not burn if carbon dioxide is present. You can use this fact to find out if you can pour carbon dioxide from a container, just as you might pour a liquid.

What to Do

Light the candle and use some melted wax from the candle to make the candle stand upright in the small dish. Pour some vinegar into the beaker. Next, drop a small amount of baking soda into the vinegar. Observe what happens when the vinegar and baking soda mix.

Slowly tip the beaker over the candle flame as if you were pouring something on the flame. However, do not let any of the vinegar and baking soda pour from the beaker onto the candle. Observe what happens to the candle flame.

Now That You Have Done the Investigation

—Could you tell that a gas formed when the baking soda was put into the vinegar? How?

—Could you see any gas that formed?

—When the beaker was tipped over the candle, could you see any gas pouring out of the beaker?

—When the beaker was tipped over the candle, what happened to the candle flame?

—Do you think any gas was poured from the beaker? Explain.

—Do you think carbon dioxide is heavier than air or lighter than air? Explain.

—Do you think this gas could be used in fire extinguishers? Explain.

Figure 5–4. In 1808, John Dalton pro-
posed the first atomic theory based on
the results of experiments. Many of
Dalton's ideas about atoms form the
basis of the atomic theory used by
scientists today.

ELEMENTS, COMPOUNDS, AND MIXTURES

What is a substance?
How is an element different from a compound?
How is a mixture like a compound? How is it
  different from a compound?

An important theory

Scientists think that all matter is made up of tiny
particles called *atoms* [AT-uhmz]. This idea about matter
is called the *atomic theory* [uh-TAHM-ihk THEE-uh-ree].
The value of a theory depends on how useful the theory
is in explaining why certain things happen. In studying
matter, scientists have found the atomic theory to be very
valuable.

Scientists often describe matter in terms of another
kind of particle. This particle is called a *molecule* [MAHL-
ih-KYOO(UH)L]. Molecules are made up of atoms. In some

kinds of matter, such as iron and copper, a single atom is thought of as also being a molecule of that kind of matter. Most molecules, however, consist of two or more atoms joined together in a certain way. In some of these molecules, all the atoms in the molecule are alike. A molecule of oxygen has two oxygen atoms joined together. Other molecules have two or more different kinds of atoms joined together. A sugar molecule is made up of carbon, hydrogen, and oxygen atoms.

You may have heard of a kind of matter being described as a *substance* [SUHB-stuhn(t)s]. Scientists use the word "substance" only to describe certain kinds of matter. A kind of matter is thought of as being a substance only if every molecule in that matter is the same. Some substances have only one kind of atom in their molecules. Such a substance is called an *element* [EHL-uh-muhnt]. Other substances have molecules made up of more than one kind of atom joined in a certain way. These substances are called *compounds* [KAHM-POWNDZ]. Whether a substance is an element or a compound, all of the molecules in that substance are alike.

★ **Iron molecules have only one kind of atom. Sugar molecules have three different kinds of atoms. What kind of substance is iron, an element or a compound? What kind of substance is sugar, an element or a compound?**

Elements

Elements are substances that have only one kind of atom. All together there are more than 100 known elements. Each element has its own kind of atom. So there are more than 100 different kinds of atoms. Some things you use everyday are elements. These include iron, tin, oxygen, and aluminum.

Only a few elements are found as pure elements in or on the earth. Gold and copper are two of them. Carbon, in the form of diamonds, is another. The table in Figure 5–5 gives a more complete list of the pure elements found in or on the earth.

ELEMENTS FOUND IN PURE FORM

Element	Phase	Abundance
Oxygen	Gas	Common
Nitrogen	Gas	Common
Hydrogen	Gas	Rare
Helium	Gas	Rare
Neon	Gas	Rare
Argon	Gas	Rare
Krypton	Gas	Rare
Xenon	Gas	Rare
Radon	Gas	Rare
Carbon	Solid	Rare
Sulfur	Solid	Common
Copper	Solid	Common
Gold	Solid	Rare
Silver	Solid	Rare
Lead	Solid	Rare
Mercury	Liquid	Rare

Figure 5–5. Which of the elements in this list have you seen in the pure form? What are the names of the pure elements shown in the pictures below?

Photos from Mary and Loren Root/Root Resources

Elements may be found as either solids, liquids, or gases. Some, such as iron and lead, are found as solids. Mercury, the silver-colored metal often used in thermometers, is found as a liquid. The air you breathe is made up of several elements which are usually found as gases.

★ **What are the names of some gases that are found in the air? What information would you need in order to know whether or not these particular gases are elements?**

Compounds

A compound is also a substance. In this way a compound is like an element. However, the molecules of a compound are made up of more than one kind of atom. That is, a compound is made up of two or more different elements. There are only about 100 known elements. Most elements can combine with other elements to form compounds. There are several thousand known compounds.

To better understand the differences between elements and compounds, think about water. You use water everyday. You know that water is a clear, colorless liquid. One drop of water looks like any other drop. But is water an element or is it a compound?

If you do the investigation on page 111, you will see that water can be changed into two other substances. Since water can be separated into other substances, it must be made up of at least two kinds of atoms. Therefore, water is a compound.

★ **When iron combines with oxygen, rust is formed. Is rust an element or a compound? Explain how you know.**

Mixtures

Have you ever mixed cereal, fruit, and milk in a bowl? If so, you have made a form of matter called a *mixture* [MIHKS-chur]. In a mixture, two or more kinds of matter are mixed together. The kinds of matter are not combined. They are simply mixed.

(*Text continues on page 112.*)

Find Out More

Iron, salt, plastic, aluminum, tincture of iodine, sugar, and sterling silver are things people use in their everyday activities. Which of these are elements? Which are compounds? Which are mixtures? What elements make up the things that are compounds? What kinds of matter make up the things that are mixtures?

Investigate

What elements make up water?

You Will Need

beaker, test-tube holder, water, wood splint, 2 test tubes, insulated copper wire, 6-volt dry cell, dilute sulfuric acid

Background

Oxygen and hydrogen are both clear, colorless gases. But there is a way to tell them apart. If a flame is held near the opening of a test tube of hydrogen, the hydrogen burns rapidly, making a loud sound. The way to test for oxygen is to start a wood splint burning and blow out the flame so the wood is just a glowing ember. The glowing end is stuck into the test tube. If oxygen is present, the wood will burst into flame.

What to Do

Pour water into a beaker until it is about half full. Fill two test tubes with water and set them in the beaker as shown. Be careful not to let any of the water run out of the test tubes. Pour about 15 milliliters of dilute sulfuric acid into the water in the beaker.

Remove the insulation from each end of 2 pieces of copper wire. Bend one end of each piece of copper wire into a hook, and slip one hook into each of the test tubes, as shown. Connect the other end of each wire to the dry cell as shown.

Observe what happens along the part of the wire inside of the test tubes. Also observe what is happening at the top of each of the test tubes. After about 5 minutes disconnect one of the wires on the dry cell. Light a wood splint. Use a test-tube holder to pick up the test tube with the greatest amount of gas in it. Keep the open end of the tube pointing down. Hold the splint near the test tube and turn the opening toward the flame. Test the other tube with a glowing piece of wood as described in the background.

Now That You Have Done the Investigation

—What appeared along the bare part of the wires when the wires were connected to the dry cell?

—What gas do you think was in the first test tube?

—What gas do you think was in the second test tube?

—What elements do you think make up water?

Figure 5–6. The colored liquids shown above are solutions—one kind of mixture. The concrete is also a mixture. Can you tell by looking that the concrete is a mixture? That the solutions are mixtures? Explain.

You can easily see that there are different kinds of matter in some mixtures. Look at a piece of broken concrete, for example. You can see different-sized pieces of rock and grains of sand. You can also see the cement that holds the pieces together. Many rocks are like concrete in that you can see different kinds of matter along broken surfaces of these rocks.

In some other mixtures it is not so easy to see that there are different kinds of matter in the mixture. Sugar and water is one mixture in which you cannot see that there are two different substances. One drop of sugar water in a glass looks and even tastes like every other drop. Mixtures that appear to be the same throughout have a special name. They are called *solutions* [suh-LOO-shuhnz]. Some solutions, such as the sugar and water mixture, are liquids. Other solutions are gases. Air is a solution of gases. Some solutions are solid. Perhaps you have seen jewelry marked sterling silver. Pure silver is too soft to use for jewelry. So the pure silver is melted and mixed with other metals, such as copper. The melted metals cool to form a solid solution called an *alloy* [AL-oy].

★ **What are some mixtures you make and use? How do you know that they are mixtures? Are any of these mixtures solutions?**

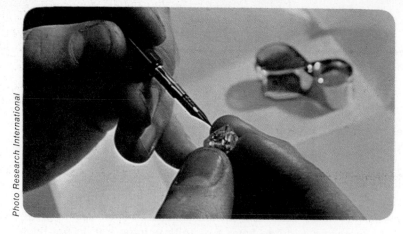

Photo Research International

Why is it important for a person who works with diamonds to know a lot about the properties of diamonds?

Knowing Properties Is Useful in Some Jobs

If you were looking for a place to mine iron, what would you look for? Iron is a dark gray metal. However, it does not occur as pure iron in the earth. Rocks with a lot of iron in them do have certain properties that help people identify them. Like iron, some of these rocks turn rusty when they are exposed to air. Others remain black in color but feel unusually heavy.

Knowing the properties of rocks and minerals is important in many jobs. Some people work at finding new places to obtain materials such as iron, aluminum, gold, oil, and gemstones. These people have to know more than just the properties of the material they are looking for. They also have to know the properties of the kinds of rock in which that material is found. For example, oil is found only beneath certain kinds of rock. Finding such rocks may mean that there is oil below.

People who cut and polish gemstones for jewelry must also know the properties of these gemstones. Some shatter if they get too warm. Others break if they are cut in certain directions. Some are so hard that only diamond powder can be used to grind them into shape.

Other people who must know the properties of various materials are those who work in laboratories testing and identifying minerals. Sometimes people send them new kinds of minerals. By testing these minerals, laboratory workers can find out if the material is different from any known kinds of matter.

Of course, not everyone interested in rocks and minerals studies the properties of rocks and minerals as part of a job. Some do it as a hobby. But many who begin studying these properties as a hobby find that such a study becomes an interesting and challenging career.

Reviewing and Extending

SUMMING UP

1. Properties that are the same for every kind of matter are called general properties. For example, all matter has volume, weight, and mass.
2. Each kind of matter also has some special properties that no other kind of matter has. It is the special properties that are used to identify kinds of matter.
3. There are three phases in which matter occurs—the solid phase, the liquid phase, and the gas phase.
4. Solids have a definite volume and a definite shape. Liquids have a definite volume but do not have a definite shape. Gases have neither a definite volume nor a definite shape.
5. According to the atomic theory, all matter is made up of tiny particles called atoms. Atoms make up another kind of particle called a molecule.
6. A substance is a kind of matter in which all of the molecules are alike. A substance may be either an element or a compound.
7. In an element, all of the atoms are alike. In a compound, the molecules are made up of two or more different kinds of atoms.
8. A mixture is formed when two or more substances are mixed. The substances can be mixed in any given amounts.
9. Solutions are a special kind of mixture which look the same throughout. Solid solutions are called alloys.

CHECKING UP

Vocabulary   Write the numerals 1–5 on your paper. Each numbered phrase describes a term from the following list. On your paper, write the term next to the numeral of the phrase that describes it.

properties   element   liquid
solid   compound   solution

1. matter that has definite volume and definite shape
2. used to tell one kind of matter from another
3. matter in which the molecules contain only one kind of atom
4. matter that has definite volume but no definite shape
5. matter in which the molecules contain at least two kinds of atoms

Knowledge and Understanding   Write the numerals 6–10 on your paper. Beside each numeral, write the word or words that best complete the sentence having that numeral.

6. At room temperature, water is (a solid, a liquid, an element).

114

7. Pure gold is melted and mixed with other metals to form a solid solution called (*an element, a compound, an alloy*).
8. Matter occurs in (*one, two, three*) different phases.
9. Air is an example of (*an element, a compound, a mixture*).
10. Pure gold is (*an element, a compound, a mixture*).

Concepts   Beside each of the numerals *11–15* on your paper, write the word or words that best complete the sentence having that numeral.

11. All _____ have a definite volume and a definite shape.
12. Gases are like liquids in that both liquids and gases have no definite _____.
13. Special _____ are used to tell one kind of matter from all other kinds of matter.
14. Liquids are like solids in that both solids and liquids have a definite _____.
15. Air is a _____ of gases.

Application and Critical Thinking   Answer the following questions as briefly as you can without leaving out any important ideas.

16. In what way or ways are a brick, water in a glass, and air in a balloon alike? What are at least two ways in which each of these three things differs from the other two?
17. Why is it important to know the properties of matter?
18. Give examples of ways in which properties determine how a kind of matter can be used.
19. Why are there so many more compounds than there are elements?

DOING MORE

1. Get a sample of some rock or mineral. Use your senses and any tools you have to find out all you can about the properties of the sample. Write a description of your sample, and put it with several other samples of rocks and minerals. Give your description to a friend and have your friend try to pick out the one you described.
2. Compounds are forms of matter that contain two or more elements. Using references, make a list of at least twenty compounds that contain only two elements. Write the names of the elements contained in each of the compounds. How many of these compounds contain the same elements? If two compounds contain the same elements, how do they differ?

CHAPTER 6

The Structure of Matter

In Chapter 5 you read that all matter is made up of atoms. There are more than 100 different kinds of atoms known today. Matter that has only one kind of atom is called an element. Matter that has two or more different kinds of atoms joined together in certain ways is called a compound. All these statements indicate that atoms are a very important part of our ideas about the makeup, or *structure* [STRUHK-chur], of matter.

The idea that matter is made up of atoms was first suggested more than 2,000 years ago. As time passed, matter was studied in many different ways. Each time something new was learned, the old ideas about atoms had to be examined in light of the new knowledge. As a result, scientists' ideas about atoms have changed many times through the years.

What were some of the early ideas about atoms and matter? How do modern ideas differ from the earlier ideas? How are the atoms of different elements alike? How are they different? How do atoms join together to form compounds? These are some of the topics discussed in Chapter 6.

The idea that matter is made of atoms is not new, but it is widely used to explain the structure of matter. Do you think this teacher is using the idea of atoms to teach about the structure of matter? Explain.

Courtesy of Science Related Materials, Inc.

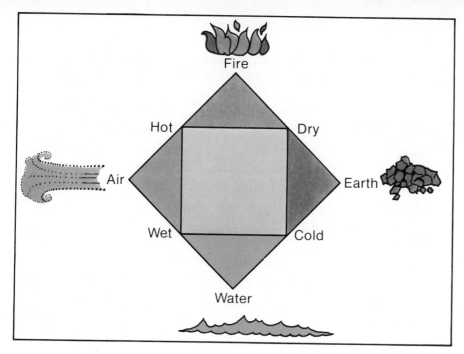

Figure 6–1. This diagram was used by people long ago to explain the four-element theory of matter. Are all of the "elements" on this diagram believed to be matter today? Are any of these "elements" what a scientist would call an element today?

THE PARTS OF ATOMS

What elements were thought to make up all matter according to the "four-element" idea of matter?

What is indirect evidence?

What are the three main parts of an atom?

Early ideas about matter

No one knows when people first began to wonder about the makeup of matter. But through the years, there have been many different ideas about matter. Some of the ideas were very different from what is known about matter today. About 400 B.C., for example, many people believed that all matter was made up of only four "elements"—water, earth, air, and fire. Each element had two of the four properties—hot, cold, wet, and dry. See Figure 6–1.

No one could ever prove this idea, and no scientists believe it today. However, at that time, the "four-element" idea seemed to explain a lot about matter. So the "four-element" idea was believed to be correct until about 300 years ago.

117

Even while the "four-element" idea was the most popular idea, other ideas about matter were also being presented. One idea, suggested in Greece about 2,000 years ago, was a lot like many of the ideas believed today. That idea included these points: (1) Matter is made up of tiny particles called atoms. (2) Atoms are too small ever to be seen. (3) All living and nonliving things are made up of atoms. (4) Each kind of atom is only a little different from other kinds of atoms. (5) Atoms cannot be broken up into smaller parts or destroyed in any way.

Long ago no one tried to do any tests to find out if either the "four-element" idea or the atomic idea was correct. Instead the ideas were simply talked about and argued about. More and more people came to believe in the "four-element" idea than in the idea about atoms. So the idea that matter is made up of atoms was forgotten for many years.

Learning about atoms

As people learned more about matter, they began to find out that water, earth, and air could be broken down into other kinds of matter. They found out that fire was not matter. The "four-element" idea began to be questioned. In the 1700's scientists agreed to use the word "element" in a new way. They agreed that an element was matter that could not be broken down into simpler forms of matter. To describe what they thought was the smallest part of an element, scientists used the word "atom"—the same word used by the ancient Greeks. However, scientists still did not really know if there were such things as atoms.

How can something as small as an atom be studied? Have you ever shaken a present to find out what was inside the box before you unwrapped it? If so, you know that you can tell from the sound if there are many or few pieces inside. You can also tell something about the size and shape of the object or objects inside by the way the box feels when you shake it.

As you shake the box, you form a picture in your mind of what is inside. You form this picture by using what you have learned about how other things sounded and felt in other boxes you have shaken. In other words, you use *indirect evidence* [IHN-duh-REHKT EHV-uhd-uhn(t)s] to find out about something you can't see.

Scientists also used indirect evidence when they began to study atoms. There was no way anyone could see atoms. So atoms themselves could not be studied. However, larger amounts of matter could be studied. From their studies, scientists found that matter behaved in certain ways. In many cases, the ways matter behaved was best explained by the idea that matter was made up of atoms. From studying larger amounts of matter, scientists began to form ideas as to what atoms were like.

★ **Suppose a marble, a wood block, and several nails are each sealed in separate identical boxes. How could you find out which item is in which box?**

Find Out More

Scientists often use cloud chambers to study the parts of atoms. Use references, such as encyclopedias, in your school library to find out about cloud chambers. How are cloud chambers used? What kinds of particles are studied using a cloud chamber? Do scientists actually see the particles being studied? If not, what do they see?

DO IT YOURSELF

Use indirect evidence

Have a friend put one or two small items into a box. Without looking inside the box, try to find out what is inside. Try such things as lifting and shaking the box, as well as any other tests you can think up. Does the box feel heavy or light? What kind or kinds of sounds come from inside the box? Make a guess as to what is inside, and then see if you are correct.

Naming the parts of atoms

For many years, scientists had no way to prove that atoms existed. They could only guess as to what atoms were like. Many scientists thought that atoms were like solid balls. However, experiments with electricity showed that an atom is made of two or more smaller parts.

Two different kinds of electric charges are known. To show that these charges are different, scientists call one kind a *positive* [PAHZ-uht-ihv] charge. The other is called a *negative* [NEHG-uht-ihv] charge. Matter that has a positive charge moves toward matter that has a negative charge. But two pieces of matter with the same kind of charge move away from each other.

The first part of an atom to be discovered was found during experiments with electricity. It was named the *electron* [ih-LEHK-trahn]. Electrons were found to have a negative charge. Scientists felt that atoms must also have a part with a positive electric charge because, overall, atoms are *neutral* [N(Y)OO-truhl]. That is, atoms do not seem to have either a positive charge or a negative charge. A part with a positive charge was discovered. It was named the *proton* [PROH-tahn]. Protons were found to be much heavier than electrons.

After studying atoms, electrons, and protons for some time, many scientists felt that there must be still more parts. Eventually a part was discovered that is about

Figure 6–2. Sir J. J. Thomson won the Nobel prize in 1906 for work which led to identifying the electron as a part of atoms.

the same weight as a proton. However, this part had no electric charge. Since it was found to be neutral, it was named the *neutron* [N(Y)OO-TRAHN].

Besides the three main parts—electrons, protons, and neutrons—scientists have discovered other parts in atoms. But, in this book, atoms will be described as having only three main parts—electrons, protons, and neutrons.

⭐ **Scientists are fairly certain that an atom has the same number of electrons as it has protons. Why are they certain of this?**

For You to Think About

Review the early Greek ideas as to what atoms were like. Which ideas do you think have been changed since scientists learned about the parts of atoms? Which ideas do you think have not been changed? How have our lives changed as a result of knowing about atoms?

THE STRUCTURE OF ATOMS

What does the model of an atom that is used by
*   scientists today look like?*
What is the electron cloud?
What parts of the atom are counted to find the
*   mass of an atom?*

A model for atoms

Many scientists have worked, and are still working, to find out what atoms are like. Since atoms cannot be seen, scientists use *models* [MAHD-uhlz] to represent what they believe atoms are like. The first model showed the atom as being a solid ball. When scientists learned that atoms were made up of parts, they made new models that were based on what they had learned. Making new models to replace those that no longer describe what is known is a part of science.

For example, the solid-ball model had to be replaced when atoms were discovered to have parts. The first part discovered—the electron—has a negative charge. Scientists realized that there also had to be a part with a positive charge. Otherwise, pieces of matter would have a negative charge.

A model was suggested that showed electrons mixed throughout a ball of matter having a positive charge. This model reminded some scientists of the pieces of fruit

Find Out More

Use references to find out about some of the early models for atoms other than the "solid-ball" model and the "plum-pudding" model. How did scientists change the models as more parts of atoms were discovered? Why aren't neutrons shown in most of the earlier models?

121

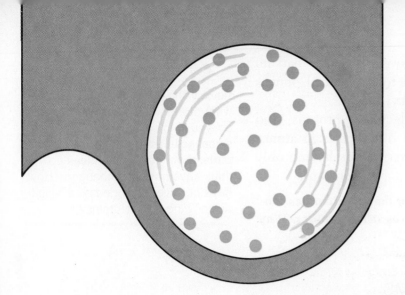

Figure 6–3. This diagram shows the "plum-pudding" model of an atom. How is this model different from the model shown in Figure 6–4?

mixed throughout a plum pudding. So this model was called the "plum-pudding" model. See Figure 6–3.

The model of atoms accepted by scientists today is like the one in Figure 6–4. The protons and neutrons are packed together in the center of the atom. This center is called the *nucleus* [N(Y)OO-klee-uhs] of the atom. The electrons of the atom move rapidly around the nucleus. Of course this model of an atom may be changed as more is learned about atoms.

★ **What kinds of models, other than models of atoms, have you made or used? Are all these models drawings? If not, what are they?**

Figure 6–4. This diagram shows what scientists today believe atoms are like. How many different kinds of parts does this model have? How many kinds of parts made up the "plum-pudding" model?

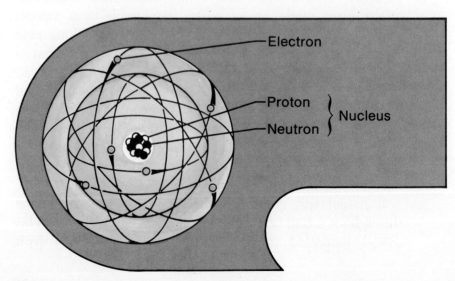

Electron

Proton }
Neutron } Nucleus

The electron cloud

The number of electrons is different for each kind of atom. A hydrogen atom, for example, has only one electron. An oxygen atom has eight electrons. In all atoms, the electrons are moving rapidly around the nucleus.

The size of the nucleus is very small when compared with the size of the whole atom. In fact, if the nucleus were the size of a basketball, the outside of the atom would be twelve blocks away from the center of the nucleus.

Scientists agree that most of the space between the nucleus and the outside of the atom is empty. But if this space is mostly empty, why is it thought of as being part of the atom? What gives an atom its shape?

Scientists believe that the electrons are constantly moving through the space around the nucleus. In fact, the electrons are moving so fast through this space that it is often described as the *electron cloud*. The term "electron cloud" does not refer to a space filled by many electrons. Instead it is a space in which only a few electrons move. In a hydrogen atom, only one electron is in the electron cloud. However, this one electron moves so rapidly it "fills" the space.

The numbers of parts

In studying matter, scientists found that each kind of atom has a different number of protons. The number of protons in an atom is called the *atomic number* of that atom. The atoms of each element found in or on the earth have atomic numbers ranging from one (hydrogen atoms) to ninety-two (uranium atoms).

Protons have a positive charge. Electrons have a negative charge. But atoms, overall, are neutral. Therefore the number of electrons is equal to the number of protons in an atom.

But what about the number of neutrons? Neutrons have no electric charge. Having a different number of neutrons will not change the electric charge of an atom. But having different numbers of neutrons will affect the mass. The mass of an atom, usually called the *atomic mass*,

Figure 6–5. This model is of a lithium atom. Which part or parts determine the atomic mass of lithium? Which part or parts determine the atomic number?

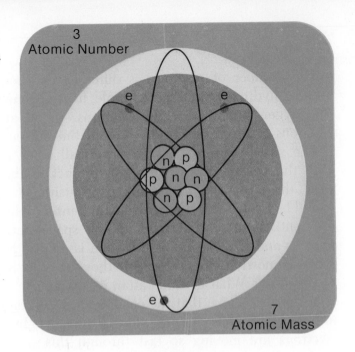

depends on the number of protons and neutrons in an atom. Each proton and each neutron is thought of as having a mass of about one *atomic mass unit,* or *amu* [AY-EHM-YOO] for short. So the mass of an atom in amu is nearly the same as the sum of the number of protons and neutrons in that atom. The mass of electrons is so small that it is not counted as part of the mass of an atom.

★ **What is the mass in amu of a carbon atom that has 6 protons, 6 electrons, and 6 neutrons? Of a uranium atom that has 92 protons, 92 electrons, and 143 neutrons?**

DO IT YOURSELF

Make a model of an atom

Use references to find out how many electrons, protons, and neutrons are in an atom of oxygen (or sodium or sulfur). Find out how the parts of this atom are arranged. Make a model showing the parts of this atom. Explain how your model shows what is known about that atom today.

ATOMS, MOLECULES, AND IONS

Which energy level determines how and why
atoms join together?
What are two ways that atoms join together?
What is an ion?

Drawings of atoms

Sometimes atoms join together, or combine, to form molecules. When atoms combine, they do so only in certain ways. Furthermore, not all kinds of atoms will combine with other atoms. The model of the atom accepted today can help explain why and how atoms combine.

The model of the atom shows the electrons moving in a space called the electron cloud. Scientists believe that, within the cloud, the electrons are more likely to be in some places than in others. These places where electrons are likely to be are called *energy* [EHN-ur-jee] *levels*.

Drawings such as the one in Figure 6–6 are often used to show how electrons are arranged in the different energy levels. The black dot in the center represents the nucleus. Each circle around the black dot represents an energy level. Blue dots, representing electrons, are on the circles.

Keep in mind that this model is not a true picture of what an atom looks like. The nucleus is drawn much larger than it should be. Energy levels are not neat little circles.

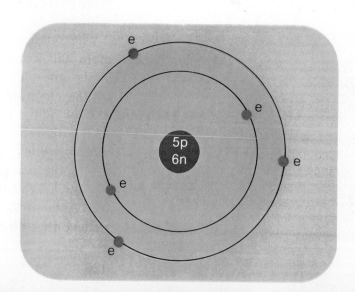

Figure 6–6. This model shows an atom having five protons (5 p), six neutrons (6 n), and five electrons. How many energy levels are shown in this model?

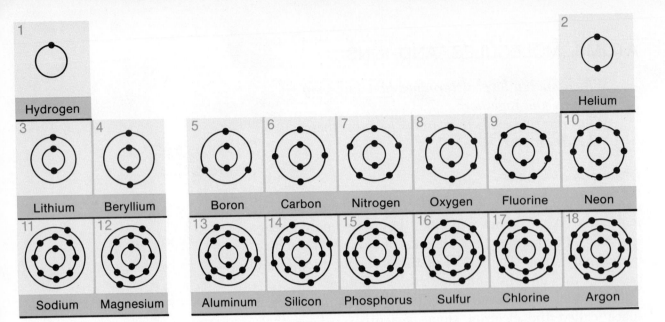

Figure 6–7. These drawings show the electron structure, but not the nucleus, of the atoms having atomic numbers one through eighteen. How are all the atoms in each column alike?

Find Out More

Find out how electrons are arranged in atoms of common elements such as iron, tin, and iodine. Make drawings of the electron arrangement for each atom.

Also, real atoms are not flat, as they are shown in the drawing. However, even with these faults, this model is useful in helping to explain how atoms join together.

Why atoms combine

Scientists think of each energy level as being filled when it holds a certain number of electrons. Look at Figure 6–7. It shows the electron arrangement of the atoms having atomic numbers one through eighteen. Notice that the energy level closest to the nucleus never has more than two electrons in it. Atoms that have more than one level never have more than eight electrons in their outer level.

The outermost level is important. Whether or not an atom will join with other atoms depends on the electrons in its outer level. How atoms join together also depends on the electrons in its outer level.

Look at the drawings of helium, neon, and argon atoms in Figure 6–7. Notice that the outer level of each of these atoms is filled. These atoms, and others with filled outer levels, do not join together with other atoms in nature.

Now look at the drawings on the other atoms in Figure 6–7. None of these atoms have a filled outer level. Scientists believe that atoms tend to have a filled outer level. Atoms

126

can have a filled outer level by joining with other atoms in certain ways.

★ **Oxygen atoms have six electrons in their outer energy level. How many electrons must an oxygen atom gain to have a filled outer level?**

Atoms to molecules

One way atoms can reach a state of having a filled outer level is for two or more atoms to form a molecule by sharing electrons. Some molecules are made of up two or more of the same kind of atom. Figure 6–8, part *A*, shows an example of such a molecule.

Other molecules are made up of two or more different kinds of atoms. Figure 6–8, part *B*, shows one such molecule—carbon dioxide. Look at Figure 6–8. Each oxygen atom has six electrons in its outer level. The carbon atom has four electrons. By sharing electrons, each of the atoms has a filled outer level.

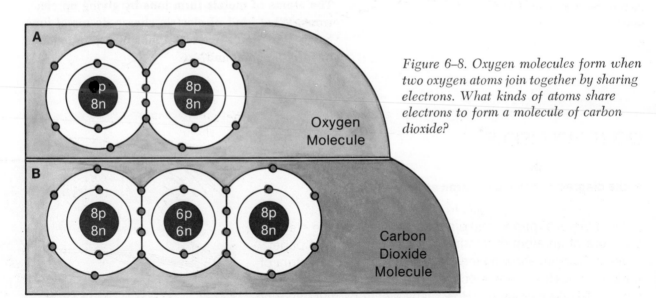

Figure 6–8. Oxygen molecules form when two oxygen atoms join together by sharing electrons. What kinds of atoms share electrons to form a molecule of carbon dioxide?

Atoms to ions

Other atoms get filled outer levels by transferring one or more electrons from one atom to another. Look at

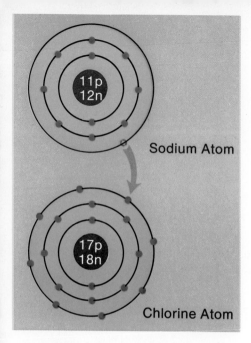

Sodium Atom

Chlorine Atom

Figure 6–9. How does the electron structure of sodium atoms and of chlorine atoms change when they join to form sodium chloride, or table salt?

Figure 6–9. The drawing shows how atoms of sodium join together with atoms of chlorine to form sodium chloride, or table salt.

A sodium atom has only one electron in its outer level. By giving up this electron, the atom is left with a filled outer level. In losing this electron, the atom is left having one more proton than it has electrons. The atom, therefore, is positively charged.

The chlorine atom has seven electrons in its outer level. By gaining the electron given up by the sodium atom, the outer level of the chlorine atom is filled. The chlorine atom then has one more electron than it has protons. So the atom is negatively charged.

When atoms lose or gain electrons, the atoms become charged particles. These charged particles are called *ions* [EYE-uhnz]. Ions with a positive electric charge are attracted to ions with a negative electric charge. This attraction holds the two kinds of ions together.

★ **The atoms of metals form ions by giving up electrons. What kind of electric charge do metal ions have? Why don't two metal ions ever join together to form a compound?**

DO IT YOURSELF

Make diagrams showing electron structure

On a piece of paper, make a diagram showing the electron structure of an atom of fluorine. On another piece of paper, make a diagram showing the electron structure of an atom of magnesium. How many electrons are in the outer energy level of the fluorine atom? How many electrons must fluorine gain to fill the outer energy level? How many electrons does magnesium need to lose to have a filled outer energy level? How many atoms each of fluorine and magnesium do you think are joined together to form magnesium fluoride?

ZEFA

To be a chemist, a person must know about atoms and molecules. What kind of education do you think a chemist must have?

Knowing About Atoms and Molecules Is Important

Most people do not have to know anything about atoms or molecules to do their job. But some jobs do require a knowledge of atoms and molecules. The people who have this kind of job are called *chemists* [KEHM-uhsts]. Sometimes a chemist is referred to as someone who studies the composition of matter and the changes in it.

Understanding how atoms form molecules is important to a chemist. Chemists use their understanding of matter in several ways. Some chemists make kinds of matter that are not found in nature. These kinds of matter are sometimes called *synthetic* [sihn-THEHT-ihk] materials. Some synthetic materials you have used include plastics, detergents, and fabrics such as nylon and rayon. Some chemists find ways to make large quantities of compounds that are not very plentiful in nature. These include such things as medicines, vitamins, and some gemstones. Many chemists work to make useful materials out of natural materials. For example, many chemists work in the oil industry. Their work is to find ways to change crude oil into useful products such as gasoline and fuel oil.

Of course a person does not become a chemist overnight. A person needs to learn a great deal about matter before becoming a chemist. So a person usually studies chemistry and other related subjects in high school and in college. Perhaps some day you will study to become a chemist. You may even be one of those who invent a new and useful compound, such as nylon or plastic.

Reviewing and Extending

SUMMING UP

1. Long ago, a popular idea was that matter was made up of only four "elements"—water, earth, air, and fire. Each element had two of four properties—hot, cold, wet, and dry.
2. The idea that matter was made up of atoms was first suggested about 2,000 years ago in Greece.
3. In the 1700's, scientists agreed to use the word "element" for matter that could not be broken down into simpler forms. The smallest part of an element was called an atom.
4. Atoms were found to be made up of three main parts—electrons, protons, and neutrons.
5. Electrons have a negative electric charge. Protons have a positive electric charge. Neutrons have no overall charge. That is, they are neutral.
6. The model of atoms accepted today has the protons and neutrons packed tightly together in the center of the atom, forming a nucleus. The electrons move rapidly around the nucleus.
7. Atoms have the same number of electrons as they have protons.
8. The number of protons in an atom is called the atomic number. The number of protons and neutrons determine the atomic mass of an atom.
9. Atoms join together to form molecules by sharing electrons. Such molecules may be made up of two or more of the same kind of atom or two or more different kinds of atoms.
10. Atoms may lose or gain electrons and become charged particles called ions. Positively charged ions are attracted to negatively charged ions.

CHECKING UP

Vocabulary Write the numerals *1–5* on your paper. Each numbered phrase describes a term from the following list. On your paper, write the term next to the numeral of the phrase that describes it.

proton	electron	neutron
ion	molecule	model

1. particle with a negative electric charge
2. particle with no electric charge
3. particle formed by atoms combining in a certain way
4. formed when atom loses or gains electrons
5. particle with a positive electric charge

Knowledge and Understanding Write the numerals *6–10* on your paper. Beside each numeral, write the word or words that best complete the sentence having that numeral.

6. The number of protons in an atom is (*greater than, equal to, less than*) the number of electrons in that atom.

130

7. The nucleus of an atom contains (*protons and electrons, neutrons and electrons, protons and neutrons*).

8. The atomic mass of an atom is determined by the number of (*protons and electrons, protons and neutrons, protons*) in that atom.

9. An atom that has gained or lost an electron is called (*a molecule, an ion, a compound*).

10. The idea that all matter is made up of atoms was first suggested about (*2,000; 300; 100*) years ago.

Concepts   Beside each of the numerals *11–15* on your paper, write the word or words that best complete the sentence having that numeral.

11. The space through which the electrons move is called the _____ of that atom.

12. The number of neutrons in an atom affects the _____ of the atom.

13. Today the atom is thought of as having a _____ of protons and neutrons in the center surrounded by rapidly moving electrons.

14. To become a negatively charged ion, an atom must *gain* one or more electrons.

15. Two atoms of oxygen combine to form a molecule by _____ electrons.

Application and Critical Thinking   Answer the following questions as briefly as you can without leaving out any important ideas.

16. The atomic number of iron is twenty-six. How can you use this information to tell how many protons are in an iron atom? How many electrons? Can you use this information to tell how many neutrons are present? Why or why not?

17. How do modern ideas about what atoms are like differ from the ideas of atoms suggested in ancient Greece?

DOING MORE

1. Collect examples of elements like iron, nickel, copper, carbon, and iodine. Make drawings showing the electron structure of the atoms for each element you have. Display each of the elements along with their drawings.

2. Scientists often use letters as *symbols* [SIHM-buhlz] to represent the names of elements. Use references, such as chemistry textbooks, to find out what the symbols are for the elements oxygen, hydrogen, iron, gold, sodium, and chlorine. Which symbols look most like the name of the element?

CHAPTER 7

Heat, Temperature, and Matter

Have you ever watched a pan of water come to a boil? If so, you know that heat causes changes in the pan and in the water. For one thing, both the pan and the water become hotter. That is, their *temperature* [TEHM-puh(r)-CHU(UH)R] changes. As the water boils, it changes into steam. So heat can cause water to change from the liquid phase into the gas phase.

Every day people use heat in many different ways. A few ways heat is used are to cook food, to warm homes, and to run automobiles. But just what is heat? Is temperature related to heat? If so, how? What effects does heat have on matter? Does heat affect atoms and molecules? If so, how? These are some of the questions discussed in Chapter 7.

Photos from Artstreet

Welding metal and cooking food are two ways heat is used. What are some other uses for heat?

Figure 7–1. Burning wood gives off a lot of heat. How does the heat affect the liquid in the kettle? How could you decide if the liquid is gaining or losing heat?

HEAT AND TEMPERATURE

What is heat? Is heat the same as temperature?
How is temperature measured?
How is heat measured?

Are heat and temperature the same?

You probably use the words "heat" and "temperature" every day. For example, you may talk about heating some food or heating your home. You may talk about the temperature in your home or outdoors. But just what do the words "heat" and "temperature" mean to scientists?

When you move or lift something, you are doing work. Work is done when a push or a pull causes something to move. You are able to do work because you have *energy* [EHN-ur-jee]. Scientists think of energy as the ability to do work. Perhaps you have seen steam pushing up the lid of a pot. In pushing the lid, the steam is doing work. The steam is able to do work because it is hot. In other words, heat causes the steam to do work. So heat is a form of energy.

Temperature is not the same as heat. However, temperature is related to heat. If matter gains heat, its temperature rises. If the matter loses heat, its temperature falls. So a change in the amount of heat in matter causes a change in temperature. Temperature, in a way, indicates the

133

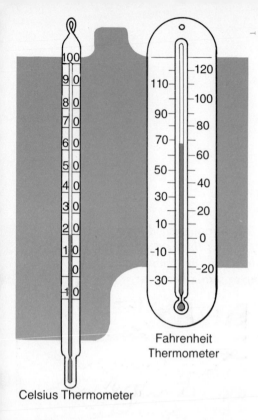

Celsius Thermometer

Fahrenheit
Thermometer

Figure 7–2. In what ways are these two thermometers alike? In what ways are they different?

amount of heat present in matter. The higher the temperature of a piece of matter, the more heat there is in that piece of matter.

Measuring temperature

Heat is measured by measuring changes in temperature. Temperature is measured in units called *degrees* [dih-GREEZ]. The instrument used to measure temperature is a *thermometer* [thuh(r)-MAHM-uht-ur]. You have probably used thermometers like the two shown in Figure 7–2.

Each of the two thermometers has a glass tube filled with a liquid. Either the glass tube or the part to which the tube is fastened is marked with lines. The lines are a scale to measure the height of the liquid in the tube. As the liquid becomes warmer, the liquid rises to a higher level. We say that the temperature is rising. As the liquid becomes cooler, the liquid falls to a lower level. We say that the temperature is falling.

You may have noticed that the two thermometers in Figure 7–2 are marked with different scales. The scale you probably use most often is the *Fahrenheit* [FAR-uhn-HYT] *scale*. According to this scale, water boils at a temperature of 212 degrees at sea level and freezes at a temperature of 32 degrees.

Most scientists use the *Celsius* [SEHL-see-uhs] *scale*. According to this scale, water boils at 100 degrees at sea level and freezes at zero degrees. So a temperature change of one Celsius degree is greater than a temperature change of one Fahrenheit degree.

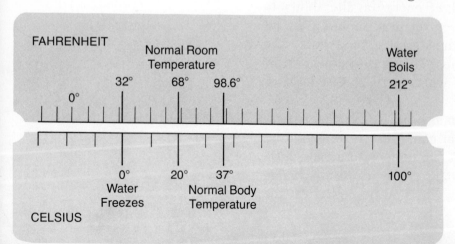

Figure 7–3. The scale shows some often-used temperatures given in both Celsius degrees and Fahrenheit degrees.

Scientists usually do not use words to write temperatures. Instead, they write the numeral, a small circle above and to the right of the numeral (the symbol for the word "degree"), and the first letter of the name of the scale being used. A scientist would write 12°C instead of twelve degrees Celsius. If the temperature is twelve degrees below 0°, a minus sign (—) is written in front of the numeral. That is, a scientist would write —12°C to show a temperature twelve degrees below zero.

★ **Why is it important to write the letter showing which temperature scale is used?**

DO IT YOURSELF

Practice reading a thermometer

Examine a thermometer. Notice which scale is used. Place the thermometer in some cold water. Wait until the liquid in the thermometer stops moving. Then read and record the temperature of the water. Now place the thermometer in some hot water. Read and record the temperature of the hot water. What scale was marked on the thermometer? What was the temperature of the cold water? The hot water? What do you think the temperature would be if you mixed the hot water and the cold water together? Try it and find out.

Measuring heat

Since temperature and heat are not the same, they are measured in different ways. Temperature is measured in either Celsius degrees or Fahrenheit degrees. Heat is also measured using two different units. One unit for measuring heat is the *calorie* [KAL-(uh-)ree]. One calorie is the amount of heat that will raise the temperature of one gram (about ¹⁄₂₈ ounce) of water one degree Celsius.

Another unit for measuring heat is the *British thermal* [THUR-muhl] *unit,* or Btu. One Btu is the amount of heat that will raise the temperature of one pound of water one degree Fahrenheit. One Btu is about 250 times as

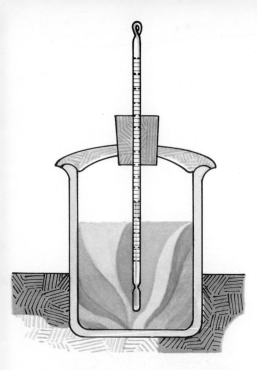

Figure 7–4. In using a water calorimeter, a person measures the change in temperature of the water in the calorimeter. How can measuring a temperature change in water help you measure heat?

Find Out More

Find out what the words *conduction* [kuhn-DUHK-shuhn], *convection* [kuhn-VEHK-shuhn], and *radiation* [RAYD-ee-AY-shuhn] mean. What do these terms have to do with heat? Give an example to show how each of the terms is related to heat.

much heat as one calorie. In the United States, air conditioners and furnaces are usually described by using Btu's. An 85,000-Btu furnace, for example, can add 85,000 Btu's of heat to a home in one hour.

Temperature is measured by using a thermometer. Heat is measured by using a *calorimeter* [KAL-uh-RIHM-uht-ur]. A calorimeter is a container through which heat cannot easily pass. A thermometer is fitted into the container. The thermometer measures changes in the temperature of matter inside the calorimeter.

A water calorimeter is shown in Figure 7–4. A measured amount of water is put into the calorimeter, and the temperature of the water is measured. A hot object is dropped into the water, and the top is quickly closed. The thermometer is used to find out how much warmer the water becomes.

Suppose 100 grams (about 3½ ounces) of water at a temperature of 10°C is in the calorimeter. The lid is raised, a piece of hot iron is dropped into the water, and the lid is quickly closed. As the iron cools off, it gives up heat to the water. This causes a rise in the temperature of the water.

How many calories of heat are given up by the iron if the temperature of the water rises ten degrees? One calorie of heat will raise the temperature of one gram of water one degree on the Celsius scale. In this example, the temperature of 100 grams of water was raised ten degrees on the Celsius scale. So the number of calories of heat given up by the iron is found as follows:

$$\text{Temperature Rise} \times \text{Mass of Water} = \text{Amount of Heat}$$

$$10°C \times 100 \text{ grams} = 1\,000 \text{ calories}$$

The water calorimeter does not measure the total amount of heat in the iron. It measures only the amount of heat given off by the iron. This is because the iron gives off heat to the water only until both the iron and the water are the same temperature. When they have reached the same temperature, the water no longer takes up heat from the iron. So, some heat is left in the iron.

Another kind of calorimeter is designed so that materials can be burned in it. The purpose is to find out how much heat is given off when a certain amount of matter is burned. Food can be burned in this kind of calorimeter to find out how much energy you can get from that kind of food.

You have probably heard the word "Calorie" used to describe food energy. Notice that this Calorie is spelled with a capital C. Sometimes a food Calorie is called a large calorie or a kilocalorie. A kilocalorie is equal to 1 000 calories.

★ **A glass of milk contains 200 kilocalories of food energy. How many calories are there in the glass of milk?**

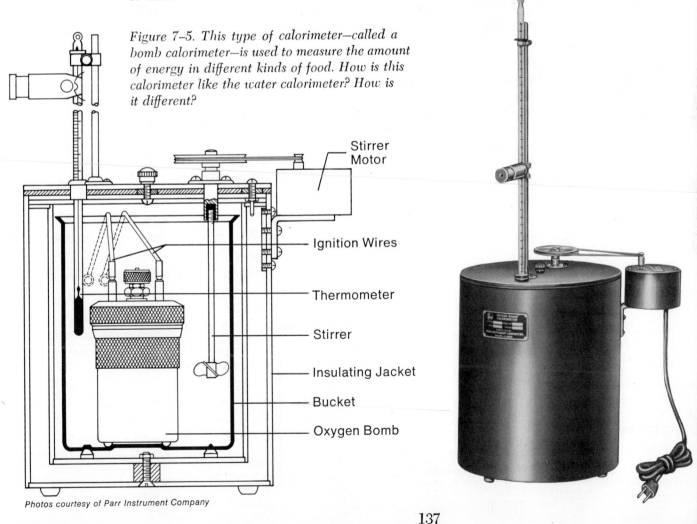

Figure 7–5. This type of calorimeter—called a bomb calorimeter—is used to measure the amount of energy in different kinds of food. How is this calorimeter like the water calorimeter? How is it different?

Stirrer Motor

Ignition Wires

Thermometer

Stirrer

Insulating Jacket

Bucket

Oxygen Bomb

HEAT AND MATTER

What do the terms "expand" and "contract" mean?
What is density? How is density affected by heat?
What happens to a liquid at its freezing point? At its boiling point?

Changes in volume

If you hold a copper wire in a flame, the wire gets hot. That is, the temperature of the wire rises. Causing a change in temperature is one of the effects heat has on matter. But heat causes other changes that are not as easily noticed. Suppose you had carefully measured the length and thickness of the wire before holding it in the flame. Then you made the same measurements while the wire was hot. You would have found that the wire was a little longer and a little thicker while it was hot.

When a solid, such as the copper wire, increases in size due to heat, it is said to *expand* [ihk-SPAND]. The change in size is not a large change. Suppose a copper wire one metre (about three feet) long is heated from 0°C to 100°C. The wire will get only 0.17 centimetre (about ⅔ inch) longer. When it cools down again, the wire will return to its original size.

Different solids expand different amounts. Look at the graph in Figure 7–6. It shows what happened when five solid rods, all one metre long, were heated from 0°C to 100°C. Each of the five rods expanded to a different length.

Find Out More

A *thermostat* [THUR-muh-STAT] is a device that uses changes in temperature to control heat. Using references, try to find the answers to these questions: How do changes in temperature affect a thermostat? Are all thermostats alike? How does a thermostat control heat? What are some things that use thermostats to control heat?

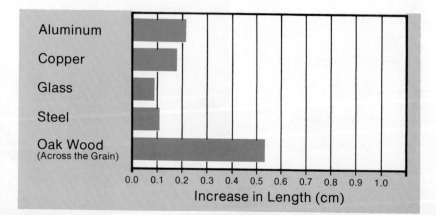

Figure 7–6. Which of the five rods expanded the most? Which expanded the least?

Aluminum

Copper

Glass

Steel

Oak Wood
(Across the Grain)

0.0 0.1 0.2 0.3 0.4 0.5 0.6 0.7 0.8 0.9 1.0

Increase in Length (cm)

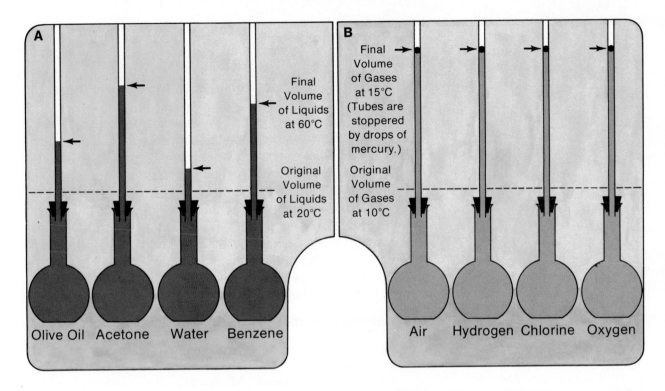

Figure 7–7. Which of the liquids expanded the most? How does the way that gases expand differ from the ways that liquids and solids expand?

Liquids and gases also expand as they become warmer. Like solids, different liquids expand different amounts. Figure 7–7, part *A*, shows how equal amounts of four different liquids expand when heated to the same final temperature. Now look at Figure 7–7, part *B*. It shows what happens to equal amounts of four different gases that are warmed to the same final temperature. All the gases expand. Unlike liquids and solids, the different gases expand the same amount.

In general, matter—solid, liquid, or gas—expands as it becomes warmer. When hot matter becomes cooler, it shrinks in size. That is, matter *contracts* [kuhn-TRAKTS] as it becomes cooler.

★ **Why are spaces left between certain parts of a bridge? What do you think might happen to the bridge if there were no spaces?**

139

DO IT YOURSELF

Compare the amounts of expansion in two different wires

Obtain two different kinds of metal wire, such as steel and copper. Both wires should be the same length and thickness. Fasten each wire between two ring stands and hang a 100-gram mass from the middle of each wire. Set a burner under each wire. Both burners should be the same distance below and the same distance from one end of the wires. In this way both wires should be heated equally and at the same place along their length. Light the burners and observe the two wires for a period of three minutes. What evidence is there to indicate that the two wires expanded? Which wire expanded more? Which of the two wires expanded faster?

Density

All matter has mass. All matter also takes up space. The amount of space a piece of matter takes up is its volume. The amount of mass in a certain volume is called the *density* [DEHN(T)-suht-ee] of that matter. The greater the amount of mass for a certain volume, the greater the density. The smaller the amount of mass for that volume, the lower the density.

A change in temperature causes a change in the density of a piece of matter. Adding or taking away heat causes a change in the size of matter. The matter might expand, or it might contract. However, adding or taking away heat does not add or take away matter. So adding heat does not change the mass.

If a piece of matter expands, it takes up more space. This means that there is less mass (a smaller amount of matter) in a certain volume. So when a piece of matter expands, its density becomes lower.

If a piece of matter contracts, the same amount of matter takes up less space. That is, there is a greater amount of mass in a certain volume. So when a piece of matter contracts, its density becomes greater.

140

Changes in phase

You know that adding heat to ice causes the ice to melt. When ice melts, it changes into water. Heat also causes water to boil. Then, the water changes into steam. Cooling, or removing heat, causes steam to change back into water. Cooling also can cause water to change into ice. So adding heat and removing heat can cause changes in the phase of water.

Other elements and compounds also undergo changes in phase when enough heat is added to or removed from them. When enough heat is added, a solid melts and changes into a liquid. If enough heat is removed, a liquid freezes and changes into a solid. For each substance there is a certain temperature at which these changes in phase occur. For example, ice melts at 0°C (32°F). This temperature is called the *melting point* of ice. Water freezes at 0°C. This temperature is called the *freezing point* of water. Each substance melts or freezes at a different temperature. For any one substance, however, the melting point and the freezing point are the same temperature.

Figure 7–8. The icicles and the flowing water represent the solid and the liquid phases of water. The gas phase—water vapor—cannot be seen. However, whenever mist forms, as in the picture on the right, the air contains a lot of water vapor. In which phase would the molecules have the greatest amount of heat energy? The least amount?

Editorial Photocolor Archives, Inc.   Photo Research International   W. Mohn/ZEFA

The different terms are used only to show the direction of the change.

If enough heat is added to a liquid, the liquid begins to boil. Each kind of matter boils at a different temperature. The temperature at which a given kind of matter boils is called the *boiling point*. However, the boiling point is not the same temperature every place or even every day. The boiling point depends on how hard the air pushes on the surface of the liquid. That is, the boiling point depends on *air pressure* [PREHSH-ur]. The lower the air pressure, the lower the boiling point.

★ **Air pressure is lower at high altitudes than it is at low altitudes. Do you think that water boils at a different temperature on the top floor of a 100-story building than it does on the first floor of that same building? Explain.**

THE KINETIC THEORY OF MATTER

What is the kinetic theory of matter?
How does the kinetic theory explain why matter expands, contracts, and changes phase?
How does the kinetic theory explain heat and temperature?

Atoms and molecules in motion

Scientists have been observing and recording the changes in matter caused by heat for many years. But scientists do more than just observe and record such changes. They also try to explain why changes happen.

Heat causes several changes in matter. Adding or removing heat changes the temperature of matter. Changes in temperature cause matter to expand or contract. As matter expands or contracts, its density changes. If enough heat is added or removed, the phase of the matter changes.

In trying to explain these changes, scientists use a theory of matter that suggests that matter is made up of tiny particles. According to the theory, the particles are always moving. Because this idea describes particles

(*Text continues on page 144.*)

Investigate

What happens to the temperature as ice is changed into steam?

You Will Need

crushed ice, burner, beaker, thermometer, ring stand, asbestos pad, matches

Background

When heat is added to ice, the ice melts and changes into water. If you keep adding heat to the water, the temperature of the water rises. Eventually the water begins to boil and change into steam. But is there a continuous rise in temperature while the ice is melting and later while the water is changing into steam? You can find out by doing this investigation.

What to Do

Half fill a beaker with crushed ice. Place a thermometer in the ice so that you can measure and record the temperature. Be sure the bulb of the thermometer does not touch the bottom of the beaker. Measure and record the temperature of the ice. Begin slowly warming the ice. Measure and record the temperature several times while the ice is melting and after all the ice has melted. Continue measuring and recording the temperature until you have recorded at least three measurements after the water has begun boiling. *Caution: Do not let all the water boil away or the thermometer may burst.*

Now That You Have Done the Investigation

—What was the temperature of the ice before you added heat?

—What was the temperature as the ice melted?

—Did the temperature rise during the time the ice was melting or only after all the ice had melted?

—At what temperature did the water begin to boil?

—Did the temperature of the water continue to rise as the water boiled or did it remain the same?

—If the temperature did not change during any time heat was being added, what was happening to the ice or water at that time? What do you think the heat was used for, if not to raise the temperature?

of matter as moving, it has come to be known as the *kinetic* [kuh-NEHT-ihk] *theory of matter*. The term "kinetic" comes from a Greek word that means moving.

But is there any evidence that particles of matter are moving? More than 100 years ago, a Scottish scientist, Robert Brown, was studying plant pollen. Pollen is like a powder made of very tiny grains. The pollen grains were placed on a drop of water. When looked at through a microscope, each grain was moving in a zigzag pattern over the surface of the water. This way of moving is called *Brownian movement*. It is explained as being caused by molecules of water bumping into the pollen grains.

Other observations indicate that molecules are always moving. What happens if a perfume bottle is left open for a while? The smell of the perfume will soon fill the room. For the smell to fill the room, perfume molecules must move from the bottle into the air of the room. If food coloring is dropped into a glass of water, the color will spread throughout the water even if the water is not stirred. In order for this to happen, the molecules of water must be bumping into, and pushing, the molecules of food coloring.

The kinetic theory of matter describes matter as being made up of tiny particles which are always moving. The idea of matter being made up of tiny particles agrees with today's ideas of matter being made up of atoms and molecules. Observations indicating that molecules are moving support the kinetic theory.

★ **What are some other examples you can give to show that atoms and molecules must be in motion?**

Explaining changes caused by heat

To be accepted, a theory must agree with or explain what is observed. A change in temperature can cause a change in the volume of a piece of matter. Adding or removing heat can cause changes in the phase of matter. These changes have been observed for many years. Are they explained by the kinetic theory?

144

Figure 7–9. Drops of water hang from the berries. What force causes a drop of water to have a rounded shape?

Scientists believe that in the gas phase, molecules are moving very fast. These molecules move so fast that they bump into one another and knock one another far apart. In the liquid phase, however, the molecules move much slower. Because they are moving slower, the molecules are held closer together. The force that holds molecules of the same substance together is called *cohesion* [koh-HEE-zhuhn]. Molecules of matter in the solid phase move even slower than molecules of the same kind of matter in the liquid phase. Cohesion holds the molecules of a solid very close together. In fact, scientists believe that the molecules are held so close together that molecules do not move from one place to another in solid matter. Instead, the molecules are thought to just move about within a very small amount of space.

If a piece of copper wire is held in a candle flame, the wire expands. According to the kinetic theory, as molecules gain energy, they move faster. As the molecules move faster, they bump into each other harder and more often. This bumping pushes each of the molecules a little farther apart. Therefore, the matter expands.

(*Text continues on page 147.*)

Investigate

Can you see moving molecules?

You Will Need

microscope, glass slide, toothpick, water, India ink

Background

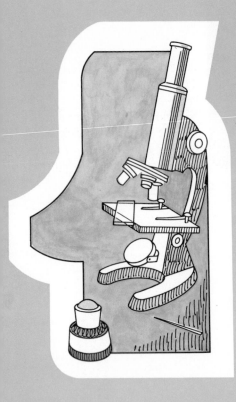

The kinetic theory of matter states that the atoms and molecules in matter are always moving. One piece of evidence that supports the idea of moving molecules is that two liquids that are placed together become mixed even if the two liquids are not stirred. Scientists say that the two liquids become mixed because of the motion of their molecules. The mixing of atoms or molecules of different kinds of matter because of the motions of the molecules is called *diffusion* [dif-YOO-zhuhn].

When you look through the microscope, you will see the ink particles moving about. The motion of the ink particles is thought to be caused by water molecules bumping into the larger ink particles.

What to Do

Set a glass slide on the stage of a microscope and place a drop of water on the slide. Use a toothpick to dip into the bottle of ink and pick up a tiny amount of ink. Touch the toothpick to the drop of water on the slide. Use the microscope to observe the particles of ink in the water.

Now That You Have Done the Investigation

—Did the ink particles stay in one place in the water or did the particles move?

—If the ink particles moved, did all the particles move in the same direction, or did they move in many different directions?

—Did you actually see molecules of water bumping into and pushing the ink particles? Is seeing ink particles move in water direct or indirect evidence for moving molecules?

—Can what you observed be explained by using the kinetic theory of matter? How?

146

When a piece of matter becomes cooler, the molecules in that matter lose energy. The molecules move slower as they lose energy. Cohesion pulls the slower-moving molecules closer together. As a result, the matter contracts.

Heat can also cause a change in the phase of matter. As a piece of solid matter gains more and more energy the molecules in that piece of matter move faster and farther apart. Cohesion can no longer hold the faster-moving molecules as close together. So the solid begins to lose its shape and become a liquid. The changing of a solid into a liquid is called *melting*.

If enough energy is gained by liquid matter, the molecules will move so far apart that the matter becomes a gas. The changing from a liquid to a gas is called *evaporating* [ih-VAP-uh-RAYT-ihng].

When molecules lose energy, they move slower. Cohesion pulls the slower-moving molecules closer together. In this way, a gas changes to its liquid phase. The changing from a gas to a liquid is called *condensing* [kuhn-DEHN(T)S-ihng]. When enough energy is lost by the

For You to Think About

When most people think of something that is frozen, they think of ice. What other kinds of matter can be thought of as frozen? At what temperatures do these kinds of matter melt?

Photo Research International

Figure 7–10. Drops of water have formed on the outside of the glass. Where did the water come from? Why did the water collect on the glass?

147

molecules, the liquid phase changes to the solid phase. The changing of a liquid to a solid is called *freezing*.

Explaining heat and temperature

Heat and temperature are closely related. However, they are not the same. The kinetic theory can be used to explain expanding, contracting, and changing phase. Can the theory also be used to explain the difference between heat and temperature?

According to the kinetic theory, molecules are always moving. Scientists agree that a moving object has energy because it is moving. This energy is called kinetic energy, or energy of motion. Since each molecule in a piece of matter is moving, each has kinetic energy. The kinetic energy of molecules is the key to explaining the difference between heat and temperature.

Today scientists believe that the temperature of a piece of matter depends on the average speed of its molecules. In any piece of matter some molecules are moving faster than others. If there are more faster-moving molecules than there are slower-moving molecules, the average speed of the molecules in that piece of matter will be greater. The greater the average speed, the higher the temperature.

A cup of boiling water has a higher temperature than a cup of warm water. The difference in temperature is due to the difference in the average kinetic energy of the molecules of water in each cup. The water molecules in a cup of boiling water have more kinetic energy, on the average, than the water molecules in a cup of warm water. So the average speed of the molecules of boiling water is greater than the average speed of the molecules of warm water.

The amount of heat energy in matter is thought of as being the sum of all the amounts of kinetic energy of every molecule in that matter. So the amount of heat in matter depends on two things: (1) the amount of kinetic energy of each molecule and (2) the number of molecules.

★ **Which contains more heat energy, a bathtub full of lukewarm water or a cup full of boiling water? Which has the higher temperature? Explain.**

ZEFA

Why are spaces being left between the sections of cement? What might happen to the cement if there were no spaces between the sections?

Working with the Effects of Heat and Temperature

Heat causes matter to expand, to contract, and to change phase. These changes caused by heat are known to most people. But some people need to know more than others do about changes caused by heat. Understanding such changes is an important part of their job.

For example, people who put up telephone or electric lines must remember not to stretch the lines too tight between the poles if the lines are hung in the summer. If the lines are strung too tightly, they will contract and break during cold winter weather. People who lay cement sidewalks and streets also need to know how different kinds of cement expand and contract. If these people do not leave enough room between the sections of a sidewalk or a street, the cement will break as it expands and contracts.

Some people work at developing new paints for the outside of houses and other buildings. Others develop new materials for use in bridges and other large structures. Each of these new materials must be tested to find out what happens when the material is subjected to changes in temperature.

These are only a few of the kinds of jobs that call for an understanding of the effects of heat and temperature. There are many other jobs in which such an understanding can prove useful. Have you thought about the kind of job you would like? If so, is a knowledge of heat and temperature important in that job?

149

Reviewing and Extending

SUMMING UP

1. Heat is a form of energy. As matter gains heat energy, the temperature of the matter rises.
2. Temperature is measured in units called degrees. Two common thermometer temperature scales are the Celsius scale and the Fahrenheit scale.
3. Heat is measured in calories or in British thermal units (Btu's).
4. One calorie is the amount of heat that will raise the temperature of one gram of water one degree Celsius.
5. One Btu is the amount of heat that will raise the temperature of one pound of water one degree Fahrenheit.
6. Changes in temperature cause matter to expand, to contract, and to change phase.
7. The idea that the atoms or molecules in a piece of matter are always moving is called the kinetic theory of matter.
8. According to the kinetic theory, as matter becomes warmer, the atoms or molecules are moving faster, hitting each other harder and more often, and pushing each other farther apart.
9. As matter becomes cooler, the atoms or molecules move slower. Cohesion then pulls and holds the slower-moving atoms or molecules closer together.
10. Heat is thought of as the total kinetic energy of all the molecules in a piece of matter.
11. Temperature is an indication of the average speed of the molecules in a piece of matter.

CHECKING UP

Vocabulary   Write the numerals 1–5 on your paper. Each of the numbered phrases describes a term from the following list. On your paper, write the term next to the numeral of the phrase that describes it.

degree	calorie	density
kinetic theory	melting	calorimeter

1. unit for measuring temperature
2. changing of a solid into a liquid
3. unit for measuring heat
4. amount of mass in a certain volume of matter
5. idea that tiny particles of matter are in constant motion

Knowledge and Understanding   Write the numerals 6–10 on your paper. Beside each of the numerals, write the word or words that best complete the sentence having that numeral.

6. The amount of heat that will raise the temperature of one gram of water one degree Celsius is one _____.

7. _____ is a force that holds slow-moving molecules together.
8. The temperature at which a liquid boils is called the _____ point.
9. Temperature is measured in units called _____.
10. The temperature at which a solid becomes a liquid is called the _____ point of that liquid.

Concepts   Beside each of the numerals *11–15* on your paper, write the word or words that best complete the sentence having that numeral.

11. When matter expands, its density (*stays the same, increases, decreases*).
12. The idea that atoms and molecules are in constant motion is called the (*atomic, kinetic, heat*) theory of matter.
13. (*Heat, Temperature, Matter*) is thought of as being the total amount of kinetic energy of all the molecules in a piece of matter.
14. For a given kind of matter, the (*melting point and the boiling point, freezing point and the boiling point, melting point and the freezing point*) are the same temperature.
15. Matter (*expands, contracts, does not change volume*) when its molecules move faster and farther apart.

Application and Critical Thinking   Answer the following questions as briefly as you can without leaving out any important ideas.

16. What are some kinds of evidence to show that atoms or molecules are always moving?
17. How can the kinetic theory be used to explain expansion?

DOING MORE

1. Completely fill a narrow-necked bottle, such as a soda-pop bottle, with very hot tap water. Set the bottle of hot water in a pan of ice water. Wait a few minutes and then observe the level of the water in the bottle. Did the water in the bottle expand or contract? How do you know? How could you measure the change in the volume of the water in the bottle?
2. Before beginning a trip, feel the tires of your family automobile to see how hot or cold they are. Also check the pressure in the tires. After driving several miles, again feel the tires and check the air pressure. Was there a change in the way the tires felt? In the air pressure? How would you describe the changes, if any, you observed? How would you explain these changes?

CHAPTER 8

Three Kinds of Changes

Telephone wires expand and contract with changes in temperature. Water freezes and ice melts as the seasons change. A rock slowly breaks down into smaller and smaller pieces. Iron and steel get rusty if they are left outside. A watch dial glows in the dark. Each of these sentences describes a change in matter.

Matter changes in many different ways. However, scientists have found that some of the ways that seem different are very much alike in terms of what happens to the matter. In fact, scientists group all changes in matter into three kinds—*physical* [FIHZ-ih-kuhl] *changes, chemical* [KEHM-ih-kuhl] *changes,* and *nuclear* [N(Y)OO-klee-ur] *changes.*

What kind of change is a physical change? A chemical change? A nuclear change? How do these kinds of changes differ from one another? Describing physical, chemical, and nuclear changes is what this chapter is about.

What changes in matter can you see happening in these pictures?

De Wys, Inc.

C. Centinio/De Wys, Inc.

Artstreet

PHYSICAL CHANGES

What is meant by the term "physical change"?
What are some examples of physical changes?

What is a physical change?

Have you ever cooked over a campfire? If so, you had to gather wood for the fire. Some of the pieces of wood were probably too large to put into the fire. These pieces had to be chopped into smaller pieces before you burned them.

When you chop a large piece of wood into smaller pieces, you change the size and the shape of the piece of wood. But wood is not changed into a different kind of matter by chopping it into smaller pieces.

Puck-Kornetzki/ZEFA

Figure 8–1. Making a pot out of clay changes the shape of the clay, but the clay is not changed into another kind of matter. What is this kind of change called?

Chopping a piece of wood into smaller pieces causes a physical change. In a physical change the appearance of matter is changed in some way. However, the kind of matter is not changed. In other words, a physical change does

153

not result in a different substance being formed. It only causes a change in the size, shape, or form of the same substance.

★ **Burning changes a piece of wood into ashes, water vapor, and several gases. Do you think the burning of wood causes a physical change? Why or why not?**

Some physical changes

Have you ever noticed what happens to a puddle after it stops raining? You might say that the puddle dries up. But what causes the puddle to dry up? If you remember the kinetic theory of matter, you'll remember that a scientist would explain it this way: Molecules of water in the puddle are moving. Some molecules move from the surface of the water into the air. The moving of water molecules into the air is called *evaporation* [ih-VAP-uh-RAY-shuhn].

During evaporation, water changes from a liquid into a gas. However, the water molecules do not change into other kinds of molecules. So evaporation is a physical change. In fact, all changes in phase are physical changes, because the kind of matter present does not change.

As matter becomes warmer, it expands. As matter becomes cooler, it contracts. Expanding and contracting change the volume and the density of matter. However, the kind of matter present is not changed. So expanding and contracting are physical changes also.

Another kind of physical change takes place when two substances are mixed together. For example, when you mix sugar in water, you make a kind of mixture called a solution. In making a sugar-water solution, the molecules of sugar become separated from each other and become scattered among the water molecules. The sugar is said to *dissolve* [dihz-AHLV] in the water. However, neither the sugar nor the water changes into another kind of matter. So dissolving is a physical change.

★ **What are some other kinds of matter you can dissolve in water? What are some kinds of matter that will not dissolve in water?**

For You to Think About

Most of the water that falls as rain comes from the oceans. How does ocean water get into the air? Ocean water is salty. Rainwater is not. Why isn't rainwater salty?

For You to Think About

The kinds of molecules do not change during a physical change. What, if anything, does happen to atoms and molecules during a physical change? Do their positions change? Do their motions change? What examples can you give to support your answers?

Use a physical change to separate a mixture

Make up a sugar-water solution. Pour the solution into a dish, and set the dish on a windowsill or shelf. Observe the dish for the next day or two. What happens to the water? What happens to the sugar? What physical change was used to separate the sugar from the water? What are some other mixtures that could be separated this way?

CHEMICAL CHANGES

What is meant by the term "chemical change"?
What happens to atoms and molecules when a
  chemical change occurs?
How do scientists classify compounds?

What is a chemical change?

If you chop a large piece of wood into smaller pieces, you cause changes in the size and shape of the wood. However, each of the smaller pieces of wood is exactly the same kind of matter as the larger piece of wood. So chopping a large piece of wood into smaller pieces causes a physical change.

If you then burn the pieces of wood, you cause still more changes in the wood. Burning causes the wood to change into ashes, water vapor, and several other gases. The molecules of the ashes, the water vapor, and the other gases are different from those of the wood. When wood is burned, then, the kinds of molecules in the wood are changed. A change in which the kinds of molecules are changed is a chemical change.

> ★ **What are some other chemical changes that you have seen or that you know about? How do you know they are chemical changes?**

Molecules and chemical changes

Water is a liquid that you use every day. Water is made up of only two elements—*hydrogen* [HY-druh-juhn] and *oxygen* [AHK-sih-juhn]. Both hydrogen and oxygen are gases at most temperatures. When hydrogen burns in oxygen, water molecules are formed. What happens to the atoms and molecules of these two gases?

You could say that hydrogen atoms and oxygen atoms join together to form water molecules. In general terms, this is correct. In the gas phase, however, both hydrogen and oxygen occur as molecules that are made of two atoms. So before the change takes place, hydrogen molecules and oxygen molecules are present. After the change, water molecules are present.

One way to show this chemical change is with a drawing such as Figure 8–2. Each atom is shown as a ball. Each ball is labeled with a chemical symbol—*O* for oxygen and *H* for hydrogen. Molecules are shown as two or more balls joined together.

One important feature of chemical changes concerns the numbers and kinds of atoms and molecules present before and after the change. Look at Figure 8–2. Count the numbers and kinds of molecules present before and after the change takes place. Now count the numbers and kinds of atoms present before and after the change.

If you counted correctly, you found that the numbers and kinds of molecules present before and after the change are different. However, the numbers and kinds of atoms present before and after the change are the same. The

Find Out More

Instead of writing out the names of elements, chemists use symbols made up of one or two letters to represent the elements. Find out what symbols are used for the elements iron, nitrogen, gold, sulfur, and chlorine. Compounds can also be shown using symbols. Find out what symbols are used to show the compounds water, sodium chloride (table salt), and ammonia.

Figure 8–2. How do the number of atoms and the number of molecules change when hydrogen and oxygen join to form water?

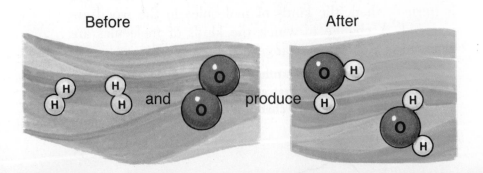

numbers and kinds of atoms present before and after any chemical change do not change. The numbers of molecules present before and after a change may or may not change. However, the kinds of molecules present always change.

Classifying compounds

There are many different kinds of compounds. No two are exactly alike in all their properties. But certain properties of one compound may be similar to those of another. Compounds with similar properties can be grouped.

One group of compounds that have similar properties is the *acids* [AS-uhdz]. All acids have hydrogen atoms joined to one or more other kinds of atoms. For example, hydrochloric acid is made up of an atom of hydrogen joined with an atom of chlorine. Furthermore, all acids have a sour taste. Lemons, limes, and grapefruit have a sour taste because of the acids in them. Of course you do not want to taste most acids. Many are very strong. Others are poisonous.

Is there an easy way to tell if a compound is an acid without tasting it? One easy way to test for acids is to use an *indicator* [IHN-duh-KAYT-ur]. An acid indicator is a substance that changes color in a certain way when it touches an acid. The acid indicator most often used is *blue litmus* [LIHT-muhs] *paper*. Blue litmus paper turns red when it touches an acid.

Another class of compounds is the *bases*. An example of a base is lye, or sodium hydroxide (NaOH). All bases contain atoms of some metal. In addition, each contains an oxygen atom joined to a hydrogen atom in a certain way. Most bases have a bitter taste. But as with acids, you do not find out if a compound is a base by tasting it. Instead, a base indicator is used. The base indicator most often used is red litmus paper. Bases turn red litmus blue.

When an acid and a base are mixed, they undergo a chemical change. Two new compounds—a salt and water— are formed. Perhaps when you hear the word "salt," you think only of the substance you put on your food. However, scientists use the word "salt" to describe a class of

(Text continues on page 159.)

Find Out More

Using references on chemistry, find out the names of some compounds, other than table salt, that a chemist would classify as a salt. Which of these have you heard of? Which have you used? Are all of them white? If not, what colors are they?

Investigate

Which household materials are acids and which are bases?

You Will Need

blue litmus paper, red litmus paper, scouring powder, lemon juice, vinegar, household ammonia, soda pop, lye (drain or oven cleaner), salt, sugar, distilled water, 9 small jars

Background

Indicators, such as litmus paper, are used to test kinds of matter to find out if the matter is an acid or a base. Acids turn blue litmus paper red but do not change the color of red litmus paper. Bases turn red litmus paper blue but do not change the color of blue litmus paper. Matter that is neither an acid nor a base will not change the color of either red or blue litmus paper.

What to Do

Put a small amount of each material to be tested into a separate jar. CAUTION: *Be sure you do not touch the lye. It can cause severe burns. If you get any on you, immediately soak the area with vinegar. Then wash the area thoroughly.* Label the jars. Add a small amount of distilled water to the jars containing the scouring powder, the salt, and the lye. Pour a small amount of water into a jar by itself.

Dip a piece of blue litmus paper into one of the jars. Observe the color change, if any, and set the piece of paper beside the jar. Do the same for each jar. Now do the same test using red litmus paper.

Now That You Have Done the Investigation

—Which materials, if any, changed the color of the blue litmus paper to red?

—Which materials, if any, changed the color of the red litmus paper to blue?

—Which materials, if any, did not change the color of either the blue or the red litmus paper?

—Which materials, if any, were acids? Which, if any, were bases? Which, if any, were neither acids nor bases?

Robert Buchbinder

Figure 8–3. Each of these packages contains a different kind of salt. Which of these salts are used in cooking? What are some other ways salts are used?

compounds. Salts do not have the same properties as either acids or bases. They do not change the color of either red litmus paper or blue litmus paper in any way. Not all salts taste salty. Some are colored green, pink, or blue instead of white. All salts can be formed from an acid and a base.

Oxygen easily combines with many other elements. Compounds formed by oxygen and one other element are called *oxides* [AHK-sydz]. Rust is an oxide. Rust is formed when iron atoms and oxygen atoms are joined together.

★ **From what elements is water formed? Could water be classed as an oxide? Explain.**

NUCLEAR CHANGES

What is meant by the term "nuclear change"?
What kinds of radiation are given off during nuclear change?
How is radiation detected and measured?

What is a nuclear change?

The sun has always interested people. Without heat and light from the sun, there would be few, if any, living things

159

on the earth. But what kind of change causes the sun to give off heat and light?

Scientists have figured out how much energy, in the form of heat and light, the sun gives off each day. They also have figured out how much fuel would have to be burned to give off the same amount of energy. Scientists have decided that the amount of heat and light given off by the sun could not result from the burning of fuel. So the kind of change taking place in the sun is not a chemical change. Furthermore, scientists do not know of any physical change that gives off that much energy. After many years, scientists have decided that the change taking place in the sun is a nuclear change. But what is meant by a nuclear change? How are nuclear changes different from physical and chemical changes?

To answer these questions, you should think again about the atomic theory. Every kind of matter is made up of tiny particles called atoms. Atoms are made up of still smaller parts—electrons, protons, and neutrons. The protons and neutrons form the nucleus in the center of atoms. A nuclear change is one that results from a change in the nucleus of an atom. Nuclear changes cause a change in the kinds of atoms present.

★ **How are nuclear changes different from physical changes? From chemical changes?**

Radiation from nuclear changes

Scientists began learning about nuclear changes almost 100 years ago. They discovered that some kinds of rock seemed to be giving off energy. If one of these kinds of rock was placed near camera film, the film was spoiled. This happened even though the film had not been unwrapped.

At that time scientists did not know how the rocks caused film to spoil. They reasoned that the rocks were giving off some kind of *radiation* [RAYD-ee-AY-shuhn]. Radiation is energy that is given off as rays or particles. Light, for example, is a form of radiation. Mat-

Figure 8–4. This piece of autunite gives off radiation. Would it be a good idea to leave a loaded camera next to this rock? Why or why not?

Mary Root/Root Resources

160

ter that gives off radiation is said to be *radioactive* [RAYD-ee-oh-AK-tihv].

Scientists began studying radioactive matter to find out what actually was being given off. In one early test, a small amount of radioactive matter was placed in a deep, narrow pit in a lead block. The lead block stopped all the radiation except that moving out through the opening of the pit. This small opening caused the radiation to come out of the pit in a narrow beam.

To show that radiation was coming out, a piece of camera film was held some distance from the opening. When the film was developed, a small dark spot was on the film at the place where the radiation hit.

Next, the north pole and the south pole of magnets were set opposite each other near the opening in the lead block. The beam of radiation passed between the two opposite poles of the magnets. See Figure 8–5. This time, when the film was developed, there were three spots on the film. The magnet had caused the beam of radiation to split into three parts. One part of the beam—later named *alpha* [AL-fuh] *rays*—was bent in one direction by the magnetic effect. Another part—later named *beta* [BAYT-uh] *rays*—was bent in the other direction. One part of the beam was not bent at all. This part was named

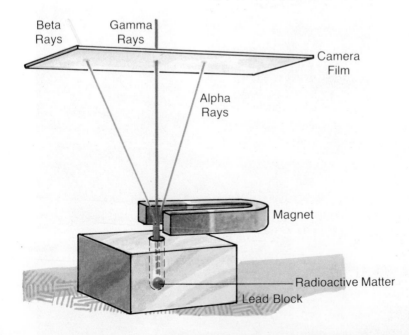

Beta Rays
Gamma Rays
Camera Film
Alpha Rays
Magnet
Radioactive Matter
Lead Block

Figure 8–5. This drawing shows how a magnetic field causes the radiation from radioactive matter to separate into three parts. Which kind of radiation is not affected by the magnet?

161

gamma [GAM-uh] *rays.* This experiment showed that three different kinds of radiation can be given off by radioactive matter.

Much has been learned about the three kinds of radiation. Gamma rays are similar to X rays, and they can go deep into most kinds of matter. Gamma rays cannot be seen or felt. But they can cause damage to living things. So people who work with radioactive matter need to be careful that they are not exposed to too much gamma radiation.

Alpha rays and beta rays are not really rays of energy. Instead, they are tiny, fast-moving particles. An alpha particle is made up of two protons and two neutrons. A beta particle is the same as an electron. Therefore, today scientists usually speak of alpha particles and beta particles rather than alpha rays and beta rays. Alpha particles and beta particles are not as harmful as gamma rays.

Detecting and measuring radioactivity

When scientists first began studying radioactive matter, they used camera film to find out if radiation was being given off. Today, scientists also use other kinds of instru-

Find Out More

Use references on nuclear changes and atomic energy to find out more about alpha particles and beta particles. Are these particles made up of even smaller particles? If so, what are the smaller particles? Do alpha and beta particles have an electric charge, or are they neutral?

Figure 8–6. This man is using mechanical hands to handle radioactive matter. Why does he use mechanical hands rather than his own hands to handle radioactive matter?

A. Devaney, Inc.

ments to study radiation from radioactive matter. One such instrument is the *cloud chamber*. Cloud chambers may be quite small or very large, but they are all alike in some ways.

The chamber is a container filled with very cold alcohol vapor. A piece of the radioactive matter to be studied is put inside the chamber. As the matter gives off alpha and/or beta particles, tiny drops of alcohol form along the paths of the particles. These "vapor trails" are easy to see and count. The particles themselves are too small to be seen. Each kind of particle—alpha or beta—making a trail can be identified. Alpha particles are larger than beta particles. They make heavy, straight trails. Beta particles are very tiny. They leave thin, wavy trails.

For You to Think About

Uranium is a radioactive element that is used as fuel in nuclear-powered electric-generating plants. How do people locate sources of uranium? Is uranium dangerous to handle? If so, what do you think can be done to make it safe to handle? What problems might occur in shipping this kind of matter from one place to another?

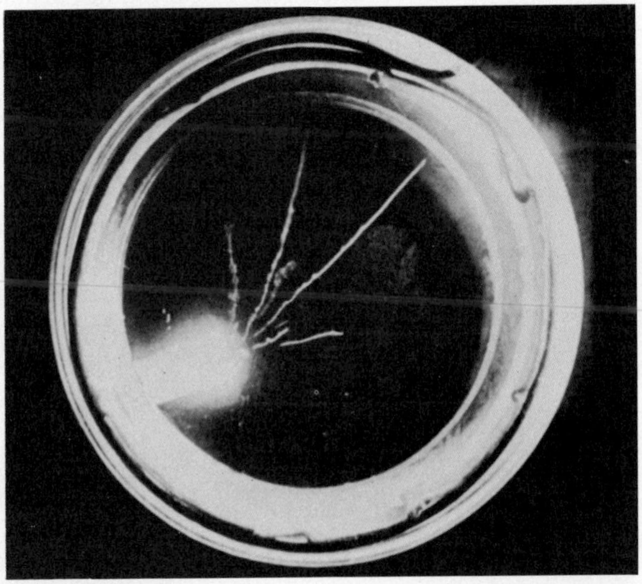

From PSSC Physics, D. C. Heath and Company, Lexington, Massachusetts, 1965

Figure 8–7. This cloud chamber contains a piece of radioactive matter. What kind or kinds of radiation do you think caused the heavy, straight "vapor trails" shown here?

Another instrument used to detect radiation from radioactive matter is the *Geiger-Müller counter*. This instrument has two main parts. One part is a tube that detects the radiation. Another part of the instrument counts the number of times radiation particles strike the tube. Usually the counter makes a clicking sound when radiation is detected. When the counter is close to radioactive matter, the counter clicks rapidly.

Investigate

How can you observe radioactivity?

You Will Need

glass jar with lid, black cloth, ink blotter, heavy wire, block of dry ice, small baking pan, alcohol, safe source of radioactive matter such as those that can be purchased from a scientific supply company, flashlight

Background

As radioactive atoms change, they give off alpha and/or beta particles. A cloud chamber is often used to study the way these particles move. The vapor trail made by an alpha particle is thicker and straighter than the vapor trail left by a beta particle. A source of radioactive matter can be purchased by your teacher from a scientific supply company. Or you could use a radium-coated watch dial.

What to Do

Cut a piece of black cloth to just fit inside the jar lid. Cut a piece of an ink blotter to just fit in the bottom of the jar. Make a clip out of heavy wire to hold the blotter in place. Now place the dry ice in the baking pan. CAUTION: *Do not handle dry ice with your bare hands.*

Under your teacher's directions, set the piece of radioactive matter on the black cloth in the jar lid. Pour some alcohol in the jar. Swirl the jar to make sure the blotter is soaked, and then pour out the excess alcohol. Without moving the lid or the radioactive matter, screw the jar into the lid. Then set the jar, lid down, on the dry ice. Wait about 5 minutes for the alcohol vapor to cool. Then, turn off the room lights and shine the flashlight through the side of the jar. Look through the jar at the black cloth. Count as many vapor trails as you can.

Now That You Have Done the Investigation

—How many vapor trails did you count?

—Were the trails straight and heavy, wavy and thin, or of both types?

—What kind or kinds of particles made the trails you saw?

164

Different kinds of jobs in nuclear power plants require different kinds of training. Why does handling radioactive matter require special training?

Working with Radioactive Matter

Today, many nuclear reactors are being used to make electricity. These reactors use certain purified forms of uranium as fuel. As more reactors are built, new sources of uranium are needed. As a result, many people have jobs finding and mining uranium ores.

The ores contain uranium. But these ores cannot be used in reactors. The ores are sent to a refinery where they are chemically changed. People who work where uranium is processed must receive special training on how to handle radioactive matter. They need this training because radioactive matter can be dangerous to living things.

Finally, there are a great many people who work in nuclear-powered electric-generating plants. Some have jobs taking care of and repairing the reactors. Others work with the steam turbines that make electricity, using steam from the reactors.

Some of the jobs just described require a great deal of training. Other jobs are learned as the people actually do these jobs. As more and more nuclear power plants are built, more and more people will have jobs working with matter that undergoes nuclear changes. Perhaps someday you will be one of these people.

Photo Research International

Reviewing and Extending

SUMMING UP

1. Scientists describe three kinds of changes in matter—physical changes, chemical changes, and nuclear changes.
2. A physical change causes some kind of change in the appearance of matter. However, the kinds of atoms present do not change.
3. Physical changes include breaking, evaporating, dissolving, expanding, contracting, and changing phase.
4. A chemical change causes a change in the kinds of molecules present. The numbers and kinds of atoms present do not change.
5. Compounds with some similar properties can be grouped together. Some groups of compounds are acids, bases, salts, and oxides.
6. A nuclear change is a change in the nucleus of an atom. Nuclear changes change the kinds of atoms present. Matter that undergoes nuclear changes is said to be radioactive.
7. Radioactive matter gives off three different kinds of radiation—gamma radiation in the form of rays, and alpha and beta radiation in the form of particles.
8. Gamma rays are similar to X rays. An alpha particle consists of two protons and two neutrons. A beta particle is the same as an electron.

CHECKING UP

Vocabulary   Write the numerals *1–5* on your paper. Each numbered phrase describes a term from the following list. On your paper, write the term next to the numeral of the phrase that describes it.

chemical change	physical change	nuclear change
alpha particle	beta particle	indicator

1. particle that is the same as an electron
2. change that forms different kinds of molecules
3. used to test for acids and bases
4. particle that is made up of two protons and two neutrons
5. change in the appearance of, but not the kind of, matter

Knowledge and Understanding   Write the numerals *6–12* on your paper. Beside each numeral, write the word or words that best complete the sentence having that numeral.

6. Expanding and contracting are examples of _____ changes.
7. _____ of water occurs when water molecules move from the surface of liquid water into the air.

8. All _____ taste sour and turn blue litmus paper red.
9. Matter which gives off alpha particles, beta particles, and gamma rays is said to be _____.
10. When an acid and a base are mixed, the compounds formed are a _____ and water.
11. The rusting of iron is an example of a _____ change.
12. Most _____ taste bitter and turn red litmus paper blue.

Concepts   Beside each of the numerals *13–17* on your paper, write the word or words that best complete the sentence having that numeral.

13. A cloud chamber is used to study (*physical, chemical, nuclear*) changes.
14. A chemical change results in different (*molecules, atoms, elements*) being formed.
15. Dissolving sugar in water is a (*physical, chemical, nuclear*) change.
16. Beta particles are (*protons, neutrons, electrons*) given off by matter undergoing a nuclear change.
17. All acids have (*hydrogen, oxygen, carbon*) atoms joined to one or more other kinds of atoms.

Application and Critical Thinking   Answer the following questions as briefly as you can without leaving out any important ideas.

18. How are physical changes, chemical changes, and nuclear changes different from each other? In what ways, if any, are they alike?
19. You have three jars, each filled with a different liquid. One liquid is an acid, one is water, and one is a base. How could you tell which liquid is which?

DOING MORE

1. Put a teaspoon of citric-acid crystals and a tablespoon of baking soda in a dry beaker. Mix them and observe what, if anything, happens. Half fill another beaker with water. Pour the citric acid and baking soda into the water. Observe what, if anything, happens. Did the water cause anything to happen that did not happen before? Why are some things marked "Store in a dry place"?
2. Uranium 238 eventually changes into lead 206. Use references such as physics books to find out how this change occurs. Does it happen in one step or in several steps? What kind or kinds of atoms are formed? What kinds of radiation are given off?

CHAPTER 9

Some Important Changes

Changes in matter are important to people. Many of the things you use every day result from changes in matter. In fact, a great many things you use come from changes in a certain kind of matter—oil.

Oil as it comes from the ground has very few uses today. Instead, the oil is changed into other, more-useful kinds of matter. Both physical changes and chemical changes are used to change oil into these other, more-useful substances.

Not all the useful changes in matter are caused by people. Some changes, such as those that occur in plants and radioactive matter, are natural changes. Natural changes can be physical, chemical, or nuclear.

Certain changes, such as those that take place in plants, have always been important in the lives of people. Other changes, such as those made to take place in oil, have only become important in modern times. In the future, nuclear changes may be very important to people. Some of these important changes are described in this chapter.

Courtesy of Marathon Oil Company

Oil from inside the earth is very valuable. However, it must be refined and changed before it is in the form of useful products, such as gasoline.

Courtesy of Marathon Oil Company

Photo Research International

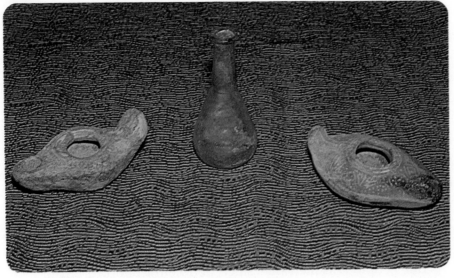

Figure 9–1. How are these old lamps different from the lamps in your home? How are they like the lamps you use?

CHANGING PETROLEUM

What were some of the early sources of oil and grease?
What kind of matter is petroleum?
How is petroleum changed into useful products?

Early sources of oil and grease

Oil and grease have been used for thousands of years. Even long ago, people used oil and grease to make wheels turn more easily. Jars and baskets were coated with oil or grease to make them waterproof. Some kinds of oil were used in cooking food. Oil was also burned in lamps for light.

Some kinds of oil and grease used long ago were obtained from animal fats. Some were obtained from certain parts of plants. Another kind of oil was found bubbling out of the ground in some places. This oil was often black and smelly. Because this oil was often found coming from cracks in rock, it came to be known as *petroleum* [puh-TROH-lee-uhm]. Petroleum means "rock oil." Long ago, petroleum

169

was not thought to be as valuable as the oils from animals or from plants. As time passed, however, more and more oil was needed. The amount of oil and grease that people could get from animals and plants was not enough.

People found ways to change petroleum into useful oil and grease. For many purposes, the oil and grease from petroleum could be used instead of oil and grease from animals and/or plants. Oil and grease for cooking, however, still had to come from animals or plants. Cooking food in oil or grease from petroleum could make you very sick or even kill you.

Petroleum became an important source for oil and grease. Soon the amount of petroleum found on the surface of the earth was too small to meet the need for oil and grease. But people reasoned that since petroleum bubbled out of the ground in some places, there must be petroleum below the ground. Wells were drilled to find these underground supplies. Today many people work at finding petroleum and drilling wells to get it out of the ground. Others work

Figure 9–2. *An early rig used to drill for oil is shown above. How does the modern rig shown at the right differ from the early one? How are they alike?*

in refineries where the petroleum is changed into more-useful kinds of matter.

What is petroleum?

You probably have not seen oil that has just been pumped from beneath the surface of the earth. Few people have. But if the people who have seen petroleum were asked to describe it, they would probably say it is a thick, black liquid. However, not all petroleum is alike. Some kinds of petroleum are thicker and darker than others. Why are there different kinds of petroleum?

One reason is that petroleum is not a single substance. It is a mixture of many different substances. Some of the substances that make up petroleum are gasoline, kerosine, waxes, and asphalt. All these different substances are made up of molecules having just two elements—hydrogen and carbon. For this reason, petroleum is often described as being a mixture of *hydrocarbons* [HY-druh-KAHR-buhnz].

Scientists believe that petroleum was formed from the remains of plants and animals that lived millions of years ago. The plants and animals that lived on one part of the earth were often quite different from those living on other parts. So the different kinds of petroleum may be the result of being formed from different kinds of plants and animals.

Separating the compounds

Petroleum is a mixture of many substances. Some, such as gasoline, heating oil, and asphalt, are themselves useful. Others are useful in making plastics, medicines, and other chemicals. The process of changing petroleum into useful substances is called *refining* [rih-FYN-ihng].

The first step in refining petroleum is to separate the different substances. Heat is used to change liquid petroleum into gases. The gases are piped into the bottom of a tall tower. Inside, the tower is divided into several levels. Each level is a little cooler than the one below.

One property of matter is that each kind of matter changes from a gas to a liquid at a different temperature.

Find Out More

Use encyclopedias and other references to answer questions such as these: What kinds of cloth are made from petroleum products? What kinds of plastics? What are some uses, other than those already mentioned, for petroleum products?

171

Figure 9–3. *Petroleum is separated into many different substances in tall towers like these. Gasoline changes to a liquid at a lower temperature than heating oil. Asphalt changes to a liquid at a very high temperature. Which of these three substances collects at the bottom of the tower? Which collects near the top of the tower?*

As the petroleum gases rise in the tower, they become cooler. At each level, some of the gases become cool enough to *condense* [kuhn-DEHN(T)S], or change to a liquid. Those substances that change to liquids at high temperatures collect in the lower levels of the tower. Those that become liquid at low temperatures collect in the upper levels of the tower.

★ **Is the separating of petroleum compounds in the tower an example of a physical change or a chemical change? Explain.**

Making new compounds

In any given amount of petroleum there is only a certain amount of each substance. People use more of some substances than they do of others. Furthermore, the amount needed of some substances, such as heating oil, changes with the seasons.

If all a refinery did was to separate the different substances in petroleum, enough gasoline and heating oil could be made to meet the changing needs of people. At the

172

same time, however, large amounts of other substances would also be made. Because there is little need for these other substances, they would be wasted.

Today, all refineries have parts in which little-used substances are changed into other, more-useful ones. One such part is a *catalytic* [KAT-uhl-IHT-ihk] *cracking unit*. In this unit, molecules of little-used substances are broken apart, or cracked. With cracking, a more-useful substance, such as gasoline, can be made from less-useful substances.

Another part is called a *reforming* [rih-FAW(UH)RM-ihng] *unit*. Here molecules are reformed, or joined to other molecules. As with catalytic cracking, the purpose is to change little-used substances into more-useful ones, such as gasoline and jet fuel.

★ **Are cracking and reforming physical changes or chemical changes? How do you know?**

For You to Think About

The amount of gasoline obtained from a certain amount of petroleum can be increased by cracking and by reforming. How do cracking and reforming change the amounts of other substances that are made from petroleum? Why are these two processes useful?

Photos courtesy of Marathon Oil Company

Figure 9–4. Reforming units such as the one on the left and catalytic-cracking units such as the one on the right are important parts of every oil refinery. Why do all refineries have such units?

173

DO IT YOURSELF

Make a report

Use various references (encyclopedias, information from oil companies, science books, and so on) to find out about the history of the petroleum industry. When was the first oil well drilled in the United States? Who drilled it? How do modern oil wells compare with the first oil well? Make a graph showing how the production of oil has increased in the United States. Report your findings to the class.

PLANTS AND CHANGES IN MATTER

Why are changes in plants important?
What changes take place in plants?
What must happen to the nitrogen in the air
before plants can use it?

Plants and energy

You use energy to grow, to work, and to play. Your energy comes from the food you eat. Energy is also used to make electricity and run machines. This energy usually comes from the burning of fuels such as coal, oil, or gasoline. But where does the energy in food and in fuels come from?

Think about the food you eat. Some of your food, such as bread and fruit, comes from plants. Other food, such as meat and fish, comes from animals. However, the animals you eat have eaten plants. So, in a way, all your food comes from plants. Therefore, all the energy you get from the food you eat comes from plants, either directly or indirectly.

You have read that scientists believe petroleum was formed from the remains of plants and animals that lived thousands of years ago. Coal is thought to have been formed from plants that became buried under deep layers of mud. So the most widely used fuels—coal and oil—also come from plants.

174

Grant Heilman

Figure 9–5. Triticale is a new kind of grain developed from wheat and rye plants. This new grain produces more food per acre than wheat or rye, is not affected by many diseases that affect wheat or rye, and can be grown in many different parts of the world. Why do you think scientists want to develop new food plants such as triticale?

In some way, then, much of the energy that people use every day comes from plants. But where do plants get their energy? And how do plants change this energy into the kinds of energy that can be used by people and other animals? Finding answers to such questions has been a major goal of scientists. For example, by understanding how plants get and store energy, scientists have been able to develop new kinds of food plants. These newer food plants produce larger amounts of food.

★ **How would you explain the statement "Plants are the food factories of the world"?**

Photosynthesis

If you have ever grown plants, you know several things about them. You know that plants need light, air, water, and certain substances from the soil in order to grow. You also know that most plants have green leaves or needles. Some plants also have green stems.

The green color of certain parts of plants is due to *chlorophyll* [KLOHR-uh-FIHL] in these parts. Chlorophyll is very important. It causes one of the most important

175

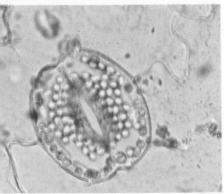

Hugh Spencer

Figure 9–6. *The tiny green bodies in this plant cell contain chlorophyll. In what way are these green bodies of use to this plant cell?*

chemical changes that take place on the earth. This chemical change is called *photosynthesis* [FOHT-oh-SIHN(T)-thuh-suhs].

Scientists have not answered all of their questions about what happens during photosynthesis. However, they have learned that during this chemical change, molecules of water and carbon dioxide are changed into molecules of sugar and oxygen. Furthermore, this change takes place only in the green parts of plants. So scientists know that chlorophyll is important to photosynthesis. Light, a form of energy, is also needed for photosynthesis to take place.

Scientists have not yet learned exactly what happens. But they are fairly sure of the following: Chlorophyll, in the green parts of plants, is able to use light energy to form sugar out of carbon dioxide and water. The light energy used in forming sugar is changed into a kind of energy that the plants can use to grow and stay alive. This kind of energy might be called food energy.

Storing extra energy

The food energy in sugar is used by plants to grow and stay alive. But plants make more sugar than they need just to grow and live. Plants are able to change the extra sugar into other substances. One of these substances is *starch* [STAHRCH].

Plants make starch molecules by causing a change in which many sugar molecules are joined together. The starch is then stored in various parts of plants. In many plants starch is stored in roots and stems. When you eat carrots or turnips, you are eating roots in which starch is stored. Potatoes are a special kind of stem in which starch is stored.

On cloudy days plants cannot make as much sugar as they can on sunny days. Sometimes plants need more sugar than they make. To get the sugar they need, plants change some of their stored starch back into sugar.

★ **What other parts of a plant have you eaten? Do you think these parts contained starch, sugar, or both? Explain.**

For You to Think About

Even though mushrooms are not green, most scientists classify mushrooms as plants. Do you think mushrooms can carry on photosynthesis? Why or why not? If not, how do mushrooms get the substances they need to grow?

176

Investigate

Is chlorophyll necessary for photosynthesis?

You Will Need

Coleus leaves, water, tongs, warm alcohol, burner, iodine solution, paper towel, 3 beakers

Background

Chlorophyll is a substance that gives plant leaves their green color. In some plants, such as *Coleus*, only part of the leaf is green. Does photosynthesis take place in only the green parts of such leaves, or does it take place in all the parts? You can find out by testing for a compound that forms as a result of photosynthesis—starch. When iodine is added to starch, the starch turns a dark blue or black color. If starch is formed only in the green parts of *Coleus* leaves, then the chlorophyll must be necessary for photosynthesis.

What to Do

Make a drawing of a *Coleus* leaf on a sheet of paper. Show the areas that are green and those that are not green.

Half fill a beaker with water, and heat the water until it boils. Place the leaf in the boiling water for several minutes. Using the tongs, remove the leaf from the water and drop it into a beaker of warm alcohol. *CAUTION: Do not heat alcohol over an open flame. Instead, to warm the alcohol, place the beaker of alcohol in a pan of very hot water.* Allow the leaf to remain in the alcohol until the green color disappears from the leaf.

When all of the color is gone from the leaf, use the tongs to remove the leaf from the alcohol. Rinse the leaf in cold water, and place it in an empty beaker. Cover the leaf with iodine solution. After 3 to 5 minutes rinse the leaf in cold water. Spread the leaf on a paper towel and compare it to your drawing.

Now That You Have Done the Investigation

—Which areas of the leaf contained chlorophyll? How do you know?

—Which areas contained starch? How do you know?

—How did the area that contained chlorophyll compare with the area that contained starch?

Food for animals

In changing sugar into starch and starch into sugar, plants use other substances they make. These substances are *proteins* [PROH-TEENZ]. Proteins make up a large part of all living things. They help living things to grow and to live by causing chemical changes.

When animals eat plants, they eat the sugar, starch, and proteins made by the plants. Animals use the sugar and starch as their source of energy. The proteins are used to make blood, muscles, and nerves. Plant proteins are very important to animals. Animals cannot make their proteins out of light, water, gases, and substances found in soil the way plants do. Animals can only change the kinds of proteins they eat into other kinds of proteins. In fact, that is why plants are so important. Plants are the only kind of living thing that can use light, water, gases, and substances found in soil to make the food that animals need.

Nitrogen fixing

One very important element in proteins is *nitrogen* [NY-truh-juhn]. Plants use nitrogen from the soil to make proteins. The nitrogen that plants use comes from nitrogen compounds. Some of these compounds are in animal wastes. Others are in the remains of dead plants and animals.

Air is made up of several gases. One of these gases is nitrogen. Nitrogen gas makes up about 80% of the air. But plants cannot use nitrogen gas to make proteins. Before plants can use nitrogen, the nitrogen atoms must become part of a nitrogen compound that dissolves in water. The changing of nitrogen gas into the kinds of compounds plants can use is called *nitrogen fixing*.

Some nitrogen fixing takes place during thunderstorms. Lightning causes nitrogen atoms and oxygen atoms to join together. These molecules are then carried to the ground by the rainwater.

Certain kinds of bacteria that live in soil also are able to carry on nitrogen fixing. These bacteria often live on the roots of certain plants. As the plants grow, the nitrogen-fixing bacteria add nitrogen compounds to the soil. In fact,

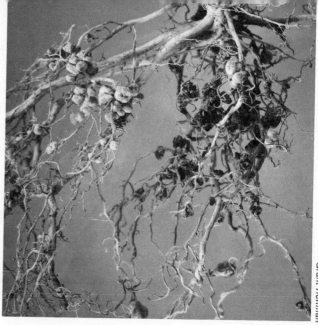

Figure 9–7. The nodules, or lumps, on these roots contain nitrogen-fixing bacteria. In what other ways does nitrogen fixing take place?

the bacteria add more nitrogen compounds to the soil than the plant they grow on needs. The extra nitrogen is used by other plants nearby.

Nitrogen fixing is important to plants. If nitrogen fixing stopped, plants would soon use up the nitrogen compounds in the soil. Without nitrogen compounds, plants would grow poorly, if at all. They could not carry out photosynthesis. The result would be less food for animals. So nitrogen fixing is also a very important chemical change.

DO IT YOURSELF

Grow clover or alfalfa

Fill a large pot with soil from your yard. Plant several clover or alfalfa seeds in the soil. After the plants have appeared above ground, dig up one of the plants and examine its roots. Dig up another plant 2 days later and another after 6 days. Use references on plants to find out what causes the nodules to form on the roots. Do all kinds of plants develop nodules? If not, what kinds of plants do? What advantage, if any, do the nodules give to the plant?

IMPORTANT NUCLEAR CHANGES

What is meant by the term "fission"?
How is nuclear fission used to make electricity?
How can nuclear changes help scientists learn
   more about living things?

Causing nuclear changes

Scientists have been studying nuclear changes for about eighty years. At first, the changes they studied were natural changes that take place in radioactive matter. These studies helped scientists learn much about atoms and their parts. But it was not until the late 1930's that scientists learned how to cause nuclear changes.

In the late 1930's, several scientists were studying the element *uranium* [yu-RAY-nee-uhm]. In their experiments they caused neutrons to smash into a piece of uranium. Later testing showed that there were small amounts of elements other than uranium in the uranium. These elements had not been present before the neutrons smashed into the uranium. The atoms of the new elements were about half the mass of a uranium atom. The scientists reasoned that the neutrons had caused some uranium atoms to undergo *fission* [FIHSH-uhn]. That is, they reasoned that the atoms split into two parts. Each part was an atom of another element.

During fission, several things other than two new atoms are formed. Two or three neutrons as well as alpha and beta particles and gamma rays are also given off. Some scientists began to wonder if the neutrons given off during fission could also cause other atoms to undergo fission. If so, it would be possible to start a *nuclear reaction* [ree-AK-shuhn] by sending neutrons into uranium. Then, the neutrons given off during fission would keep the reaction going by splitting more uranium atoms. This would give off more neutrons, so that even more atoms would split. The reaction, once started, would keep going until all the matter had changed. Such a reaction is called a *chain reaction*.

If a chain reaction is not controlled, a lot of energy is given off all at once. This causes a powerful explosion. If the reaction is controlled, the energy is given off in smaller amounts over a long period of time. If the energy is given off over a period of time, the energy can be used to do work.

The first controlled chain reaction was started on December 2, 1942. Many scientists began thinking of ways to use this nuclear change to help people. But World War II had started just two years earlier. So the first use of nuclear fission was in a bomb.

★ **How is fission different from the nuclear changes in radioactive matter that result only in alpha particles, beta particles, and gamma rays being given off?**

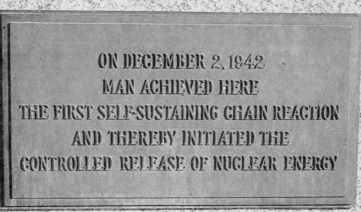

Robert Buchbinder

ON DECEMBER 2, 1942
MAN ACHIEVED HERE
THE FIRST SELF-SUSTAINING CHAIN REACTION
AND THEREBY INITIATED THE
CONTROLLED RELEASE OF NUCLEAR ENERGY

Figure 9–8. The plaque marks the place where scientists started the first controlled chain reaction. However, the first use of nuclear fission was in bombs, such as the one that caused this explosion over Nagasaki, Japan. Is the nuclear fission that takes place in a bomb an example of a controlled or an uncontrolled chain reaction?

181

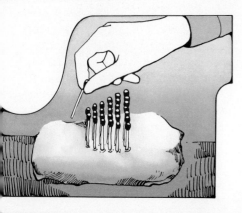

DO IT YOURSELF

Demonstrate a chain reaction

Flatten a piece of modeling clay. Stick wooden kitchen matches into the clay in a triangular pattern, as shown in the diagram. Be sure that the matches are no more than one centimetre apart from each other. Light the match at one point of the triangle. What happens? How do the matches demonstrate a chain reaction? Is this an example of a controlled or of an uncontrolled chain reaction?

Find Out More

Find out more about nuclear reactors. Use newspaper articles, magazine articles, and other references to answer questions such as these: Can a nuclear reactor explode? How are chain reactions controlled in a reactor? How are people that work in nuclear power plants protected from harmful radiation?

Electricity from nuclear changes

Since the end of World War II, scientists have been able to make nuclear fission serve peaceful uses. One such use is the making of electricity. Today, there are several nuclear-powered electric-generating plants in the United States and in other countries.

An important part of such a plant is the *nuclear reactor* [ree-AK-tur]. Inside the reactor, a controlled chain reaction takes place. This chain reaction gives off a lot of energy. Some of the energy is in the form of radiation that could be harmful. Care is taken in building these power plants to make sure that such radiation does not get outside the plant.

Most of the energy given off by the chain reaction is in the form of heat. The heat is used to make water boil and change into steam. Then the steam is used to run a turbine that turns the electric generator.

In using steam to make electricity, nuclear power plants are like power plants that burn coal or fuel oil. The main difference between nuclear power plants and those that burn coal or oil is the way water is changed into steam.

Artificial radioactivity

In studying nuclear changes, scientists made many interesting discoveries. One is that substances that are not normally radioactive can be made radioactive. To make a substance become radioactive, some of the substance is put inside a reactor. Atoms of the substance soak up some of the neutrons given off by the fissioning uranium. The extra neutrons make the substance become radioactive. This kind of radioactivity is called *artificial* [AHRT-uh-FIHSH-uhl] *radioactivity.*

Artificial radioactivity has been very useful. One way it has been used is to study plants. Scientists know that plants need certain substances in order to grow. But how do these substances get into plants? And, what happens to the substances after they get into plants? Answers to questions such as these have been found by using artificial radioactivity.

First an element that plants need is made radioactive. Then the radioactive element is used to form compounds. These compounds are then put into the soil in which plants are growing. As the radioactive substances are taken

Find Out More

Use encyclopedias and other references to find out how artificial radioactivity is useful to doctors, both in detecting and in treating certain disorders. Make a report on what you find out.

Jack Novak/Photo Research International

Figure 9–9. These plants are being given radioactive substances. How can giving radioactive substances to plants help scientists learn about plants?

Faust/Photo Research International

Figure 9–10. The apple seedling shown in this autoradiogram was grown in soil containing radioactive calcium. The parts of the plant containing the radioactive calcium caused dark areas to appear on the piece of film. Into which part or parts of this plant did the radioactive calcium move? What part or parts do not seem to contain radioactive calcium?

into the plants, the path of the substances can be followed by using a Geiger-Müller counter or some other detector.

Scientists have discovered that some substances move to certain parts of the plant and remain there. Special camera film can be used to show where the radioactive matter is. See Figure 9–10.

Radioactive substances can also be used to find out what kinds of chemical changes take place in plants. Scientists keep careful records as to how much radioactive matter is put into the soil. Later they run tests to find out how much of the radioactive matter is taken up by the plants. They also test to find out which substances made by the plants have the radioactive matter in them.

★ **Scientists are sure that the carbon used by plants to make sugar comes from carbon dioxide in the air and not carbon compounds from the soil. How might scientists have found out this information?**

Workers in the Petroleum Industry

The petroleum industry is one of the largest industries in the world today. The petroleum industry involves a lot more than just drilling for oil and changing the oil into gasoline. Petroleum also contains the raw material used to make plastics, fertilizers, pesticides, medicines, synthetic fabrics, and many other products. The jobs of finding oil, refining it, and selling the many products made from it are all part of the petroleum industry. Many men and women work at these jobs.

Some jobs with oil companies require several years of college. One such job is that of the geologist who searches for new places to drill for oil. Another is that of the chemist who tries to find better ways to refine petroleum and to discover new products that can be made from petroleum.

Many other jobs in the oil industry are learned on the job. These include setting up drilling rigs, drilling for oil, and running machines in the refineries and chemical plants.

Not everyone who works for an oil company works with oil. The oil industry, like all other industries, provides jobs for accountants, clerks, computer programmers, secretaries, and many other kinds of workers.

Each year more and more petroleum is used. So, oil companies will continue to hire men and women for many different jobs. Perhaps when you begin your career, you will be one of these people.

Geologists like these know a great deal about the rocks of the earth. Why do oil companies hire people who know about rocks to look for oil?

Courtesy of Marathon Oil Company

Reviewing and Extending

SUMMING UP

1. Petroleum is a mixture of many different substances. All of these substances are made up of molecules having just two elements—hydrogen and carbon.
2. The process of changing petroleum into useful products is called refining.
3. Little-used substances are changed into other, more-useful ones by cracking and reforming.
4. The green color of certain parts of plants is due to chlorophyll. Chlorophyll plays an important role in a chemical change called photosynthesis.
5. In photosynthesis, plants use light to change carbon dioxide and water into sugar.
6. Plants change the extra sugar made during photosynthesis into starch and protein.
7. In order to make protein, plants need nitrogen. However, plants can only use nitrogen from certain kinds of nitrogen compounds.
8. The changing of nitrogen in the air into the kinds of nitrogen compounds plants can use is called nitrogen fixing.
9. Fission is the splitting of atoms into two almost equal parts. Neutrons given off by fissioning atoms can cause the fission of other atoms in a chain reaction.
10. Substances that are not normally radioactive can be made radioactive by putting them into a nuclear reactor. Such radioactivity is called artificial radioactivity.

CHECKING UP

Vocabulary Write the numerals *1–5* on your paper. Each numbered phrase describes a term from the following list. On your paper, write the term next to the numeral of the phrase that describes it.

petroleum	photosynthesis	chlorophyll
fission	nuclear reactor	catalytic cracking unit

1. causes certain plant parts to have green color
2. word that means rock oil
3. splitting of atoms into almost equal parts
4. process by which plants use light energy to make sugar
5. where a controlled chain reaction takes place

Knowledge and Understanding Write the numerals *6–10* on your paper. Beside each numeral, write the word or words that best complete the sentence having that numeral.

6. The process of changing petroleum into useful substances is called (*condensing, refining, fissioning*).

7. Petroleum is a (*mixture of hydrocarbons, mixture of chlorophylls, single substance*).

8. Inside a nuclear reactor, a controlled (*chemical, physical, chain*) reaction takes place.

9. Photosynthesis takes place only in (*refineries, nuclear reactors, green plants*).

10. (*Starch, Protein, Sugar*) is formed from carbon dioxide and water during photosynthesis.

Concepts   Beside each of the numerals *11–15* on your paper, write the word or words that best complete the sentence having that numeral.

11. Light energy is taken up by the _____ in the green parts of plants.

12. _____, given off by some uranium atoms undergoing fission, cause other atoms to also undergo fission in a chain reaction.

13. _____ are the only living things that can make food out of light, air, water, and substances in the soil.

14. The process of joining together molecules of little-used substances in petroleum to make molecules of more-useful substances is called _____.

15. In the tower used to separate the different substances in petroleum, the substances that condense at the lowest temperatures collect in the _____ levels of the tower.

Application and Critical Thinking   Answer the following questions as briefly as you can without leaving out any important ideas.

16. Describe three ways petroleum is changed into useful substances. Which, if any, are physical changes? Chemical changes?

17. How could you find out if a plant uses iron from the soil?

DOING MORE

1. The nuclear reactions that take place in the sun are not due to fission. Use physics books or other references to answer questions such as these: What kind of nuclear reaction takes place in the sun? How does this reaction differ from fission?

2. Plant two to four bean seeds in each of two containers of moist soil. Put one container in a dark closet and the other container on a sunny windowsill. Add water as necessary to each container to keep the soil moist. Check the containers each day for a week after the plants appear above the soil. Were there differences between the plants grown in the dark and those grown in the light? If so, describe any differences you observed.

Pros and Cons

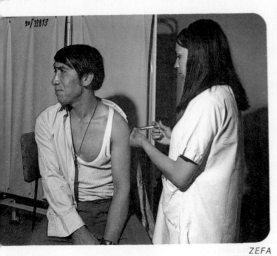

ZEFA

A. Devaney, Inc.

Most medicines and insecticides are made from chemicals. What are some other uses for chemicals?

Chemicals—Should We Continue to Use Them as We Do Now?

People use chemicals in many ways. In many cases, the chemicals are used in large amounts. Some people feel that learning how to make and use many different kinds of chemicals has been one of the most important achievements of this century. These people feel that chemicals will play an even more important role in our world in the future.

Other people have a different point of view. These people feel that too many chemicals are being used. They say that chemicals, when used in large amounts, are dangerous to people and to other living things. So even though the use of chemicals has been helpful in some ways, there are reasons to consider limiting the use of chemicals. That is, there are some pros and some cons regarding the use of chemicals.

Farmers today use many chemicals. Insecticides are used to keep insects from destroying crops. Herbicides are used to control weeds. Fertilizers are used to make plants grow better. By using these chemicals, farmers are able to grow far more food on less land than they could years ago. Many farmers say that without the help of chemicals, they could not farm profitably.

Growing food is not the only use for chemicals. Most medicines in use today are made from chemicals. Because so many medicines can be easily made from chemicals, few people die from diseases such as measles and pneumonia today. In addition, chemicals are often added to food to help preserve the food, make it taste better, or be more attractive.

Plastics and synthetic fabrics, such as nylon and rayon, are other important products made from chemicals. Plastics are used to make boats, toys, dishes, windows, and many other things that would otherwise be made of wood, metal, or glass. Synthetic fabrics can be made to feel and look like cotton, wool, or silk cloth. The synthetic cloth costs far less to make than cotton, wool, or silk cloth. So, clothes made of synthetic fabrics cost less than clothes made of other materials. Also, synthetic fabrics are often easier to clean than other kinds of cloth.

In fact, there are few things that you use that do not depend in some way on chemicals. But using chemicals in factories often produces waste products that must be got rid of. Sometimes these waste products go into the air through smokestacks. Some waste products get into rivers and lakes through sewers. In either case, the wastes can cause harmful pollution.

Using chemicals on farms has also caused some problems. Some insects have become immune to the chemicals. That is, they are no longer killed by the insecticides. Furthermore, some insecticides are believed to affect birds. If this is true, it could mean that fewer insect-eating birds are being hatched.

Fertilizers have also caused some problems. Fertilizer can be washed off the fields and carried into rivers by rainwater. The fertilizer makes the river plants grow very fast. As these river plants grow, they use up much of the oxygen in the water. Then fish begin to die because there isn't enough oxygen for them to breathe.

Even chemicals that have been used as medicines and food additives have been found to have harmful effects. These

Photos from Dr. E. R. Degginger

Using chemicals has caused some problems. What kinds of problems caused by the use of chemicals are shown in these pictures?

chemicals are taken off the market as soon as the harmful effects are discovered. But, by then, some people may have already suffered because of the chemicals.

As you have read, using chemicals has made life easier and better for many people. However, there are some problems that have developed from the use of chemicals. Should we continue to use more and more chemicals? Or should we limit the use of chemicals? Would limiting the use of chemicals cause other problems? How would you go about deciding how to answer such questions?

Investigate On Your Own

1. You can make an indicator from the leaves of red cabbage and find out how an acid (vinegar) and a base (ammonia) affect it. Shred two red cabbage leaves. Boil the shreds in a small amount of water until the water is a deep red color. Squeeze the juice from the leaves and pour the liquid into a jar or beaker to cool. Slowly pour some vinegar into the purple liquid. Does a color change occur? If so, what kind of change? Now slowly pour some ammonia into the jar and stir the liquid. What happens to the color this time? Add more ammonia. Does the color change more? Now you know how this indicator changes color in the presence of an acid (vinegar) and a base (ammonia). Use it to test other household liquids to find out which, if any, are acids and which, if any, are bases. If you did the investigation on page 158, test the same liquids using the red cabbage indicator. Compare the results you obtained using the different indicators.

2. Plants give off a gas when they carry on photosynthesis. To find out which gas plants give off, fill a large beaker or wide-mouth jar with water. Place an aquarium plant in the beaker. Then place a funnel over the plant, as shown in the diagram. Fill a test tube with water and invert the tube over the funnel. Observe the test tube for two or three days. Does the tube remain full of water, or does it become filled with a gas? If there is gas in the tube, where

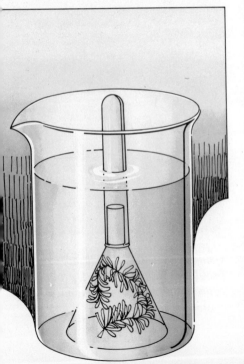

did the gas come from? Do you think the gas is carbon dioxide or oxygen? Test the gas with a glowing splint to find out. If the gas is carbon dioxide, the splint will stop glowing. If the gas is oxygen, the splint will burst into flame.

Read On Your Own

Aylesworth, Thomas G., *The Alchemists: Magic into Science.* Reading, Massachusetts: Addison-Wesley Publishing Co., Inc., 1973.
This book presents a humorous history of alchemy, which led to modern-day chemistry. Some famous alchemists and their work are described.

Coulson, E., Trinder, P., and Klein, A., *Test Tubes and Beakers: Chemistry for Young Experimenters.* Garden City, New York: Doubleday and Company, Inc., 1971.
Interesting, easy-to-do experiments and ways to make your own laboratory equipment are two of the best features of this book.

Fenton, C. L., and Fenton, M. A., *Riches from the Earth.* New York: The John Day Company, 1970.
Many useful elements and compounds found in the earth are described. There is also information as to where they are found and how they are used.

Gallant, Roy A., *Explorers of the Atom.* Garden City, New York: Doubleday and Company, Inc., 1974.
How the parts of the atom were discovered is described in this book. There is also information about many of the people who contributed to our understanding of atoms.

Stepp, Ann, *The Story of Radioactivity.* Irving-on-Hudson, New York: Harvey House, Inc. Publishers, 1971.
This book describes what is meant by radiation and some different kinds of radiation. It also describes the uses for and dangers from radioactive matter.

UNIT **3**

Dr. Hans Kramarz/ZEFA

ENERGY

For Work and Motion

Have you ever thought of all the kinds of work you do just in school? Try making a list of the kinds of work you do. Are you sure everything you listed is what a scientist would call work? In the kinds of work you listed, is something made to move? Is motion important in doing work? If so, how is it related to work? What has energy to do with either work or motion? Is there only one kind of energy, or are there many kinds of energy? You will be able to learn more about these and other ideas about energy, work, and motion in this unit.

Chapters

CHAPTER 10

Work, Power, and Energy

Suppose your family automobile is stuck in mud, sand, or snow. Getting it out takes a lot of work. You can do this work by pushing it out yourself. Or, you can call for a tow truck to come and pull it out. You do the same amount of work that the tow truck does if you move the stuck automobile the same distance the tow truck moves it. However, the tow truck does this amount of work much faster than you do. The tow truck does the work faster than you do because the tow truck has more power than you do.

But, neither you nor the tow truck could move the automobile without *energy* [EHN-ur-jee]. Energy is used to do work. You get energy from the food you eat. The tow truck gets energy from the gasoline burned in its engine.

Understanding work, power, and energy is important in using machines and engines. But what is meant by these three terms? How are they related? These are some of the questions that will be explored in this chapter.

Photos from John D. Firestone & Associates, Inc.

In each picture, work is being done. What sources of energy are being used to do the work?

WORK

How does a scientist use the word "work"?
Can work be measured? How?
What units are used to measure work?

What is work?

Ms. Andrews asked the class, "Who did work last night?" She listed what students said on the chalkboard.

Mary—studied for four hours
Leroy—held a heavy bag of potatoes while standing in a store checkout line
Paul—tried to, but couldn't, move a large cabinet by pushing it
Anita—took the garbage out

"Look at this list. Who did work?" asked Ms. Andrews. "Everybody," answered the class.

"A scientist would say that only one person did work," said Ms. Andrews.

Why did Ms. Andrews say that? Do scientists use the word differently than you do? Think about the word "work." Most people use this word to describe many different things. Sometimes thinking is called work. Reading, shopping, talking, and the moving of objects are other things people often call work.

Using a word with more than one meaning can cause confusion. Scientists want everyone to know the exact meaning of every word. For example, scientists have agreed on the exact meaning of the word "work."

Several things must happen before a scientist says that work has been done. First, a push or a pull must act on an object. A push or a pull that acts on an object is a *force* [FOH(UH)RS]. Second, the push or the pull must make the object move while the push or the pull is acting on the object. If you push against a wall and the wall doesn't move, a scientist would say that no work is done. No work is done because the force you use does not cause the wall to move while you are pushing on it.

Think again about the kinds of things the students called work. Their teacher said that only one person did work. She meant that only one person did what a scientist would call work. Which person was it?

Mary studied for four hours. Because studying is not a push or a pull, she did not do work. Leroy held a bag of potatoes. He pulled up on the bag to keep gravity from pulling it down, but the bag did not move while he was holding it. So, he did not do any work either. Paul tried to move a cabinet by pushing on it. Even though Paul pushed and pushed and got very tired, he did not do any work because the cabinet did not move.

Anita took the garbage out. To lift and carry, she had to cause pushes and pulls to act on the garbage. Her pushes and pulls caused the garbage to move. Anita did what a scientist would call work.

A good way to explain what work is, then, is to say that work is done when a push or a pull causes an object to move or to change the way it is moving. This includes several things. An object that is not moving may be started moving. An object that is already moving may be made to go faster, to go slower, or to stop. Or, a moving object can be made to move in another direction.

★ **Would you do more work pushing open an unlocked door or pushing as hard as you can against a locked door? Explain.**

Figure 10–1. Riding a bicycle can be a lot of fun. Do you think any work is done riding a bicycle? Explain.

Measuring work

Work is done when a force causes an object to move or to change the way it is moving. But knowing that work has been done does not tell how much work has been done. How is work measured?

Whenever work is done, a push or a pull—that is, a force—must cause an object to move while the push or the pull is acting on the object. To measure the amount of work done, you need to know two facts. One is the amount of force used to make the object move. The other is how far the object moves while the force is acting on it.

When the amount of force used and the distance an object moves while a force acts on it are known, the amount of work done can be found. The amount of work done is equal to the amount of force used multiplied by the distance the object moves while the force acts on it. Here is another way to write this:

$$\text{Force} \times \text{Distance} = \text{Work}$$

For You to Think About

You push a shopping cart and cause the cart to move. Have you done any work? How do you know? Suppose you stop pushing on the cart, but the cart keeps moving. Are you doing any work now? How do you know?

Units for measuring work

Scientists all over the world have been using *metric* [MEH-trihk] units to measure for a long time. In many countries all people use metric units for measuring. Most people in the United States, however, use units called English units. Now people in this country are being urged to use metric units. In this section metric units for measuring work will be described and used. English units will also be given, usually in parentheses ( ).

The metric unit for measuring distance is the *metre* [MEET-ur]. One metre is a little longer than three feet. The metric unit for measuring force is the *newton* [N(Y)OOT-uhn]. A newton is not a large amount of force. It is a little less than ¼ pound.

Earlier it was stated that the amount of work is equal to the force times the distance. For example, suppose you used a force of 23 newtons (about 5 pounds) to lift a bag of sugar. You lifted it a distance of 2 metres (about

197

6½ feet). That is, the bag of sugar moved a distance of 2 metres while you used a force of 23 newtons on it. You can find out how much work you did as follows:

$$\text{Force} \times \text{Distance} = \text{Work}$$

$$23 \text{ newtons} \times 2 \text{ metres} = 46 \text{ newton-metres}$$
$$(5.17 \text{ pounds} \times 6.56 \text{ feet} = 33.9 \text{ foot-pounds})$$

★ **You use a force of 46 newtons to move a box. Do you do more work, less work, or the same amount of work moving the box five metres as you would moving the box ten metres? Explain.**

DO IT YOURSELF

Measure the amount of work you do in walking up stairs

Use a metre stick to measure the vertical height of a stairway. Record the height of the stairway. Now weigh yourself and record your weight. Change your weight from pounds to newtons. (Hint: One pound is equal to 4.5 newtons.) Find out how much work you would do in walking up the stairs. To do this, multiply your weight in newtons by the vertical height of the stairway in metres.

POWER

What does a scientist mean by the word "power"?
How is power measured?
Why did James Watt describe machines in terms of horsepower?

What is power?

Suppose you used a force of 150 newtons (about 34 pounds) to move a box of books 10 metres (about 33 feet). You would have done 1 500 newton-metres (about 1,100

Figure 10–2. Bulldozers, such as this one, are used to move dirt. Could a person with a shovel move as much dirt as this bulldozer can? If so, why are bulldozers, instead of people with shovels, used to do this work?

foot-pounds) of work. You would have done the same amount of work whether you took ten seconds or thirty seconds to move the box. But, the faster you worked, the sooner the work would have been done.

The amount of work done in a given period of time, say one second, is the rate of work. Scientists use the word "power" when they speak of the rate of work.

In the example, you would have done 1 500 newton-metres of work in moving the box of books. However, the rate of work would have been three times faster if you did the work in ten seconds instead of in thirty. That is, it would have taken more power to move the box in less time.

Think about this example: A bulldozer digs up and moves a lot of dirt in a short time. A bulldozer has a lot of power. A person could dig up and move as much dirt as a bulldozer. But a person does not have as much power as a bulldozer. So a person would have to work for a long time to do as much work as a bulldozer does in a short time.

Measuring power

Power is measured by dividing the amount of work done by the time it takes to do the work. This can be shown as follows:

$$\text{Work} \div \text{Time} = \text{Power}$$

199

Earlier it was stated that work is equal to the amount of force used multiplied by the distance an object moves while the force is acting. So another way to find out how much power is used is with the following formula:

$$(\text{Force} \times \text{Distance}) \div \text{Time} = \text{Power}$$

Think again about the example in which you moved the box of books. How much power would you have used if it took you ten seconds to move the box? Power is found by dividing the amount of work (1 500 newton-metres) by the length of time (10 seconds). Your power would be 150 newton-metres per second.

$$1\,500 \text{ newton-metres} \div 10 \text{ seconds} = 150 \frac{\text{newton-metres}}{\text{second}}$$

$$\left(1{,}107 \text{ foot-pounds} \div 10 \text{ seconds} = 110.7 \frac{\text{foot-pounds}}{\text{second}}\right)$$

But if you took thirty seconds to move the box, your power would only be 50 newton-metres per second.

$$1\,500 \text{ newton-metres} \div 30 \text{ seconds} = 50 \frac{\text{newton-metres}}{\text{second}}$$

$$\left(1{,}107 \text{ foot-pounds} \div 30 \text{ seconds} = 36.9 \frac{\text{foot-pounds}}{\text{second}}\right)$$

The faster you move the box, the more power you use.

Instead of using the term "newton-metres per second," scientists use the word *watt* [WAHT]. This word may make you think of light bulbs and electricity. However, the word "watt" can also be used to describe the power of other things. One watt is the same as one newton-metre of work done in one second. If you moved the box of books in ten seconds, your power was 150 watts. How much power did you use if you moved the books in thirty seconds?

A watt is a very small amount of power. Some engines have more than 200 000 watts of power. When people describe large amounts of power, they use the word *kilowatt* [KIHL-uh-WAHT]. One kilowatt is equal to 1 000 watts. Therefore, an engine with 200 000 watts of power is a 200-kilowatt engine.

★ **Could you figure out how much power a person used if you knew only the amount of force used and the distance through which the force acted? Explain.**

Another word to describe power

Scientists use the terms "watt" and "kilowatt" to describe power. But have you ever heard of a 260-kilowatt automobile engine? Probably not. Most people do not describe automobile engines and other engines in watts or kilowatts. The power of these engines is usually given in horsepower.

Horsepower was first used as an amount of power about 200 years ago. A Scottish inventor, James Watt, wanted to sell his new invention, the steam engine, to the owners of a coal mine. At that time horses were used to run most of the air pumps and to lift coal from the mine. The mine owners wanted to know how the amount of work done by Watt's steam engine compared with the amount of work done by a horse.

Watt measured the amount of work done by horses. He also measured how long it took to do the work. He found that a horse could lift about 550 pounds one foot each

(*Text continues on page 203.*)

Grant Heilman

H. Lüetticke/ZEFA

Figure 10–3. Can more land be plowed in one day with a horse-drawn plow or with a tractor-drawn plow? Does the answer to this question depend on the power of a tractor compared with that of a horse? Which do you think has more power?

Investigate

How much power do you use in going up stairs?

You Will Need

metre stick, bathroom scale, stopwatch

Background

If you did the activity in the last section, you found out how much work you do in walking up a stairway. This activity adds one more measurement—time. By knowing how much work you do and how fast you can do it, you can find out how much power it takes to walk up the stairs and how much power it takes to run up the stairs.

What to Do

Measure and record the vertical height of a stairway in your home or school. Weigh yourself. Record your weight in newtons. (Hint: One pound is equal to 4.5 newtons.) Have someone measure and record the time it takes you to walk up the stairs. Also measure and record the time it takes to run up the stairs.

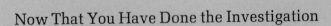

Now That You Have Done the Investigation

—How much work was done walking up the stairs?
—How much work was done running up the stairs?
—How much power (in watts) was used to walk up the stairs?
—How much power (in watts) was used to run up the stairs?
—How much horsepower was used each time you went up the stairs? (Hint: One horsepower is equal to 746 watts.)

Figure 10–4. This model of Watt's steam engine is like the engines that were first used to pump water out of mines and run machines in factories. In what way or ways is this engine like more modern engines you have seen? In what way or ways is it different?

second. This is about the same as lifting 2 475 newtons 0.30 metre each second. Watt called this rate of work one horsepower. One horsepower is equal to 746 watts.

A one-horsepower engine can do this amount of work each second all day long. Some engines work without stopping for weeks, months, and even years. A horse cannot work even a whole day without stopping.

★ **Does a two-horsepower engine or a two-kilowatt engine have more power?**

Power in people and machines

How much power can a person have? That depends on the person. Some weight lifters can lift 1 750 newtons (about 390 pounds) a distance of 2 metres (about 6.5 feet) in one second. For that one second, the weight lifter's power is 3 500 watts, or 3.5 kilowatts. This is almost 5 horsepower.

So, some weight lifters can be almost as powerful as a 5-horsepower engine. However, a weight lifter is that powerful only for about one second. Then that weight lifter must rest. Most weight lifters need a long period of rest before they can lift this amount of weight again.

Most people do not have this amount of power. But a person who is used to lifting heavy objects can work at a rate of about 75 watts (newton-metres per second) for several hours. This is about the same amount of work that could be done by a 0.1-horsepower engine.

203

ENERGY

What does a scientist mean by the term "energy"?
What are some kinds of energy?
What are two ways in which objects can gain potential energy?

What is energy?

Energy is closely related to work. In fact, the term "work" is often used to explain what scientists mean by the term "energy." Energy is described as the ability to do work. If something has energy, it is able to do work.

To scientists, there is only one meaning for the term "work." That is, work is done only when a force causes a change in the way something is moving. However, there is more than one kind of energy. Scientists often divide energy into two groups.

Kinetic energy

All moving things have the ability to do work. The snow in a snowslide can knock down trees and crush

Figure 10–5. What kind of energy—potential or kinetic—does a waterfall have? The water behind a dam? The winds of a hurricane? Is work being done in any of these pictures? How do you know?

204

houses. A falling tree branch can knock a hole in a roof or break a window. In these examples, the snow and the branch are moving. Moving things have a kind of energy called *kinetic* [kuh-NEHT-ihk] energy.

Think of other things that have kinetic energy. A moving car has kinetic energy. A moving car might do work in knocking over a lamppost. When you throw a baseball, the ball has kinetic energy. If the ball is thrown at something like a can or a bottle, the ball can do work knocking it over. Heavy iron balls on chains are used to knock down old buildings. An iron ball is made to swing against the walls of a building. While the iron ball is swinging, it has kinetic energy.

Potential energy

Can things that are not moving have energy too? Even when they aren't moving, some things have the ability to do work. Their energy is stored. Stored energy is called *potential* [puh-TEHN-chuhl] energy.

Water behind a dam and a rock on the edge of a cliff have potential energy. Water behind a dam is higher than

Art Sawyers/Van Cleve Photography

J. Battin/De Wys, Inc.

the water below the dam. If the water is allowed to flow down through the dam, it can do work turning a water-wheel. A rock on the edge of a cliff can also do work if it falls. It may hit other rocks or trees and make them move.

A stretched rubber band also has potential energy. If the rubber band is let go, it will snap back to its usual shape. While it is moving, it can do work pushing a small object forward.

> ★ **Does a book on a shelf have potential energy or does it have kinetic energy? How do you know? How could the book do work?**

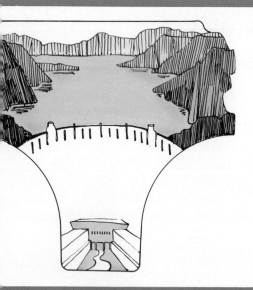

DO IT YOURSELF

Explain examples of potential energy

Examine the following list of things with potential energy. For each example, explain briefly how the potential energy could be used. That is, tell how each thing on the list could do work.

> a. water behind a dam
> b. automobile battery in a parked car
> c. rocket fuel in a storage tank
> d. large red ball on a shelf
> e. stretched bowstring
> f. rock on the edge of a cliff

Changes in potential energy

One way to understand potential and kinetic energy better is to examine some more examples of these forms of energy. Think about an arrow being fitted against the bowstring of a bow. Then the bowstring is pulled back and held. Before the bowstring is let go, the bow and bowstring have potential energy. When the bowstring is let go, the arrow is pushed for a short distance by the

Figure 10–6. Before either a pile driver or a bowstring can do work, its potential energy must be increased. How is the potential energy of a pile driver increased? Of a bowstring?

moving bowstring. Since the push is a force and the arrow moves some distance, work is done on the arrow.

When the bowstring is let go, its potential energy is changed into kinetic energy of the moving arrow. But how did the bowstring get potential energy? Someone had to do work to pull the bowstring back. Energy was put into the bow and bowstring by someone doing work. Pulling back the bowstring increases the potential energy of the bow and the bowstring.

In this example, you should have noticed two important facts: (1) Work must be done on an object to increase its potential energy. (2) Potential energy can be changed into kinetic energy.

Now think about this example: A pile driver is a kind of machine. It is used to pound steel posts into the ground. The pile driver has a heavy weight which is raised above the post. Then the weight is dropped on top of the post. This pushes the post a short distance into the ground.

Work is done raising the weight above the post. This increases the potential energy of the weight. As the pile driver falls its potential energy is changing into kinetic energy. When the weight hits the post, the kinetic energy is used in pushing the post into the ground.

The bowstring and the pile driver have different kinds of potential energy. Energy was stored in the bow because it was bent out of shape. When the bowstring is let go, the bow snaps back to its usual shape. Things that return to their usual shape after being pushed or pulled out of shape are *elastic* [ih-LAS-tihk]. When an elastic object is pushed or pulled out of shape, it has potential energy. As it returns to its usual shape an elastic object is able to do work.

The potential energy of the pile driver increases when the weight is raised to a higher place. When the weight is dropped, gravity pulls it down. Things that are raised above a floor or the ground have potential energy due to gravity.

★ **In the examples of the bowstring and the pile driver, potential energy changed into kinetic energy. Do you think kinetic energy can be changed into potential energy? If so, explain.**

For You to Think About

Do you think an automobile battery has potential energy? What about the gasoline in the automobile gas tank? Does it have potential energy? If you think so, explain why you think so. How can the energy (if any) in the battery and in the gasoline be used to do work?

DO IT YOURSELF

Examine energy in a rubber band

Hold a rubber band in your hand and stretch the band a little. Does it have potential energy? Can it do work? Let go of one end of the band. Does the band have kinetic energy?

Stretch the rubber band as far as you can. Let go of one end. Does the rubber band snap back faster this time? When did the rubber band have the most potential energy? When did it have the most kinetic energy?

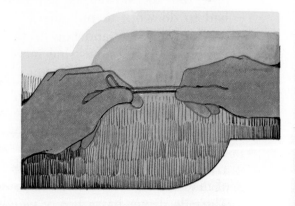

Photos courtesy of Chrysler Corporation

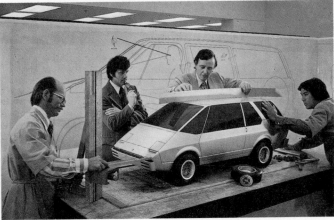

Work, Power, and Energy for Automobiles

If asked to name something that does work, has power, and uses energy, many people would name an automobile. The automobile industry, which also includes buses and trucks, is very much a part of living today. In fact, millions of people earn their living in some field related to the automobile industry.

Automobiles get their energy from gasoline, which is made from oil. Many people work in the oil industry. Some are scientists who work on new ways to find and manufacture oil products. Some sell oil, gasoline, and other things made from oil. Many other people earn their living making automobiles. These jobs include designing the automobiles, putting the parts together, and testing the new models. Others sell or repair automobiles. Several years of college are needed to become a design engineer. Other kinds of work, such as assembling, repairing, and testing automobiles, are learned on the job.

Automobiles, trucks, and buses need batteries, light bulbs, and many other parts. These are made by other people and sold to the automobile manufacturers. Delivery of these parts, and other things, is often done by trucks. Thousands of people earn their living driving trucks in the United States.

Someday you will be thinking about the kind of job you want. Perhaps it will have something to do with the automobile industry. If so, you will have something to do with work, power, and energy.

Designing automobiles and building them are only two kinds of jobs that have something to do with the automobile industry. What are some other jobs that depend on automobiles? Do you know anyone whose job is somehow related to automobiles?

Reviewing and Extending

SUMMING UP

1. Scientists say that work is done only when a force causes an object to change the way it is moving.
2. The amount of work done is equal to the amount of force used multiplied by the distance the object moves while the force is acting on it.
3. The amount of work done in a given amount of time is the rate of work, or power.
4. The amount of work done divided by the amount of time it takes to do the work gives the amount of power.
5. Energy is described as the ability to do work. If an object has energy, it can do work.
6. The kind of energy an object has because it is moving is called kinetic energy. Energy that is stored in an object is called potential energy.
7. Work must be done on an object to increase its potential energy. The potential energy of an object can change into kinetic energy.

CHECKING UP

Vocabulary Each of the phrases numbered *1–5* describes a term from the following list. On your paper, write the term next to the number of the phrase that describes it.

potential energy	power	energy
kinetic energy	work	watt

1. rate at which work is done
2. kind of energy moving objects have
3. ability to do work
4. stored energy
5. unit of power

Knowledge and Understanding Beside each of the numerals *6–10* on your paper, write the word or words that best complete the sentence having that numeral.

6. If a force causes an object to change the way it is moving, a scientist would say that _____ is being done.
7. A moving automobile has _____ energy, simply because it is moving.
8. A metric unit used in measuring work is the _____.
9. The newton is a unit of _____.
10. _____ is described as the ability to do work.

210

Concepts Beside each of the numerals *11–15* on your paper, write the word or words that best complete the sentence having that numeral.

11. When a book falls from a shelf, potential energy is changed into (*kinetic energy, force, power*).
12. If a book is raised from a low shelf to a higher shelf, it (*loses, gains, has the same amount of*) potential energy.
13. The amount of work a machine can do in a given amount of time is the (*force, energy, power*) of the machine.
14. A machine that does 200 newton-metres of work per second has (*the same, more, less*) power than a machine that does 400 newton-metres of work per second.
15. If a person pushed on a heavy object but did not move it, (*work, no work, power*) was done.

Application and Critical Thinking Answer the following questions as briefly as you can without leaving out any important ideas.

16. Can a two-kilowatt engine do as much work as a five-kilowatt engine? Explain your answer.
17. Does gasoline in the tank of a parked automobile have kinetic or potential energy? Explain your answer.
18. In finding out the amount of work done on a job, do you need to know how long it took to do the job? Why or why not?

DOING MORE

1. Tie a heavy string around a brick. Tie the brick to a spring balance. Notice the reading on the balance as you lift the brick to a table top. Measure the height of the table. How much work did you do? Now pull the brick across the table top with the spring balance. Pull the brick the same distance you did in lifting it from the floor. How much work did you do this time? Was more work done lifting or sliding the brick?
2. Look at the following sentences. Each one contains the word "work." For each sentence, decide if the word "work" is used as a scientist uses it. If not, write the sentence over so that the sentence does not include the word "work."
    a. John's painting is a work of art.
    b. Laura did a lot of work moving tables.
    c. My flashlight won't work.
    d. Thinking up an answer to this problem is a lot of work.

CHAPTER 11

Conversion and Conservation of Energy

When an automobile engine is "running," fuel is being burned. The burning of the fuel causes several things to happen. Parts of the engine are made to move. Heat is given off. The battery is charged with electric energy. The automobile is able to move. All of these things happen because the potential energy of the fuel is changed into other forms of energy. The changing of one form of energy into another is an energy *conversion* [kuhn-VUR-zhuhn].

Some energy conversions take place in nature. For example, lightning might strike a tree and set it on fire. The energy stored in the wood of the tree is given off as heat and light. People have also learned how to cause energy conversions, such as the ones that take place in an automobile.

What happens to energy during an energy conversion? Is some energy lost? Is new energy formed? Or does the total amount of energy stay the same? These and other questions about energy will be explored in this chapter.

H. Mantel/ZEFA

Courtesy of Tennessee Valley Authority

Energy conversions change one form of energy into another. Sometimes energy conversions result in changes in matter.

FORMS OF ENERGY

What are six forms of energy?
Which form of energy is given off by the sun?
Why is heat different from other energy forms?

Ways to describe energy

Up to now, only two words have been used to describe energy. Moving things were said to have kinetic energy. Any kind of stored energy was called potential energy.

But the terms "kinetic" and "potential" are not always the best words to use in describing energy. This is because both moving and stored energy can come from different sources. In order to describe these different sources, energy is often thought of as having six different forms. These forms are *mechanical* [mih-KAN-ih-kuhl], *magnetic* [mag-NEHT-ihk] and *electric, chemical* [KEHM-ih-kuhl], *nuclear* [N(Y)OO-klee-ur], *radiant* [RAYD-ee-uhnt], and *heat*.

Energy of moving matter

The name "mechanical energy" makes most people think of automobiles and other large machines. But other things also have this kind of energy. In fact, scientists think of

Figure 11–1. Does this car parked on a hill have potential or kinetic energy? Imagine what might happen if the brakes were released. Would the kind of energy change?

this kind of energy as the kind that a piece of matter has because it is moving or can move. Sometimes moving matter is described as having kinetic mechanical energy. Matter that is not moving because it is being held back in some way is often described as having potential mechanical energy.

★ **What kind of energy does a bowling ball rolling down an alley have? What kind of energy does an automobile parked on a steep hill have?**

Energy that attracts

If a magnet is held near some steel paper clips, they move toward the magnet. In causing a force that makes the paper clips move, the magnet does work on the paper clips. The form of energy used to do this work is magnetic energy. But magnetic energy is not the only kind of energy that causes a force to pull on things.

Another kind is electric energy. For example, just after you have washed your hair and dried it thoroughly, try this. Comb it for a while and then hold the comb near some small pieces of paper. The paper pieces will suddenly "jump" and stick to the comb. After a while some of the pieces begin to "jump" away from the comb.

Why does this happen? Your hair rubbing on the comb builds up electricity on the comb. This electricity is used to do work on the paper. That is, the paper moves because of electric energy. The comb and paper show one kind of electric energy. Another kind of electric energy is found where electricity flows through a wire.

Magnetic energy and electric energy are closely related. Magnets can be used to make electricity flow through wires. Electricity can be used to make some kinds of metals into magnets.

Energy from changes in matter

Have you ever watched something burn? When matter burns, it changes into other kinds of matter such as ashes, gases, and water. Changes such as this are called chemical changes. Energy that was stored up in the matter that

Find Out More

Electricity can be used to make some metals magnetic. Magnets made this way are called electromagnets. Find out what kinds of metals are used to make electromagnets. Where are these kinds of magnets used? Is the metal still a magnet when the electricity stops flowing?

214

Figure 11–2. Nuclear power stations, such as this one near Morris, Illinois, use the energy given off during nuclear changes to generate electricity.

burned is given off as heat and light. Because this stored energy is given off during a chemical change, it is called chemical energy.

Another kind of change in matter also gives off energy. All matter is made of tiny particles called *atoms* [AT-uhmz]. Atoms are made of even smaller parts. One or more of these smaller parts form the center of each atom. This center is called the *nucleus* [N(Y)OO-klee-uhs] of the atom. Some kinds of atoms change into other kinds of atoms. They change because the nucleus in each of these atoms splits into two or more parts.

Such a change in the nucleus is called a nuclear change. When a nuclear change takes place, energy is given off. Energy that comes from such changes is called nuclear energy.

There is a lot of interest in nuclear energy today. Scientists have learned how to cause and to control nuclear changes. Many people think that the energy from nuclear changes will become very important because it can be changed into electric energy.

215

Figure 11–3. Solar panels, such as those on the roof of this house, can change sunlight into heat and electricity. How can such changes be useful to people living in this house?

Energy from hot objects

Nuclear changes take place in the sun. These nuclear changes make the sun very hot. Hot objects, such as the sun, give off a form of energy called radiant energy. Radiant energy moves away, or radiates, from hot objects.

There are several kinds of radiant energy. One kind is known to almost everyone. That kind is visible light, or light that can be seen. But many kinds of radiant energy cannot be seen. Some of these are ultraviolet, or "black," light; infrared light; microwaves; and X rays.

★ **Some houses have been built that use radiant energy from the sun for heat. Are such houses a good idea? Why or why not? Are there places where such houses may not be practical?**

Is heat a form of energy?

When a fuel is burned, chemical energy is given off as heat and light. Heat is also given off when nuclear changes take place. The heat given off by fuels and nuclear changes can be used to do work. For example, heat is used to run automobiles. It is also used to change water into steam. The steam can be used to make electricity or run other machines. Does this mean that heat is a form of energy?

Not all scientists agree, but many do think of heat as a form of energy. In an automobile engine, for example, the burning of fuel causes heat. The heat causes

Find Out More

People have learned how to change electric energy into the different kinds of radiant energy. What are some of the uses for visible, ultraviolet, and infrared light? What are some of the uses for microwaves? For X rays?

216

gases in the engine to spread out and push on the pistons of the engine. In a toaster, wires get hot when electricity flows through them. In each of these examples, heat is given off when another form of energy is being used. So even though heat is often thought of as a form of energy, heat is not given off unless another form of energy is also present.

DO IT YOURSELF

Observe an energy conversion

Light a wooden match. As soon as the wood part of the match is burning, set the burning match in a metal pie pan. Be careful not to burn yourself. Hold your hand over, but not in, the flame. Wait for the match to burn out. Compare the burned match to one that has not been burned.

Did burning change the match? If so, what changes could you see? Was the matter still wood after it was burned? If not, what was it like? What did you feel when you held your hand over the match? What kind of energy does a wooden match have before it is burned? What kind or kinds of energy do you think the match gave off as it burned?

ENERGY CONVERSIONS

What is an energy conversion that starts by itself called?
What energy conversions occur in a pendulum?
What is one kind of energy conversion that takes place in an automobile?

Ways conversions start

Some people hang flowerpots from their ceilings with a rope. A hanging flowerpot has potential mechanical energy because of its height above the floor. If the rope breaks, the flowerpot falls. What happens to its potential energy?

As the flowerpot falls, it gets closer to the floor. The closer to the floor it gets, the less potential energy the flowerpot has. But as it moves toward the floor, the kinetic energy of the flowerpot becomes greater. It becomes greater because the flowerpot is moving faster. So as the flowerpot falls, it seems to lose potential energy, but it seems to gain kinetic energy. What happens is that the potential energy of the hanging flowerpot changes into the kinetic energy of the falling flowerpot.

When the flowerpot falls, potential energy is changed into kinetic energy. This energy conversion starts "by itself." That is, no other form of energy is used to start the energy conversion. This kind of conversion is *spontaneous* [spahn-TAY-nee-uhs].

Not all energy conversions are spontaneous. Wood does not start to burn by itself. Neither does gasoline. In each case heat, another form of energy, is needed to start an energy conversion. When outside energy is used, the conversion is *nonspontaneous*.

★ **List some spontaneous and nonspontaneous energy conversions. What are some of the forms of energy in these energy conversions?**

Find Out More

A hypergolic fuel is used to lift rockets off the surface of the moon. What is a hypergolic fuel? Why is this kind of fuel used by rockets "lifting off" from the surface of the moon? Is the burning of a hypergolic fuel an example of a spontaneous reaction, or is it an example of a nonspontaneous reaction?

Courtesy of National Park Service

Figure 11–4. An energy conversion causes the water and the steam of the geyser to shoot into the air. The sign below warns of another energy conversion. Are these conversions spontaneous or nonspontaneous?

Richard Reynolds

Potential to kinetic

At one time or another, just about everyone has played on a swing. Most people enjoy swinging back and forth. But did you know that energy conversions take place when you swing back and forth? A swing is a kind of *pendulum* [PEHN-juh-luhm]. A pendulum is a mass hung from a fixed point so that it is free to swing. As a pendulum swings, potential energy changes into kinetic energy and then back to potential energy again.

Think about a pendulum that is not moving. That is, it is at rest. So it has no kinetic energy. The mass is hanging as low as the string will allow it to hang. Unless the string breaks, the potential energy of the mass is as low as it can be. So for this example, think of the mass as having zero potential energy in this position. Where, then, does the energy for energy conversions come from?

The pendulum is started swinging by pulling it to one side (point *A*), which raises the mass to a higher level. Energy is used to pull the mass to one side and raise it. This energy is now stored in the pendulum. When the pendulum is let go, it moves toward point *B*, which is lower than point *A*. As it moves, the pendulum loses potential energy. At the same time it gains kinetic energy. At point *B*, the pendulum is moving faster than at any other point in its swing. This is the lowest point of the swing. The amount of potential energy is again zero. All of the energy added to the mass when it was pulled to one side has been changed into kinetic energy.

Back to potential

The pendulum continues to move toward point *C*. The mass rises higher. It is also moving slower. The kinetic energy is changing back into potential energy. At point *C*, the pendulum stops moving for an instant. Again it has about the same amount of potential energy it started with. It is not moving, so its kinetic energy is zero.

Slowly, the swing of the pendulum gets shorter. Finally it stops. What causes it to slow down and stop? Some of

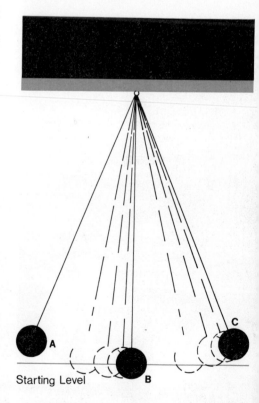

Figure 11–5. As a pendulum swings back and forth potential energy changes to kinetic energy and back to potential energy. At which position does each of these energy conversions begin?

Starting Level

219

Figure 11–6. The iron ball used to knock buildings down is a kind of pendulum. When the ball hits a wall, it usually does not continue swinging forward. Nor does it bounce back. Why does the ball stop swinging? What do you think happens to the kinetic energy the ball had while it was swinging?

Grant Heilman

the energy of the pendulum is used to push the air aside. Some energy is used as the string twists and turns. These are small amounts of energy. However, as the energy of the pendulum is used to do these things, the pendulum has less and less energy in its swing. It slows down and stops.

★ **What other events can you think of in which energy is changed from potential to kinetic or from kinetic to potential?**

DO IT YOURSELF

Make an energy-conversion poster

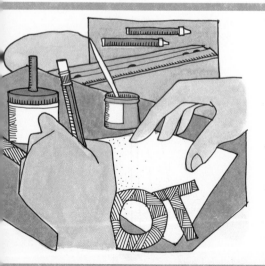

Make a poster showing the kinds of energy conversions that occur in an automobile and where they take place. Make the poster using pictures you draw or ones you cut out of magazines and newspapers. Label each picture to tell the kind or kinds of energy conversions that take place. What kinds of energy are used by a moving automobile? What kinds of energy are used to charge the battery? Where does all the energy to run an automobile come from? What happens to its kinetic energy when a moving automobile stops?

CONSERVATION OF ENERGY

What are the laws of conservation?
What is unusual about radioactive matter?
What happens to matter and energy in a nuclear change?

Laws of conservation

Up to now, nothing has been said about the amounts of energy at each step in a chain of energy conversions. Suppose you lift a box up to a shelf. The box now has more potential energy than it had before you lifted it. This energy came from the work you did in lifting the box. The energy you used to do the work came from food you had eaten. Several energy conversions took place to change the energy in your food into the energy of the box on the shelf.

Is all of one form of energy changed into another form of energy during an energy conversion? Or is some energy lost with each energy conversion? In the 1800's many scientists were interested in such questions. Many energy conversions were studied. From these studies, scientists were convinced that energy is not created or destroyed during an energy conversion. The fact that the amount of energy stayed the same, or was conserved, came to be known as the *law of conservation* [KAHN(T)-sur-VAY-shuhn] *of energy.*

Other scientists were studying changes in matter. They found that the kinds of atoms in chemical changes do not change. Only the ways the different atoms join together changed. They also found that the mass of the kinds of matter formed during a chemical change was the same as the mass of the kinds of matter used. These scientists were convinced that the mass of matter was not changed during a chemical change. That is, matter was not created or destroyed. This came to be known as the *law of conservation of mass.*

For many years scientists were sure that neither energy nor matter was created or destroyed. They knew that energy could be changed from one form to another. Matter could also be changed from one form to another. But in all the changes in energy or matter that they studied, no energy or matter ever seemed to be created or destroyed.

Discovering a new kind of energy

As time passed, a kind of energy was discovered that didn't obey the law of conservation of energy. This energy was coming from a kind of rock called *pitchblende* [PIHCH-BLEHND]. X rays, heat, and other kinds of energy were being given off by pieces of this kind of rock. This energy did not seem to be coming from an energy conversion. Instead, the energy seemed to be created. Furthermore, some scientists predicted that this kind of rock would keep giving off energy for several thousand years.

Marie Curie was one of the persons who studied pitchblende. She found that this rock was made up of several different kinds of matter. When she separated the different kinds of matter, she found that one certain kind was giving off energy. Marie Curie named this matter *radium* [RAYD-ee-uhm]. Later, other kinds of matter that give off energy over a long period of time were discovered. Because they give off kinds of radiant energy, such as X rays, they are described as being *radioactive* [RAYD-ee-oh-AK-tihv].

A lot has been learned about the energy given off by radioactive matter. The energy in this kind of matter does

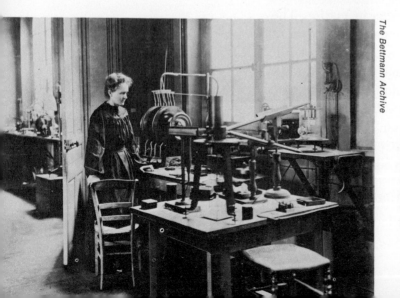

Figure 11–7. Marie Sklodowska Curie, the discoverer of the radioactive elements radium and polonium, is shown at work in her laboratory. Do you think she knew about the danger involved in handling radioactive matter? Explain.

not come from any chemical change. It does not result from a conversion of electric or magnetic energy. Changes in temperature do not change the amount of energy that is given off. But the question of where the energy comes from was not answered right away.

★ **Can the law of conservation of energy be used to explain radioactive matter? Explain.**

Changing the laws

Where does the energy in radioactive matter come from? This question was one that many scientists tried to answer. The old ideas about matter and energy could not be used to explain radioactive matter. A new idea was needed. Albert Einstein thought of a way to explain this puzzle. He suggested that matter was being changed into energy. Careful measurements have since shown this to be true.

This caused much concern to scientists. Remember, up to this time, they believed that neither matter nor energy could be created or destroyed. This discovery meant that the laws of conservation of mass and energy had to be changed.

Today, scientists talk about the *conservation of mass-energy.* They have found that energy can be created. But matter is used when this happens. They have also found that matter can be created. But energy is used to create matter. In this way, the total amount of mass-energy remains the same when matter changes to energy or energy changes to matter.

Remember, both matter and energy are conserved in most changes. Neither matter nor energy is created or destroyed in the changes most people see every day, such as the burning of fuels and the using of electricity to make heat, light, or sound. The only kind of change where matter or energy is created or destroyed is a nuclear change.

★ **Why do many people say all matter has potential energy?**

Find Out More

There are several different kinds of radioactive matter known today. What are the names of the kinds of radioactive matter? Are all of them found in nature? What are some uses for these kinds of matter?

Investigate

What happens to the amount of matter during a chemical change?

You Will Need

soda-pop bottle, small balloon, balance, short piece of string, 60 millilitres (about $\frac{1}{4}$ cup) of vinegar, 7 grams (about a tablespoon) of baking soda

Background

When baking soda and vinegar mix, a chemical change takes place. In this case, a solid (the baking soda) and a liquid (the vinegar) change into another kind of liquid (water), a solid that is dissolved in the liquid, and a gas (carbon dioxide). In order to measure the total amount of matter before and after the chemical change takes place, it is necessary to keep the gas from escaping into the room air. In this investigation, a small balloon is used to trap the gas.

What to Do

Put about 7 grams of baking soda into a small balloon. Pour about 60 millilitres of vinegar into a soda-pop bottle. Ease the neck of the balloon over the neck of the bottle in a way that no baking soda falls into the vinegar. Tie a short piece of string over the balloon around the neck of the bottle. This will keep the balloon from "popping off" the bottle. Use a balance to weigh the balloon-bottle setup and record this information. Now, raise the balloon so that the baking soda falls into the vinegar. Observe the chemical change that takes place. When the reaction stops, again weigh the balloon-bottle setup.

Now That You Have Done the Investigation

—Was the chemical change you observed an example of a spontaneous change, or was it nonspontaneous? How do you know?

—After the chemical change took place, did the materials of the balloon-bottle setup weigh more than, less than, or the same as they did before the change?

—What kind or kinds of energy were involved in this change?

—What law of conservation was shown by this activity?

People Who Work with Energy

Today people are using more and more energy. Energy is used to make electricity, to run the machines in factories and on farms, and to run the engines of cars, buses, trucks, trains, and airplanes. Because of this, many people have jobs that involve finding new sources of energy and ways to make energy conversions.

Some people have jobs looking for new sources of coal, oil, and uranium. Others design the power plants that use these fuels. Some people design engines for machines. Almost all the people who have these kinds of jobs go to college to learn how to do these kinds of work.

There are other people who also have jobs that involve sources of energy. There are people who mine for coal or uranium and drill for oil. Others work to keep the machines used in these jobs running properly. Some of the fuels need to be processed in factories called refineries. Refineries need many different kinds of workers. People who work in mines, drill for oil, work on machines, or work in refineries often do not go to college. Many of them learn how to do their work on the job.

Grant Heilman

Lothar Schröter/ZEFA

Our need for energy provides many kinds of jobs, including designing power plants and offshore oil-well drilling. What other jobs do you know of that have to do with energy?

225

Reviewing and Extending

SUMMING UP

1. Mechanical energy is the kind of energy matter has because it is moving or because it can move. Mechanical energy can be either kinetic or potential.
2. Energy that attracts objects may be either magnetic energy or electric energy. These two forms of energy are closely related.
3. Chemical energy and nuclear energy result from chemical changes and nuclear changes in matter.
4. Hot objects give off radiant energy. Forms of radiant energy are visible light, ultraviolet light, infrared light, microwaves, and X rays.
5. Heat is also thought of as a form of energy. However, heat is not given off unless some other form of energy is also present.
6. The changing of one form of energy into another form is called an energy conversion.
7. An energy conversion that begins without the use of outside energy is called spontaneous.
8. The original laws of conservation stated that neither matter nor energy could be created or destroyed.
9. In radioactive matter energy seemed to be created. It was found that matter was being changed into energy.
10. Today scientists speak of the law of conservation of mass-energy. Whenever energy is created, matter is used. If matter is created, energy is used.

CHECKING UP

Vocabulary Each of the phrases numbered *1–5* describes a term from the following list. On your paper, write the term next to the number of the phrase that describes it.

spontaneous	mechanical	conversion
radiant	nuclear change	magnetic

1. takes place when the nucleus of an atom splits
2. kind of energy an object has because it is moving or can move.
3. kind of energy given off by hot objects
4. changing of one form of energy into another form
5. starts without outside energy being used

Knowledge and Understanding Beside each of the numerals *6–10* on your paper, write the word or words that best complete the sentence having that numeral.

6. (*Potential, Electric, Mechanical*) energy is the kind of energy a moving object has.

7. The sun gives off (*chemical, radiant, mechanical*) energy.
8. Inside a car engine, (*radiant, mechanical, chemical*) energy is changed into mechanical energy and heat.
9. Any energy conversion that starts by itself is (*nonspontaneous, chemical, spontaneous*).
10. Magnetic energy and (*chemical, electric, nuclear*) energy are closely related.

Concepts   Beside each of the numerals *11–15* on your paper, write the word or words that best complete the sentence having that numeral.

11. When a pendulum is at the highest point of its swing, it has the greatest amount of _____ energy.
12. At first, radioactive matter puzzled scientists because somehow _____ was being created.
13. Hot objects like the sun give off several kinds of _____ energy.
14. Chemical energy being changed into electric energy is an example of an energy _____.
15. According to the law of conservation of _____, when energy is created, matter is destroyed.

Application and Critical Thinking   Answer the following questions as briefly as you can without leaving out any important ideas.

16. Suppose you have a model car that runs on batteries. What kinds of energy conversions result in the car's moving?
17. List five forms of energy. What is one way that people use each of these forms?
18. What are some kinds of energy conversions that take place in you?

DOING MORE

1. Use a hammer to drive a nail into a piece of wood. Pull the nail from the board and feel it. How does the nail feel? Describe the energy conversions that took place.
2. Use a balance to find the mass of a flashcube. Cause the cube to flash. Weigh the flashcube again. Did a chemical change take place? How do you know? Did the cube change in mass when it flashed? Explain how the law of conservation of mass-energy applies to this example.
3. Report to other members of your class on the kinds of energy conversions that are important in your daily life.

CHAPTER 12

Motion

Have you ever pushed a really full shopping cart? If so, you had to push hard to start the cart moving. But once the cart was moving, it was easy to keep it moving. In fact, you may have noticed that the cart moved for a short distance after you stopped pushing on it.

Sometimes a moving cart bumps into something. If it bumps into shelves with glass bottles on them, one of the bottles may fall and break. Has this ever happened to you? If so, you may have wondered why things hit the floor so fast. You may have wished at that time that things fell more slowly or didn't fall at all.

Carts you push and falling bottles are examples of moving objects. Almost everywhere you look, you see something that is moving. But how can you decide if things are moving? What causes them to move? What causes things to fall to the ground? These and other questions are part of the study of *motion* [MOH-shuhn]. That is what this chapter is about.

In which picture is the Ferris wheel moving? How do you know?

Photos from Artstreet

Larry P. Trone

Artstreet

Figure 12–1. Are the motions of the birds different from those of the boys? If so, how? Is there a way in which these motions are like each other? Are all motions alike in some way?

DESCRIBING MOTION

What do you need to know before you can describe something as moving?
How are speed, distance, and time related?
How can graphs be used to describe motion?

What is motion?

In flying from the ground to a tree branch, a bird may follow a curved path. Falling leaves move in many directions on a windy day. However, a stone seems to fall straight down when it is dropped, even on a windy day. The bird, the leaves, and the stone in these examples are all objects in motion. Yet the motion of each one is different from that of the others. With all these different ways of moving, is there an easy way to describe what is meant by the term "motion"?

Think about what happens when something moves. Suppose a bird moves from the ground to a tree branch. The

229

bird starts in one place and ends up somewhere else. In going from the ground to the branch, the bird changes its *position* [puh-ZIHSH-uhn]. Whenever something changes its position, we say it moves. In fact, motion is often defined as a change in position.

★ **Can an object move without going from one place to another? Explain your answer.**

Is it moving?

How can you tell if something is moving or not? Imagine that you are in a moving automobile and that a book is on the seat next to you. Is the book moving or is it not moving? People in different places might answer this question in different ways. To people in the automobile, the book is not moving. That is, the position of the book is not changing when it is compared with the positions of other things inside the automobile. But what might someone standing beside the road say? That person might say that the automobile and everything in it are moving. When compared with the position of the person standing beside the road and of the other things along the road, the position of the automobile and everything in it is changing. Therefore, the automobile and everything in it are in motion.

You cannot decide if something is in motion if you can only see that thing. You must also be able to see other things around it. Whether or not you see something as being in motion is related to the way you see the things around it.

Speed, time, and distance

It takes time for something to go from one place to another. The less time it takes to go a given distance, the faster that thing is moving. The word "speed" is used to describe how fast something is moving. Speed is another name for rate of motion.

Speed, time, and distance are closely related. If two of the three are known, you can find the third. If you

Figure 12–2. Does the airplane in this picture seem to be moving? Do the men seem to be moving? How did you decide? Suppose the picture only showed an airplane against a plain background. Could you decide if the airplane was moving then? Why or why not?

know the speed of something and how long it moves at that speed, you can find out how far it moves. For example, a train is moving at a speed of 50 kilometres (about 30 miles) per hour. How far does it go in 3 hours? You can find out as follows:

$$\text{Speed} \times \text{Time} = \text{Distance}$$

50 kilometres per hour $\times$ 3 hours = 150 kilometres
(31 miles per hour $\times$ 3 hours = 93 miles)

At other times you might want to know how long it will take you to get someplace. You might plan to drive a distance of 270 kilometres (about 170 miles) at a speed of 90 kilometres (about 55 miles) per hour. You can find out how long the trip will take this way:

$$\text{Distance} \div \text{Speed} = \text{Time}$$

270 kilometres $\div$ 90 kilometres per hour = 3 hours
(168 miles $\div$ 56 miles per hour = 3 hours)

On a train you usually do not know how fast you are going. Suppose it takes 8 hours to go a distance of 800 kilometres (about 500 miles). You can find the speed for this trip as follows:

$$\text{Distance} \div \text{Time} = \text{Speed}$$

800 kilometres $\div$ 8 hours = 100 kilometres per hour
(497 miles $\div$ 8 hours = 62 miles per hour)

★ **You go on a trip of 240 kilometres. What is your speed if it takes 5 hours to complete the trip?**

Ways to describe motion

The Jackson family had a picnic at a park five kilometres (about three miles) from their home. Mr. Jackson walked to the park at a speed of five kilometres per hour. Liz and Sally rode their bikes at a speed of ten kilometres (about six miles) per hour. Mrs. Jackson drove to the park. Her speed was twenty-five kilometres (about 16 miles) per hour. Of course, on trips like these, each person would

---

Find Out More

You may have heard the term *velocity* [vuh-LAHS-uht-ee]. Find out what this term means. Does it mean the same as speed? If not, how is velocity different from speed?

speed up or slow down for different reasons. However, to keep the example simple, assume that their speeds did not change during the whole trip.

One way to compare the trips to the park is to use a table of data. The table of data in Figure 12–3 shows each trip to the park.

Another way to describe each trip is by using a *distance-time graph* [DIHS-tuhn(t)s–TYM GRAF]. See Figure 12–3. A distance-time graph is a line drawn on paper that has been marked in a certain way. Distance is marked along the side of the paper. Time is marked along the bottom.

Look at the graph in Figure 12–3 carefully. Notice the line for the two girls' trip. Data from the table are shown on the graph as black circles. All the circles are connected with a straight line. The straight line shows that the two girls traveled at a *constant* [KAHN(T)-stuhnt], or unchanging, speed.

The person who took the shortest time to get to the park had the greatest speed. The part of the graph that will tell you who had the greatest speed is the *slope* [SLOHP] of the lines. The nearer a line is to being straight up and down, the steeper is its slope. The line with the steepest slope shows the greatest speed. Which of the lines has the steepest slope?

Figure 12–3. The table gives data for each of the trips to the park. The same data is shown on the graph. From the graph, can you tell which of the Jacksons traveled at the greatest speed?

DATA FOR EACH PERSON'S TRIP			
Time (hours)	Distance (kilometres)		
	Father	Daughters	Mother
0.1	0.5	1.0	2.5
0.2	1.0	2.0	5.0
0.3	1.5	3.0	
0.4	2.0	4.0	
0.5	2.5	5.0	
0.6	3.0		
0.7	3.5		
0.8	4.0		
0.9	4.5		
1.0	5.0		

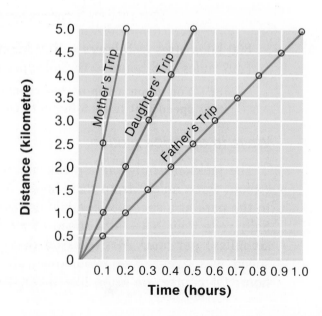

232

You should have noticed two important things on this distance-time graph: (1) A constant speed is shown by a straight line. (2) The slope of a line shows the speed. The steeper the slope, the greater the speed.

★ **If a straight line on a distance-time graph shows a constant speed and the slope of the line shows the amount of speed, what would a straight, level (no slope) line show?**

DO IT YOURSELF

Draw distance-time graphs

Use the data in the table to draw three distance-time graphs on a piece of graph paper. Mark time units along the bottom of the paper. Mark distance units along the side of the paper. Use a different color or kind of line for each car.

Which line has the steepest slope? What does this line tell about the speed of that car? Which car did not travel at a constant speed? How do you know? How does a line showing constant speed compare with a line showing changing speed?

TIME (seconds)	DISTANCE (metres)		
	Car A	Car B	Car C
0	0	0	0
1	4	1	2
2	8	3	4
3	12	8	6
4	16	10	8
5	20	16	10
6	24	22	12
7	28	24	14
8	32	24	16

WHY OBJECTS MOVE

What is friction?
What is inertia? How are inertia and the need
for seat belts related?
Which will move faster, a small mass or a large
mass, if a small force is used to push it?
What does "action equals reaction" mean?

Unbalanced forces

Suppose you wanted to move a book that is lying on a table. There are many different ways you could do this. You could push the book. Or, you could tie a string around the book and pull it. Lifting is another way you could make the book move.

Perhaps you can think of still other ways to move the book. But no matter how the book is moved, some kind of push or pull—that is, a force—must act on the book before it will move. However, there is *friction* [FRIHK-shuhn] wherever two things, such as the book and the table, rub together. In a way, friction is a force that tends to keep the book from moving. Before the book will move, the force acting on the book must be greater than the forces that are keeping the book from moving. That is, the forces acting on the book must be unbalanced.

The first law of motion

About 300 years ago Sir Isaac Newton wrote down some ideas about motion. These ideas have been so useful in explaining motion that today they are called the laws of motion. Perhaps reading about these laws will help you gain a better understanding of why things move in certain ways.

The first law of motion deals with why a force is needed to change the state of motion of an object. The law states that if an object is at rest, or not moving, it tends to stay at rest. If an object is moving, it tends to keep moving. Furthermore, it tends to keep moving in a straight line and at the same speed. This property of matter (that of not

For You to Think About

We use many ways to reduce friction—ball bearings, grease, oil, and so on. Would it be good if there were no friction at all? How would a lack of friction affect your walking? How would it affect the use of automobiles? Can you think of any ways in which you can increase friction?

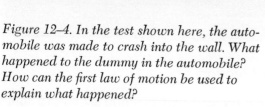

Figure 12–4. In the test shown here, the automobile was made to crash into the wall. What happened to the dummy in the automobile? How can the first law of motion be used to explain what happened?

changing its state of motion unless unbalanced forces act on it) is called *inertia* [ihn-UR-shuh]. All matter has inertia.

Suppose you are riding in an automobile which speeds up rapidly. What happens to you? You might say that you are pushed backward. You can understand what you feel if you remember that you have inertia. That is, you tend to keep moving at the same speed. But the back of the seat causes a force to act on you, pushing you forward. So you are not really being pushed backward. Instead, the seat is pushing you forward.

Suppose you are riding in an automobile and not using a seat belt. What happens if the automobile stops suddenly? You keep moving forward until something causes a force to act on you, stopping your forward motion. If you are in the front seat, it will be the dashboard or the windshield that stops you. If you are in the back seat, it will be the back of the front seat that stops you. In either case you could be badly hurt, or even killed. If you keep the first law of motion in mind, you will probably use your seat belt when riding in an automobile.

★ **What do you think would happen if you were standing in the aisle of a bus, and the bus speeded up rapidly? If the bus stopped quickly? Explain.**

Figure 12–5. In order for the canoe to move, the force used to move the canoe must overcome inertia and friction. What determines the amount of inertia? What causes friction?

The second law of motion

You probably have noticed that pushing an empty shopping cart is easier than pushing a full shopping cart. Why is this so? A full shopping cart has a greater mass than an empty cart. You have to use more force to make the greater mass of the full cart move than you do to make the empty cart move.

The second law of motion states that the force acting on something, the mass of the thing, and the resulting change in speed are related. A small force acting on something with a large mass will not cause a great change in speed. A large force acting on something with a small mass will cause a great change in speed.

Remember that friction also plays a part in the way things move. A force that makes something move must be large enough to overcome both friction and inertia.

The second law of motion also helps explain why things speed up or slow down. A force may act on an object by pushing or pulling in the same direction the object is moving. Then the object will speed up. Or, a force may act on an object by pushing or pulling in a direction opposite to that in which the object is moving. Then, the object will slow down.

★ **How would you use the second law of motion to explain why friction causes a moving object to slow down?**

236

The third law of motion

Suppose you and a friend are on skates. You stand facing each other and push each other away. Would just one person move, or would both of you move? Each of you causes a force to act on the other person. The forces are in opposite directions. Therefore, each of you will move backward, away from the other person.

Now suppose you and your friend face each other again. This time you do not push on your friend. Instead, you just stand there as your friend pushes on you. Will you move backward while your friend stays in the same place? Will your friend move backward while you stay in the same place? Or will you both move backward?

Try it and see. The result may surprise you. Both you and your friend will move backward. You move because your friend pushes on you. Your friend moves because you "push" on your friend. This may seem odd since you did not try to push your friend.

The forces that cause both you and your friend to move can be explained by the third law of motion. One way to state this law is to say "action equals reaction." In this

(*Text continues on page 239.*)

For You to Think About

Suppose you dive into a lake from a small rowboat. As you move forward the boat moves backward. If you dive off a larger boat, such as the kind used to pull water-skiers, will the larger boat move more or less than the smaller rowboat? If you dive off an ocean liner, how will the ocean liner be affected? Explain your answers.

Figure 12–6. How can the third law of motion be used to explain the lift-off of a rocket? What is the action? What is the reaction?

Investigate

How can you demonstrate the third law of motion?

You Will Need

soda-pop bottle with smooth, straight sides; cork or rubber stopper; tissue paper; vinegar; baking soda; petroleum jelly; round pencils or dowel rods

Background

When baking soda and vinegar mix, they react to form the gas carbon dioxide. In a closed container, pressure increases as the gas forms. The effects of this pressure can be used to demonstrate the third law of motion.

What to Do

Smear some petroleum jelly around the outside of a cork that will just fit inside the mouth of the bottle. Pour about half a cup of vinegar into the bottle. Set the pencils in a row as shown. Place one or two tablespoons of baking soda on a piece of tissue, roll the paper, and twist the ends closed. Put the wrapped tissue in the bottle and quickly fit the cork into the mouth of the bottle. Do not force the cork in tightly. Set the bottle on the pencils and observe what happens.

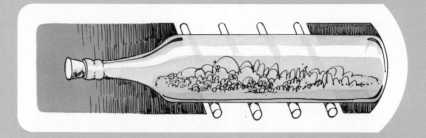

Now That You Have Done the Investigation

—Did the cork fly out of the bottle? If so, in which direction did it go?
—Did the bottle move? If so, in which direction did it move?
—How could the third law of motion be used to explain what you observed?
—How could the second law of motion be used to explain what you observed?

case, a *reaction* [ree-AK-shuhn] is an action in the opposite direction. You could also state the law like this: When one object causes a force to act on a second object, the second object causes a force to act on the first. The force caused by the second object is equal to the force caused by the first object. But it is in the opposite direction.

MOTION OF FALLING OBJECTS

What force causes objects to fall?
What happens to the speed of heavy objects that fall short distances through air?
What happens to the speed of heavy objects that fall long distances through air?

Why objects fall

Even in early times people tried to explain why things move. They could explain some motions as a result of forces. That is, they knew a cart moved because an animal or a person pulled or pushed it. However, the motion of falling objects was not easy to explain. No force seemed to act on falling things.

Because no force seemed to be acting, people thought that things fell without a force acting on them. They thought that all things that were heavier than air had a true resting place on the surface of the earth. Falling was the way these things returned to their true resting place. Today, scientists believe that any change in motion is the result of a force. This is stated in the second law of motion. So some kind of force must cause an object to fall. But what force is it?

Sir Isaac Newton was the first person to explain falling as the result of a force. He stated that a force of *attraction* [uh-TRAK-shuhn] exists between all things—from grains of sand on a beach to the planets and stars. This force was called *gravitational* [GRAV-uh-TAY-shnuhl] *attraction.*

Newton described the effects of gravitational attraction. However, he did not explain what causes it. You may be

Figure 12–7. Is there gravitational attraction between the astronaut and the moon? How do you know? Do you think this attraction is greater than or less than the attraction between the earth and the astronaut when the astronaut is on the earth? Why?

Courtesy of NASA

surprised to learn that even today, scientists do not know what causes it.

★ **What common term is used to refer to the gravitational attraction between the earth and objects on the earth?**

Why you don't see the earth move

Suppose you are holding a heavy stone. Then you drop it. You see the stone fall to the earth. One way to explain what you see is to say that the earth attracts the stone. However, gravitational attraction has been explained to mean that the stone and the earth attract each other. That is, the stone pulls on the earth with just as much force as the earth pulls on the stone. Why, then, don't you see the earth move up to meet the stone?

The answer to this question has to do with the difference between the mass of the earth and the mass of the stone. The mass of the earth is billions and billions of times greater than the mass of the stone. The stone may fall one or two metres. At the same time, the earth would move so little that the distance could not even be measured, much less seen.

Speeding up because of gravity

As objects fall they move faster and faster. That is, they *accelerate* [ihk-SEHL-uh-ʀᴀʏᴛ]. Furthermore, they accelerate at a constant rate. This acceleration has been found to be 9.8 metres (about 32 feet) per second for each second the object is falling. This means that a falling object is moving 9.8 metres per second faster at the end of each second than it was one second earlier.

On the earth, objects move through air as they fall. Air causes a force to act which slows the speed of a falling object. This is not noticed in heavy objects unless they fall far enough to move at great speed. For the following example assume that air has no effect on the falling object.

Suppose you are in a balloon that is 490 metres (about 1,600 feet) high. The balloon is not moving. Now suppose you drop something out of the balloon. The diagram at the right shows the speed of the object and the total distance it has fallen at the end of each second.

The same data is shown below on a distance-time graph. The distance-time graph shows the speeding up as a curved

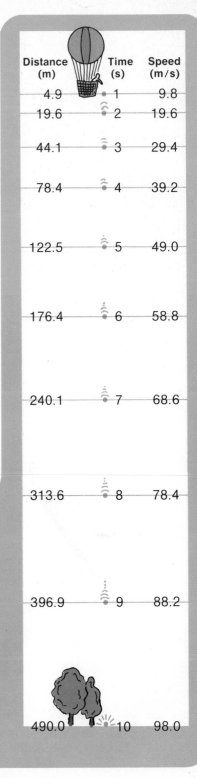

Distance (m)	Time (s)	Speed (m/s)
4.9	1	9.8
19.6	2	19.6
44.1	3	29.4
78.4	4	39.2
122.5	5	49.0
176.4	6	58.8
240.1	7	68.6
313.6	8	78.4
396.9	9	88.2
490.0	10	98.0

Figure 12–8. A falling object does not move at a constant speed. How would the graph be different if the falling object were moving at a constant speed?

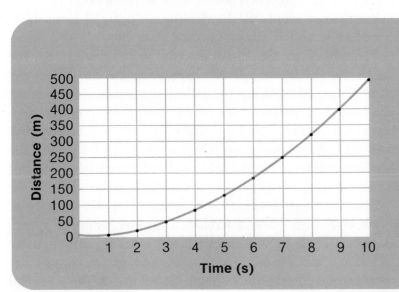

line. The steeper the slope on such a graph, the greater the speed. The graph shows that the speed of the falling object is increasing each second.

Terminal speed

Some people enjoy a sport called skydiving. In this sport people jump out of a plane hundreds of metres above the ground. They fall, sometimes for over a minute, before opening their parachute. If skydivers kept accelerating for each second of fall, their speed would be 588 metres per second (more than 1,300 miles per hour) at the end of one minute! But this speed is not reached. Instead, after falling for about ten seconds, a *terminal* [TURM-nuhl] *speed* of about 55 metres per second (about 125 miles per hour) is reached. When skydivers reach terminal speed, they no longer accelerate as they fall. Instead they fall at a constant speed.

Why do skydivers not fall faster than 55 metres per second? The reason has to do with the air. Air causes a force to act on skydivers. This force is often called air *resistance* [rih-ZIHS-tuhn(t)s]. Have you ever held your hand out of the window of a moving car? If so, you have felt the force caused by air on a moving object. If you have tried this at different speeds, you have noticed that the faster the car went, the harder the air seemed to push on your hand. And it always pushed your hand in the direction opposite to the direction you were moving. So the faster the skydivers fall, the greater is the air resistance.

At some point during the fall of skydivers, air resistance just balances the force of gravity. From this point on skydivers no longer speed up. They do not stop falling, but they do stop speeding up. During the rest of the fall, the skydivers move at a constant speed unless something causes a change in air resistance.

Skydivers can control their terminal speed somewhat. Look at Figure 12–9. To reach a greater terminal speed, skydivers "ball up" as shown in A. In this position there is less surface for the air to push on. Air resistance decreases, and the skydivers begin to fall faster. But as speed

Figure 12–9. Skydivers change position and use parachutes to control their terminal speed. Which skydiver will have the fastest terminal speed? Which will have the slowest?

increases, so does air resistance. Soon a terminal speed —faster than the original terminal speed—is reached again. Skydivers can slow their rate of falling by spreading their arms and legs as shown in *B*. There is more surface for the air to push on. Air resistance increases and a slower terminal speed results.

When skydivers open their parachute, as shown in *C*, air resistance increases greatly. The terminal speed slows to about five metres per second (about twelve miles per hour). This is slow enough to land safely.

★ **Why do objects such as feathers, table-tennis balls, and sheets of paper fall more slowly from high places than do objects such as marbles, ball bearings, and baseballs?**

243

Investigate

Do objects with different masses fall at the same rate?

You Will Need

ruler with a groove, three marbles or ball bearings of different sizes

Background

What happens when things with different masses are dropped from the same height at the same time? For a long time people believed that the one with the greater mass would fall the fastest and hit the ground first. As far as we know, no one ever tested this idea until about A.D. 1600. Galileo was the first person known to run actual tests to find out if things with different masses fall at different speeds. You can also test this idea by using marbles or ball bearings with different masses.

What to Do

Place three marbles (or ball bearings) of different sizes in the groove of a ruler. Stand on top of a table and carefully raise the ruler above your head. Turn the ruler over so that all the objects fall to the floor from the same height at the same time. Listen for the sounds made when the objects hit the floor. Repeat the test.

Now That You Have Done the Investigation

—Could you tell which object hit the floor first? If so, explain why you think that object hit the floor first.

—Were forces caused by the air important in this investigation?

—Would air-caused forces be more important or less important if the same objects were dropped from a height of 1 kilometre (about 3,300 feet)? Explain.

—Would the force caused by air pushing on an object be more important or less important if one of the objects you dropped had been a table-tennis ball? Try it and see. Explain what you observed.

Plotting courses for rockets and guiding airplanes as they land and take off calls for an understanding of motion.

Motion Is Important in Many Jobs

Who needs to know about motion and the forces that cause it? The answer is that almost everyone does. Some people need to know about motion as part of their job. Others use what they know in sports or in hobbies, such as flying model airplanes.

One job that calls for a great understanding of motion is plotting a course for a rocket to the moon. The mass of the rocket changes as the fuel is used up. The forces acting on the rocket change as the rocket gets farther from the earth. Also, the moon, the earth, and the rocket are all moving through space at different speeds. All these factors, and others, must be considered. Of course, not many people do this kind of work. But those who do must understand motion very well.

Pilots and ship navigators use what they know about motion. People who design or use large machines also need to understand motion and the cause of motion. Even people who play sports, such as baseball or football, or race motorcycles or automobiles need to know about motion. Understanding motion helps these people do their job better. Perhaps someday you will have a job in which you will use what you know about motion.

Reviewing and Extending

SUMMING UP

1. Motion is often described as a change in position. Whether or not you see something as moving depends on how you see the object relative to its surroundings.
2. The word "speed" is used in referring to how fast something is moving. Speed, time, and distance are closely related. If you know two of the three, you can find the third.
3. Where things rub together, friction acts as a force that tends to keep them from moving.
4. Any piece of matter has inertia. That is, matter tends not to change its state of motion unless unbalanced forces act on it. (The first law of motion)
5. When unbalanced forces act on an object, the change in motion of the object depends on the mass of the object and the amount of force acting on it. (The second law of motion)
6. When one object causes a force to act on another object, the second object causes an equal but opposite force to act on the first. (The third law of motion)
7. Objects fall to the earth because of a force called gravitational attraction.
8. Air resistance changes the motion of falling objects. Air resistance can cause an object to stop accelerating and fall at a constant speed, called terminal speed.

CHECKING UP

Vocabulary Write the numerals 1–5 on your paper. Each numbered phrase describes a term from the following list. On your paper, write the term next to the numeral of the phrase that describes it.

motion	inertia	terminal speed
speed	graph	friction

1. rate of motion
2. tendency to resist a change in the state of motion
3. change in position
4. resistance to motion between objects that rub together
5. depends on the air resistance on a falling object

Knowledge and Understanding Write the numerals 6–10 on your paper. Beside each numeral, write the word or words that best complete the sentence having that numeral.

6. To put an object in motion, the forces acting on the object must be (*balanced, decreasing, unbalanced*).
7. (*Distance, Speed, Position*) refers to the rate of motion.
8. On a distance-time graph, constant speed is shown as a (*curved, straight, jagged*) line.

9. The phrase "action equals reaction" describes the (*first, second, third*) law of motion.

10. According to the (*first, second, third*) law of motion, an object at rest tends to remain at rest.

Concepts   Beside each of the numerals *11–15* on your paper, write the word or words that best complete the sentence having that numeral.

11. If unbalanced forces act on an object in a direction opposite to the one in which the object is moving, the object will _____.

12. If there were no air resistance, falling objects would never reach a _____ speed.

13. If you know the amount of time you travel and the distance you go during that time, you can find your _____.

14. _____ is the property of all matter that causes matter not to change its state of motion unless unbalanced forces act on it.

15. You do not see the earth and a falling stone move toward each other because the _____ of the earth is much greater than that of a stone.

Application and Critical Thinking   Answer the following questions as briefly as you can without leaving out any important ideas.

16. Use the laws of motion to explain what can happen to people who are not wearing seat belts in an automobile accident.

17. Air resistance causes a skydiver to reach a terminal speed. How would the skydiver's terminal speed be affected if there were no air? If the air were as "thick" as water?

DOING MORE

1. Participate in a "tug-of-war" game with your classmates. Try to even up the teams so that each team pulls on the rope with the same amount of force but in opposite directions. If each team pulls with the same amount of force, does the position of the rope change? Do you think an object can be set in motion if balanced forces are acting on it? Why or why not?

2. Stand on a table and drop a small stone to the floor. Does the stone slow down or speed up as it falls? Now make a parachute out of string, a square piece of paper, and tape. Fasten the parachute to the stone. Again, stand on the table and drop the stone. Does the stone seem to fall faster, slower, or about the same speed? Would a larger parachute slow the fall of the stone more? Try it and see.

247

CHAPTER 13

Work and Machines

Have you ever been asked to describe a machine? If so, perhaps you thought of something like a bulldozer. A bulldozer is a large machine with many moving parts. It is used to lift and move heavy loads. A bulldozer is used to help do work.

There are many kinds of machines you use. Some of these are pencil sharpeners, doorknobs, and ramps. Most of the machines you use are not large and have few moving parts. They are called simple machines. Simple machines also help people do work. But what are simple machines? How do simple machines help people do work? You can find out by reading this chapter.

How does each of these machines help people do work? Which of these machines have only a few, if any, moving parts?

Michael D. Sullivan

USING MACHINES

How do machines help people do work?
What is mechanical advantage?
Do you ever get more work out of a machine, such as an automobile jack, than you put into it? Why or why not?

Why people use machines

Have you ever watched someone raise a flag to the top of a flagpole? If so, you have seen a machine being used. At the top of the flagpole is a grooved wheel called a *pulley* [PUL-ee]. As a person pulls down on one end of a rope hanging over the pulley, the other end of the rope, with the flag fastened to it, rises.

But why is a pulley used to raise a flag? The pulley doesn't decrease the amount of force needed. Nor does the pulley decrease the distance through which the rope must be pulled. That is, using the pulley does not change the amount of work done in raising the flag.

However, using a pulley does make the work easier to do. With a pulley, a person can stand on the ground to raise the flag. Without one, a person would have to use a ladder or climb the flagpole.

Machines make work easier in ways other than changing the direction in which a force acts. For example, do

249

you think you could lift an automobile? It takes a force of about 4 500 newtons (about 1,000 pounds) to lift just one wheel of an automobile off the ground. By using an automobile jack, a person can lift one wheel of an automobile using a force of about 150 newtons (about 35 pounds). The jack changes the small force a person uses on the jack into a much larger force acting on the automobile.

A fishing pole changes a force in still another way. When you get a bite, you raise the tip of the pole. The end you are holding moves only a short distance. The tip of the pole, from which the line hangs, moves a much greater distance and at a faster speed.

The pulley, the automobile jack, and the fishing pole are all machines. They all change a force used to do work. In fact, a machine is anything that is used to change the force a person uses to do work. Machines change forces in three different ways: (1) They can change the direction of a force. (2) They can increase the amount of the force. (3) They can cause a force to act through a greater distance and, at the same time, at a greater speed.

★ **When you use a bottle opener to open a bottle of pop, in what way or ways does the opener change the force you use?**

For You to Think About

What are some machines that are used to change the direction of a force? To increase the amount of a force? To increase the speed of a force? To increase the distance through which a force acts? Can the same machine do more than one of these things at the same time? Can it do all of these at the same time?

David W. Corson/A. Devaney, Inc.

Figure 13–2. A fishing pole changes the force acting on the handle of the pole, causing the tip to move through a greater distance and, at the same time, at a greater speed. What other things can you think of that change a force in this way?

Mechanical advantage

The reason a person uses a machine is that using a machine gives a certain *advantage* [uhd-VANT-ihj]. This advantage is called the mechanical advantage of the machine. It is the number of times the machine multiplies the force acting on the machine. The force acting on the machine is called the *effort* [EHF-urt]. The force the machine overcomes is called the *resistance*.

If the effort needed to move an object is equal to the resistance, the machine being used has a mechanical advantage of one. The pulley on top of the flagpole is a machine with a mechanical advantage of one. In using an automobile jack, the effort needed is smaller than the resistance. Therefore, an automobile jack has a mechanical advantage greater than one. A fishing pole, on the other hand, has a mechanical advantage less than one. It takes a greater effort to lift the line (and the fish) using the pole than it would if you just pulled up on the line. However, by using a pole, the line is made to move farther and at a faster speed than it would move if you just lifted the line.

Something for nothing?

There is an old saying that you cannot get something for nothing. Is this true for a machine such as an automobile jack, which has a mechanical advantage greater than one? In such machines the effort is smaller than the resistance. For example, by using only 150 newtons (about 35 pounds) of force, you can lift 4 500 newtons (about 1,000 pounds). Isn't that an example of getting more out of a machine than you put into it?

If you think only of the amount of force, you do get more out of such machines than you put into them. However, you do not get more work out of any machine than you put into it. The amount of work done is equal to the amount of force used multiplied by the distance the force acts on an object. In using a jack, you have to move the jack handle a lot to get the automobile to move a little. If you measure the amount of work you do on the jack and the amount of work the jack does in lifting the automobile, you find something unexpected. The amount of work you do on the jack is always more than the amount of work the jack does in lifting an automobile.

Why is this so? Where does the extra work go? Where parts of a machine rub together, there is friction. Work must be done to overcome this friction in the machine. So you do more work on a machine than the machine does on the object being moved. But using a machine makes the work easier to do. If it didn't, there would be no reason to use a machine.

★ **What do you think happens to the expected mechanical advantage of a machine if there is a lot of friction? What are some things that can be done to lower the amount of friction?**

Figure 13–3. Friction caused the bottom of the space capsule at the right to become very hot and burn. What was the capsule rubbing against to cause friction? The motorcycle below is being greased. Will greasing increase or decrease friction in the motorcycle?

Alfa Studio

Courtesy of NASA

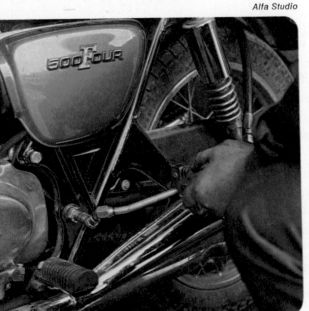

Investigate

What is the mechanical advantage of an automobile jack?

You Will Need

automobile jack, metre stick

Background

The mechanical advantage of a machine is usually found by measuring the effort force and the resistance force. However, forces are not always easy to measure. There is another way to figure out the approximate mechanical advantage of a machine. This way involves measuring the distance the effort moves and measuring the distance the resistance moves. Then, the distance the effort moves is divided by the distance the resistance moves.

What to Do

Measure the height of the end of the jack handle while it is in an up position. Also measure the height of the part that lifts the automobile. Push the handle down. Again, measure the height of the end of the jack handle as well as the height of the part that lifts the automobile. Use these four measurements to figure out the distance the handle (effort) moves and the distance the part that lifts the automobile (resistance) moves. Now use the following formula to figure out the mechanical advantage of the jack.

$$\frac{\text{Distance the Effort Moves}}{\text{Distance the Resistance Moves}} = \text{Mechanical Advantage}$$

Now That You Have Done the Investigation

—What was the mechanical advantage of the jack?

—In machines with a mechanical advantage greater than one, which force do you think will move farther—the effort or the resistance?

—In machines with a mechanical advantage less than one, which force do you think will move farther—the effort or the resistance?

253

LEVERS

How many classes of levers are there?
What class of lever has the fulcrum between
the resistance and the effort?
What are three kinds of wheel-like machines
that act like levers?

Classes of levers

Perhaps you have seen a crowbar used to pry two pieces of wood apart. When used like this, the crowbar is a kind of simple machine called a *lever* [LEHV-ur]. A bottle opener is also a kind of lever. A shovel is often used as a lever, too. To most people, a lever is a straight rod or bar that moves around a fixed point. This fixed point is called a *fulcrum* [FUL-kruhm].

The crowbar, the bottle opener, and the shovel are all used in different ways. That is, they belong to different classes of levers. Levers are divided into three classes, based on the positions of the effort, the resistance, and the fulcrum. See Figure 13–4. When a crowbar is used to pry pieces of wood apart, the effort and the resistance are at the two ends. The fulcrum is between them. A crowbar used in this way is a first-class lever.

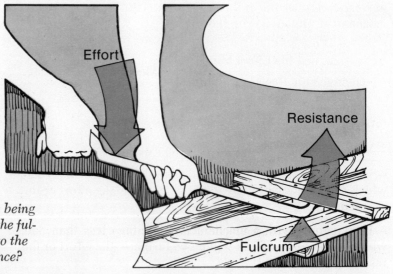

Figure 13–4. The crowbar is being used as a first-class lever. Is the fulcrum of this crowbar closer to the effort or closer to the resistance?

Many bottle openers have a hook that fits under the edge of the bottle cap. The fulcrum is on top of the cap. Because the resistance (the edge of the bottle cap) is between the fulcrum and the effort, the bottle opener is a second-class lever.

A shovel is often used as a third-class lever. When you lift a load of snow or dirt, the effort to lift it comes from your hand on the shaft part of the handle. Your other hand on the end of the handle acts as the fulcrum.

★ **What other things do you use that are levers? To which class does each one belong?**

Vannucci/De Wys, Inc.

Figure 13–5. A snow shovel can be thought of as a kind of lever. Is the shovel being used as a first-class lever, as a second-class lever, or as a third-class lever? How do you know?

Levers and work

Like all simple machines, levers help do work by changing forces. First-class levers change the direction of a force. Second-class and third-class levers do not. Levers can also be used to change the amount of a force. How much a force is changed depends on two lengths. One is the length of the effort arm. This length is the distance between the fulcrum and the effort. The other is the length of the resistance arm. This length is the distance between the fulcrum and the resistance. Dividing the length of the effort arm by the length of the resistance arm gives the mechanical advantage of a lever. So the longer the effort arm, the greater the mechanical advantage.

When a crowbar is used to pry pieces of wood apart, the fulcrum is very close to the resistance. So the crowbar has a mechanical advantage greater than one. The longer the handle of the crowbar, the greater the mechanical advantage.

Not all first-class levers have a mechanical advantage greater than one. A seesaw is a kind of first-class lever in which the fulcrum is usually in the center. Suppose a friend is sitting on one end of the seesaw. Unless your friend pushes up, you would have to pull the high end down to get on. Furthermore, you would have to pull down with a force equal to your friend's weight. When the resistance arm is equal to the effort arm, as in the seesaw, the mechanical advantage is one.

★ **How do you and a friend sit to seesaw if your friend weighs more than you do?**

Figure 13–6. Which, if any, of these first-class levers has a mechanical advantage greater than one? Which, if any, has a mechanical advantage equal to one? Is the mechanical advantage of any of these levers less than one? How are you able to find the mechanical advantage of a lever?

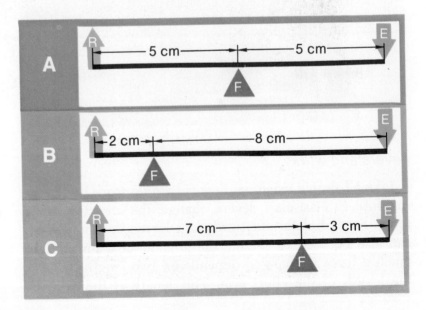

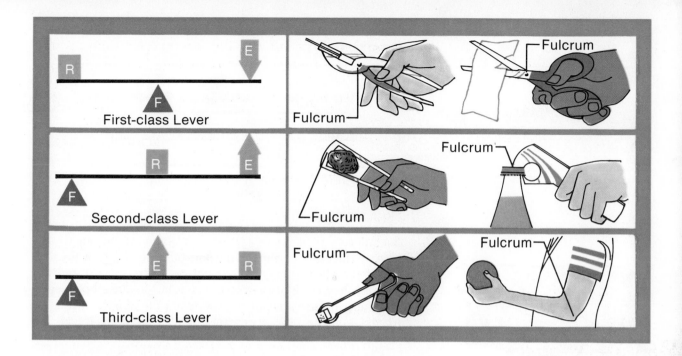

Labels within figure:
R   E
First-class Lever
F

Fulcrum
Fulcrum

R   E
Second-class Lever
F

Fulcrum
Fulcrum

E   R
Third-class Lever
F

Fulcrum
Fulcrum

A first-class lever can also have its fulcrum closer to the effort than to the resistance. In this case, the effort used is greater than the resistance. Such first-class levers have a mechanical advantage less than one.

In second-class levers, such as the bottle opener, the effort arm is always longer than the resistance arm. This means that all second-class levers have a mechanical advantage greater than one. On the other hand, third-class levers, such as the shovel, always have a resistance arm that is longer than the effort arm. Their mechanical advantage is always less than one.

With levers that have a mechanical advantage greater than one, the amount of effort needed is smaller than the amount of resistance. However, the resistance does not move as far as the effort does. On the other hand, by using a lever with a mechanical advantage less than one, the resistance can be made to move farther and faster than the effort does. But the effort used is greater than would be needed without using the lever.

Figure 13–7. Many of the things you use every day are levers. Which of the examples of different kinds of levers have mechanical advantages greater than one? Which have mechanical advantages less than one?

★ **Is the direction of the force changed when a first-class lever is used? When a second-class lever is used? A third-class lever?**

257

Investigate

How does moving the fulcrum affect a first-class lever?

You Will Need

ruler, length of string, 2 rubber bands, 3 pencils, fist-sized rock (about ½ kilogram or about 1 pound)

Background

The fulcrum of a first-class lever is always between the effort and the resistance. Moving the fulcrum changes the length of the effort arm (distance between the fulcrum and the effort) and the length of the resistance arm (distance between the fulcrum and the resistance). Changing the lengths of the effort arm and the resistance arm changes the mechanical advantage of the lever.

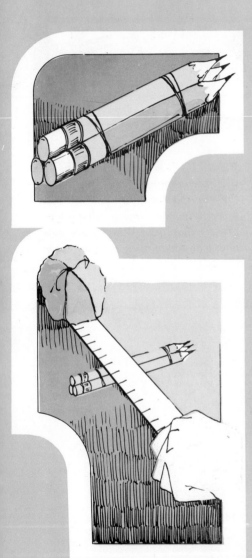

What to Do

Lift the rock to get an idea of how heavy it feels. Now use a length of string to tie the rock to one end of a ruler. The ruler will act as a lever. For a fulcrum, use 3 pencils held together with rubber bands as shown in the diagram. Put the fulcrum in the middle of the ruler. Lift the rock by pushing down on the other end of the ruler. Decide if the rock feels heavier, lighter, or about the same as it did when you first lifted it. Also notice the direction the effort moves and the direction the resistance moves. Repeat these steps with the fulcrum in several different positions between the rock and your hand.

Now That You Have Done the Investigation

—When the fulcrum was in the middle, did the rock feel (1) heavier, (2) lighter, or (3) about the same as when you first lifted it?

—Where was the fulcrum when the rock felt the lightest?

—Where was the fulcrum when the rock felt the heaviest?

—Which direction does the effort move? Which direction does the resistance move?

—How does changing the position of the fulcrum change the amount of effort needed to lift the rock?

258

Wheels that act like levers

Not all machines thought of as being levers are straight rods. Some wheel-like machines also act like levers. In fact, one wheel-like machine that acts like a lever has already been described. This machine is the pulley.

Pulleys are used in two ways. Some, such as the one on a flagpole, are fastened in a fixed place. Only the wheel turns. The pulley itself does not move. Such pulleys are called fixed pulleys. Another way to use a pulley is to fasten one end of the rope and hang the pulley on the rope. The load to be moved is then hung from the pulley. This type is called a movable pulley. As the rope is pulled up, both the pulley and the load move higher.

All pulleys act like levers even though they do not look like straight rods. But there are two kinds of pulleys. Does this mean that the two kinds of pulleys act like different classes of levers? Both a fixed pulley and a movable pulley are shown in Figure 13–8. Straight levers have been drawn over each one.

Figure 13–8. Sometimes a pulley is described as a "continuous lever." How do these drawings help explain that description?

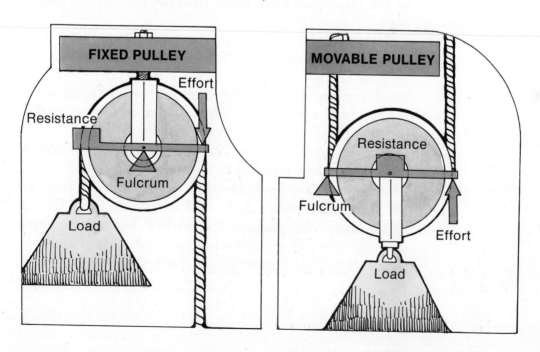

In using a fixed pulley, the fulcrum is in the center of the pulley. Both the effort arm and the resistance arm are the same length. Therefore, the mechanical advantage of a fixed pulley is one. The resistance moves the same distance as the effort.

With a movable pulley, the resistance hangs from the center of the pulley. The fulcrum is thought of as being the point where the fixed end of the rope first touches the wheel. With such pulleys, the effort arm is twice as long as the resistance arm. They have a mechanical advantage of two. So you only use about half as much force as the resistance weighs. However, you pull the rope twice as far as the resistance moves.

Find Out More

Sometimes fixed and movable pulleys are used together. This combination is called a block and tackle. What are some uses for a block and tackle? Why is a block and tackle used? How can you figure out the mechanical advantage of a block and tackle?

A gear is another kind of wheel-like machine that acts like a lever. Gears are wheels with "teeth" around the outside edges. Sometimes two gears are connected by a chain. A bicycle uses gears this way. One gear is between the pedals. The other is on the rear wheel. The teeth of the gears fit into open spaces in the chain. The gear on the pedals is larger than the one on the wheel. So you use more effort to make this gear turn than you would to make the smaller one turn. However, the smaller gear on the rear wheel turns faster than the gear on the pedals does.

Gears can also move other gears without a chain. This is done by making the teeth of one gear fit between the teeth of another. The gears inside watches and clocks are fitted together this way. By using gears of different sizes, the hands of a watch or a clock are made to turn at different speeds.

A third kind of wheel-like machine that acts like a lever has a wheel fastened to the end of an *axle* [AK-suhl]. Sometimes a handle is fastened to the outside edge of the wheel. Sometimes the wheel is nothing more than a crank. Then, the machine doesn't look like a wheel and axle. But it is still called a wheel and axle. Wheel-and-axle machines include doorknobs and the pedals on a bicycle.

Figure 13–9. In what way are all these machines alike? ▶

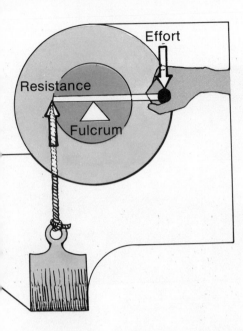

Figure 13–10. *The drawing shows how a wheel-and-axle machine is like a lever. What class of lever is this wheel and axle like? Is the mechanical advantage of this wheel and axle greater than one or less than one?*

But how can a wheel and axle act like a lever? A straight lever is drawn over the wheel and axle in Figure 13–10. The fulcrum is in the center of the axle. The length from the fulcrum to the edge of the wheel is like the effort arm of a straight lever. The length from the fulcrum to the edge of the axle is like the resistance arm of a straight lever. The larger the wheel part, the less effort needed.

★ **What are some ways that wheel-like levers change forces?**

INCLINED PLANES

What is an inclined plane?
How does an inclined plane help a person do work?
What other simple machines are thought of as forms of inclined planes?

The inclined plane

Have you ever watched furniture movers put heavy boxes and furniture into a truck? Perhaps you noticed that they do not lift heavy things from the ground up into the truck. Instead, they use a ramp to help get very heavy things into the truck.

Sloping surfaces, like the ramp, are another kind of simple machine. They are *inclined* [ihn-KLYND] *planes.* Inclined planes are used to move things from one level to a higher level. Unlike levers and pulleys, which move when they are used, the inclined plane itself does not move when it is used.

Suppose you wanted to raise a barrel weighing 450 newtons (about 100 pounds) from the ground to a platform one metre (about 3 feet) high. Unless you are very strong, you would have trouble lifting the barrel by yourself. However, you could make an inclined plane by resting one end of a board on the ground and the other end on the platform. Then you could roll the barrel up the board and onto the platform.

262

When you use the board, you have to move the barrel farther than you would if you just lifted it. However, rolling the barrel up the inclined plane is easier than lifting it up to the platform. That is, an inclined plane gives you a mechanical advantage.

To find the mechanical advantage of an inclined plane, you need to know two distances. One is the distance over which the object moves. This is the effort distance. The other is the height from the ground to the highest part of the inclined plane. This is the resistance distance. Dividing the effort distance by the resistance distance gives the mechanical advantage of the inclined plane. Because the effort distance is always greater than the resistance distance, inclined planes always have a mechanical advantage greater than one.

With an inclined plane, the longer the effort distance, the greater the mechanical advantage. But the greater the mechanical advantage, the farther the object has to be pushed or pulled. As with all machines, using an inclined plane does not lessen the amount of work. It only makes the work easier to do.

★ **Describe some inclined planes you have seen or used. Explain why you think they are inclined planes.**

DO IT YOURSELF

Change the resistance distance of an inclined plane

Use several books to support one end of a board. Tie a string around a brick, and then fasten the string to a spring scale. Find the weight of the brick and record it. Now slowly pull the brick up the inclined plane. What is the reading on the scale? Remove a book to lower the height of the inclined plane. Again, slowly pull the brick up the board. What is the reading on the scale now? Does a high or a low inclined plane give you the greatest advantage?

The wedge

A *wedge* [WEHJ] is very much like an inclined plane. A wedge has long sides that slope from a pointed end to a wider end. In fact, you might think that wedges and inclined planes are used the same way. However, they are not.

An inclined plane doesn't move when it is used. When you push a box up an inclined plane, the effort (your pushing) acts on and moves the resistance (the box). In using a wedge to lift a box, you place the pointed end of the wedge under the box. Then you push the wedge under the box. In other words, your effort acts on and moves the wedge instead of the box.

The screw

A screw is a simple machine that is a kind of inclined plane. One way to describe a screw is to say that it is an inclined plane wrapped around a round object, such as a broomstick. You may be able to understand this better by looking at Figure 13–11. A right triangle is cut out of a piece of paper. Notice that the long side of the triangle has a slope like that of an inclined plane. The paper triangle is then wrapped around a pencil. The long side of the triangle coils around the pencil like the ridge on a screw. This ridge is called the thread of a screw.

⭐ **The tops of some jars are screws. What are some other uses for screws?**

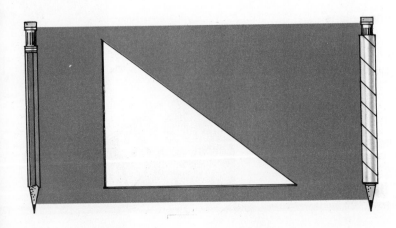

Figure 13–11. One side of the paper triangle is like an inclined plane. That is, it is a slope. What happens to this slope when the paper triangle is wrapped around a pencil?

Paul Schrock/FPG

Ted H. Funk/FPG

Carpenters and other craftsmen often use simple machines. In what other jobs are simple machines used?

Simple Machines Are Used in Many Jobs

You use simple machines every time you open a door or sharpen a pencil. Screwdrivers, pliers, hammers, and automobile jacks are some simple machines that many people use every day. However, some people use simple machines more often than other people. These people use simple machines in their jobs. A carpenter uses planes and saws with wedge-shaped blades. Drill bits are a kind of screw. Hammers are sometimes used as a lever to pull nails.

Automobile mechanics also depend on many simple machines. Some work is done using screwdrivers, wrenches, and pliers. For other kinds of work, they may use a jack. Or, they may use a block and tackle made of several pulleys to raise part of the automobile.

There are many other jobs that depend upon using simple machines. Therefore, many people have jobs making such machines. Other people design simple machines. People are always looking for ways to improve the efficiency or increase the mechanical advantage of a machine. Perhaps someday you will use or make simple machines in your job.

Reviewing and Extending

SUMMING UP

1. A machine is anything that is used to change the force a person uses to do work.
2. Machines can (1) change the direction of a force, (2) increase the amount of a force, or (3) cause a force to act through a greater distance and at a greater speed.
3. Mechanical advantage is the number of times a machine multiplies the force acting on the machine.
4. The force acting on a machine is called the effort. The force a machine overcomes is called the resistance.
5. You can never get more work out of a machine than you put into the machine.
6. Levers are machines that balance or turn on a fixed point called a fulcrum. Levers can be either straight rods or wheel-like.
7. Levers are divided into three classes depending on the positions of the effort, the resistance, and the fulcrum.
8. Levers that look like wheels include wheel-and-axle machines, pulleys, and gears.
9. Inclined planes are sloping surfaces over which a resistance is moved.
10. The wedge and the screw are kinds of inclined planes.

CHECKING UP

Vocabulary Each of the phrases numbered *1–5* describes a term from the following list. On your paper, write the term next to the number of the phrase that describes it.

fulcrum	resistance	inclined plane
effort	pulley	mechanical advantage

1. number of times a machine multiplies a force acting on the machine
2. sloping surface that goes from one level to a higher level
3. force acting on a machine
4. fixed point on which a lever balances or turns
5. force a machine overcomes

Knowledge and Understanding Beside each of the numerals *6–10* on your paper, write the word or words that best complete the sentences having that numeral.

6. If you use a screwdriver to pry a lid off a can, you are using a (*first-class, second-class, third-class*) lever.

7. The ridge that coils around a screw is called the (*fulcrum, thread, resistance*) of the screw.

8. The wedge is a machine that is a form of (*lever, wheel, inclined plane*).

9. There are (*five, three, two*) different classes of levers.

10. A machine cannot (*make work easier, do more work than is put into the machine, change the direction of a force*).

Concepts Beside each of the numerals *11–15* on your paper, write the word or words that best complete the sentence having that numeral.

11. The fulcrum of a wheel and axle is in the center of the ____ .

12. In a ____-class lever the effort is between the fulcrum and the resistance.

13. A fixed pulley acts like a ____-class lever.

14. An inclined plane always has a mechanical advantage ____ than one.

15. A ____ can be described as an inclined plane wrapped around a rod.

Application and Critical Thinking Answer the following questions as briefly as you can without leaving out any important ideas.

16. In what ways do fixed pulleys differ from movable pulleys? What class of lever does each of these pulleys resemble?

17. What are three ways machines change forces? Give an example of a machine for each of the three ways.

18. How does the position of the fulcrum determine the mechanical advantage of a lever?

19. How does friction affect the mechanical advantage of a simple machine?

DOING MORE

1. Use a spring balance to weigh a roller skate. Make an inclined plane that is 1.5 metres (about 5 feet) long and 0.3 metres (about a foot) high. Use the spring balance to pull the roller skate up this inclined plane. How does the effort compare to the weight of the skate? What is the mechanical advantage of the inclined plane?

2. Prepare a bulletin board on simple machines. Use pictures that show simple machines in use. Classify and label each picture.

CHAPTER 14

Engines

What would your life be like if there were no engines? There would be no automobiles, buses, trucks, or airplanes. Large ships would use sails to cross the oceans. People would row or paddle small boats. There would be fewer things in stores because many of the things you buy are made by using engines. Engines are a very important part of people's life today. And yet people have been using engines for less than 300 years.

How did people do work before engines were invented? Are all engines alike? If not, how do engines differ? What kinds of engines do people use today? These are some of the questions that will be answered in this chapter.

Photos from The Bettmann Archive

Sailing ships and stagecoaches were once important means of travel. Why are they no longer important? Do you think they will ever be important again? Why?

WHY USE ENGINES

What is an engine?

What is the difference between internal-combustion engines and external-combustion engines?

How did people do work before engines were invented?

What are engines?

Engines are machines that change heat energy into mechanical energy. The mechanical energy is used to do work. Engines come in all sizes, from the tiny ones used in model airplanes to the huge ones used in electric power plants. Engines also use many different kinds of fuel. Some fuels are oil, gasoline, and coal. But even though engines may differ in size and the kind of fuel they use, all engines can be put into one of two groups.

Engines are grouped according to where the fuel is burned. In some engines, the fuel is burned inside the engine. This kind of engine is called an *internal-combustion* [ihn-TURN-uhl–kuhm-BUHS-chun] engine. Engines used in automobiles, airplanes, and rockets belong to this group.

In other engines, the fuel is burned outside the engine. This kind of engine is an *external-combustion* [ehk-STURN-uhl–kuhm-BUHS-chun] engine. But how can an engine change heat into mechanical energy if the fuel burns and gives off heat outside the engine?

To understand this, think about a steam engine which is one kind of external-combustion engine. A large tank, called a boiler, is filled with water. Heat from the burning fuel changes the water in the boiler into steam. The steam is then piped into the engine where it does work. Because of this, the engine may be some distance from where the fuel is burned. The giant engines used in many electric power plants are external-combustion steam engines.

Before engines

Since engines do so much work today, you may wonder how work was done before engines were invented. People

Figure 14–1. These pictures show some ways work was done before engines were invented. Where did the energy come from for doing the kinds of work shown in these pictures?

did have simple machines to help do work. The lever, the inclined plane, the wheel and axle, the pulley, and the screw were invented thousands of years ago. Larger machines, made of several simple machines, have been used almost as long for grinding grain and raising water. However, even with machines to help, energy was needed to do work.

At first, the energy to do work came from people themselves. That is, a person had to lift, pull, or push something to do work. As larger and heavier machines were built, many people had to work together to use these machines. Animals were also used to do some kinds of work. But even large animals were not strong enough to do all kinds of work. People found they needed other sources of energy for doing work.

Two other sources of energy that people learned to use long ago were wind and moving water. Both wind and water can act with great force. In places where strong winds blew, towers with sails, called windmills, were used. The winds pushed on the sails causing them to turn and run machines. Where there were fast-moving streams and rivers, large waterwheels were used. Water pushed on the paddles of the waterwheel causing it to turn and run machines.

★ **Suppose moving water and wind were the only sources of energy for running machines today. Do you think this would cause any problems? If so, what kinds of problems?**

DO IT YOURSELF

Make a display

Wind power and water power are still used in many places. Make a display showing ways in which wind power or water power is used today. Use diagrams or models to show how a windmill or a water wheel changes the mechanical energy of wind or water into useful work.

What happens if the wind changes direction? Can a windmill also be made to face in different directions? Is the use of wind power or water power different today than it was 100 years ago? If so, how?

Using steam

For many years, moving water was a very important source of energy for doing work. Factories were built beside streams and rivers. However, many places had no moving water. Factories could not be built in these places unless some other source of energy was used. A source of energy was needed that could be used anywhere and at any time.

People have known for a long time that burning fuels give off a lot of heat. They have also known that heat causes water to boil. When water boils it changes into steam, a gas. Gases, such as steam, tend to spread out or *expand* [ihk-SPAND]. As steam expands, it can act with great force. You may have seen steam cause the lid of a pot to rise. If the steam could not escape from the pot, the force caused by the steam would be great enough to burst the pot.

Find Out More

How did discoveries about steam lead to the invention of steam engines? Who were some of the people who made important discoveries about steam and steam engines? How are steam engines used today? How did the first steam engine differ from modern steam engines?

271

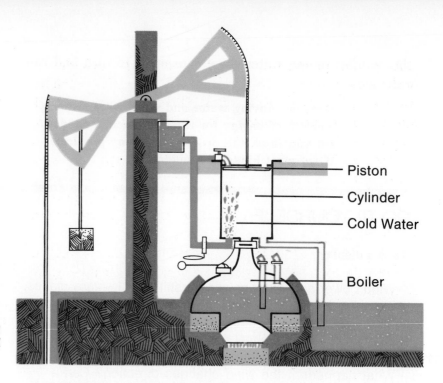

Figure 14–2. The diagram shows what an early steam engine looked like. What caused the piston to move upward in the cylinder? What caused the piston to move downward?

Eventually people were able to find ways to use the force of steam to do work. They discovered a way to make steam engines. The first steam engines were used to pump water from coal mines in England.

EXTERNAL-COMBUSTION ENGINES

What is meant by the term "reciprocating"?
How is a steam turbine different from a reciprocating steam engine?
Which kind of steam engine is used in most electric power plants today?

Reciprocating engines

The first kind of engine invented was a steam engine. It was an external-combustion engine. In the first engine, steam from a boiler did work on a moving part inside the engine. This part was a thick metal plate called a *piston* [PIHS-tuhn]. The piston moved back and forth inside a large metal pipe called the *cylinder* [SIHL-uhn-dur]. See Figure 14–2.

272

As steam moved from the boiler into the cylinder, it pushed the piston to the top of the cylinder. The cylinder was then cooled with cold water. The steam changed back into water. With no steam below the piston, the pressure below the piston became very low. Air moving through an opening in the top of the cylinder pushed the piston down. More steam entered the cylinder, and these steps were repeated. The piston had a back-and-forth, or *reciprocating* [rih-SIHP-ruh-KAYT-ing], motion. So, this engine was called a reciprocating steam engine.

This first steam engine used a large amount of fuel to do very little work. Ways to improve the steam engine were soon discovered. Using steam to push the piston in one direction and air pressure to push it in the other direction wasted a lot of heat. A way of making the steam push first on one side of the piston and then on the other was discovered. By doing this, the cylinder stayed hot all of the time. Less heat was wasted warming the cylinder and more of the heat was used in doing useful work.

At one time, the reciprocating steam engine was the only kind of engine being used. All factories had one or more of these engines. They were also used in riverboats and large ships. Railroads came into being because of these engines.

Find Out More

Find out more about how steam engines have been changed over the years. Make simple diagrams that show the parts of some of the early steam engines. How was reciprocating motion changed into turning motion? What were some uses other than as pumps for early steam engines? How did the invention of engines affect transportation?

Roy H. Blanchard/Alpha

Figure 14–3. This kind of railroad locomotive—often called an "iron horse"—has a reciprocating steam engine. At one time such locomotives played an important role in moving people and goods across the United States. Why are locomotives like this used very little today?

Even some early automobiles had this kind of external-combustion engine.

★ **Energy must be used to overcome friction. What are some places in a reciprocating steam engine where friction occurs? How does friction affect the amount of useful work an engine can do?**

The steam turbine

The reciprocating steam engine was the only kind of steam engine for a long time. Then, about 100 years ago, a new kind of steam engine was invented. This engine was the steam *turbine* [TUR-buhn].

In a reciprocating engine, steam pushes a piston back and forth. This back-and-forth motion must be changed into a turning motion to run other machines. This takes many moving parts. Where there are many moving parts, there is a lot of friction. In the steam turbine, on the other hand, the steam causes parts of the engine to have a turning motion. Fewer moving parts are needed to make a turbine run other machines. There is less friction. The diagram in Figure 14–4 shows how a turbine works.

Today, steam turbines are used to make electricity in all nuclear power plants and in most coal-burning power plants. Ways to improve steam turbines are always being

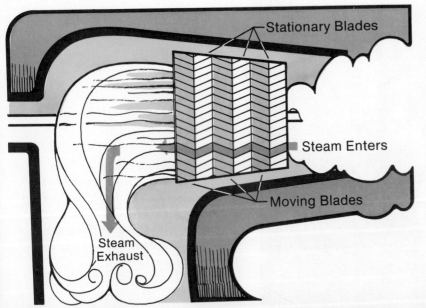

Figure 14–4. The moving blades are fastened to the shaft that passes through the center of the turbine. The shaft and blades turn. The stationary blades are not connected to the shaft. They do not turn. Instead, they direct the steam so that it pushes on each set of moving blades.

sought because electric energy is so important. At present, it costs less to make electricity using steam turbines than by any other way.

★ **How is a steam turbine different from a reciprocating steam engine? Which kind of engine do you think uses less energy to overcome the friction of its moving parts? Explain.**

DO IT YOURSELF

Make a simple steam turbine

Make a simple steam turbine like the one in the diagram. Make the turbine wheel out of a styrofoam disk. Cut the blades out of a plastic coffee-can lid or a plastic-coated paper plate.

Put a small amount of water in a flask. Fit a one-hole rubber stopper with a piece of bent tubing in the hole into the flask. *CAUTION: Do not press the stopper into the flask too tightly.* Set the flask over a burner. Point the bent tube at the blades as shown. Heat the water until it boils and then turn the flame down. What happens when the steam hits the blades? Why do you think this happens? Is your steam turbine an external-combustion or an internal-combustion engine? How do you know?

INTERNAL-COMBUSTION ENGINES

What are some of the different kinds of internal-combustion engines?

How does a two-stroke cycle differ from a four-stroke cycle?

What law of motion causes both jet airplanes and rockets to fly?

Piston engines

You may never have seen a steam engine. However, there is one kind of engine which you probably have seen.

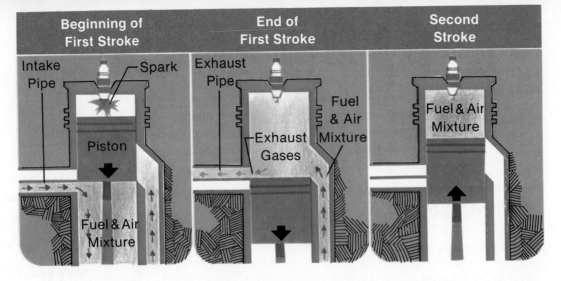

Figure 14–5. These diagrams show what happens inside a piston engine with a two-stroke cycle.

It is the type of engine used in such things as automobiles, model airplanes, and lawn mowers. It is the internal-combustion engine.

Like the first steam engine, the first internal-combustion engine was a piston engine. An internal-combustion piston engine is classed by how many times the piston moves in the cylinder to complete the burning of the fuel. Each move of the piston from one end of the cylinder to the other is called a *stroke* [STROHK]. The number of strokes needed to let fuel into the cylinder, burn the fuel, and remove the used gases is called the *cycle* [SY-kuhl]. Some piston engines have a two-stroke cycle. Others have a four-stroke cycle.

In lawn-mower engines, only two strokes—one in each direction—complete the cycle. At the start of the first stroke, fuel between the piston and the top of the cylinder is started burning by an electric spark. The burning fuel gives off heat and gases which expand rapidly. This pushes the piston to the other end of the cylinder, uncovering two openings in the cylinder wall. Pipes are fitted to each of the openings. One, the *exhaust* [ihg-ZAWST] pipe, is for the used gases, or exhaust, to leave the engine. The other pipe lets fresh fuel (mixed with air) into the cylinder. See Figure 14–5.

During the second stroke the piston moves back toward the top of the cylinder, covering the two openings. The fresh fuel and air are squeezed into a smaller amount of space. That is, they are *compressed* [kuhm-PREHST]. When the piston reaches the top, the fresh fuel is started burning. A new cycle is started.

Most automobile engines have a four-stroke cycle. This means the piston moves the length of the cylinder four times, or twice in each direction to complete one cycle. Four-stroke engines differ from two-stroke engines in ways other than the number of strokes. Movable parts, called *valves* [VALVZ], let fuel into the cylinder and let used gases out. These valves are fitted into the top of the cylinder. See Figure 14–6.

To begin the cycle, the piston moves toward the bottom of the cylinder. The intake valve opens, and fuel mixed with air enters the cylinder. When the piston reaches the bottom, the intake valve closes. The piston then moves toward the top again. As it moves upward, the fuel-air mixture is compressed.

As the piston moves downward again, the fuel is started burning by an electric spark. The hot gases given off by

Figure 14–6. These diagrams show the strokes that occur in an engine with a four-stroke cycle. How are these steps like those in a two-stroke engine? How are they different?

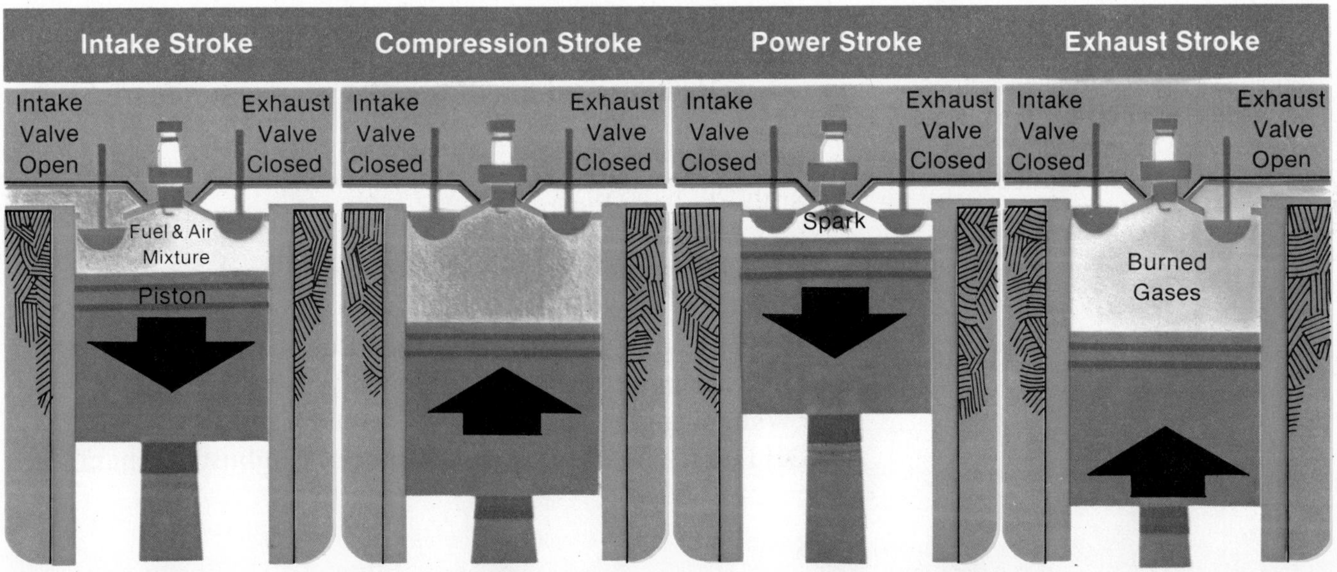

| Intake Stroke | Compression Stroke | Power Stroke | Exhaust Stroke |

Intake Valve Open   Exhaust Valve Closed   Fuel & Air Mixture   Piston

Intake Valve Closed   Exhaust Valve Closed

Intake Valve Closed   Exhaust Valve Closed   Spark

Intake Valve Closed   Exhaust Valve Open   Burned Gases

the burning fuel cause a powerful push on the piston. Then, the piston moves upward for a second time in this cycle. The exhaust valve opens, and the used gases are pushed out of the cylinder by the rising piston. When the piston reaches the top of the cylinder, the exhaust valve closes completing the cycle.

★ **Why is there more force on the piston when the fuel starts burning than when the fuel-air mixture is being compressed in piston engines?**

Diesel engines

One kind of internal-combustion piston engine is somewhat different from those already described. These engines are called *diesel* [DEE-zuhl] engines. Diesel engines do not use gasoline as a fuel. Instead, they use a very thin oil called diesel fuel. The other difference is in the way the fuels are started burning. In gasoline engines, the fuel is started burning by an electric spark. Diesel engines do not use electric sparks. What then starts fuel burning in a diesel engine?

Perhaps you have used a hand pump to put air in a bicycle tire. If so, you may have noticed that the bottom of the pump and the tire get warmer as air is squeezed into the tire. You may wonder why this happens. The air is compressed by the pump. When gases are compressed, they get hot. The more they are compressed, the hotter they get. When the piston in a diesel engine rises, the air in the cylinder is compressed. This compressed air gets very hot. Fuel sprayed into this hot air starts burning right away.

The Wankel engine

The newest kind of internal-combustion engine is called the *Wankel* [WAHNG-kuhl] engine. In a way, the Wankel engine is a kind of piston engine. But it does not have pistons that move back and forth inside cylinders. Instead, the Wankel engine has a triangle-shaped part called a *rotor* [ROHT-ur]. The rotor turns in a special combustion cham-

Find Out More

Use various references to learn about another kind of internal-combustion engine—the gas turbine. How are gas turbines like steam turbines? How are they different? What advantages do gas turbines have over piston engines? Are there disadvantages in using gas turbines? If so, what are they? What are some ways gas turbines are used today?

278

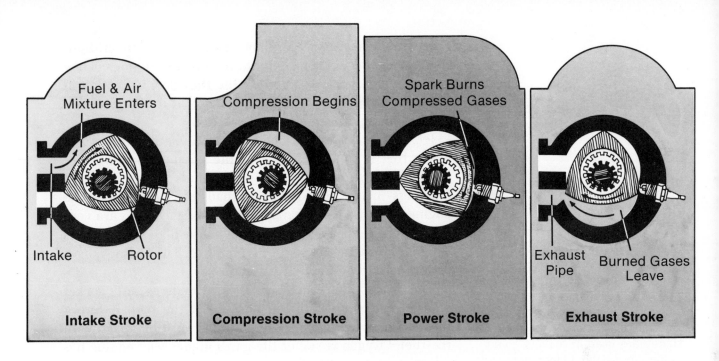

Figure 14–7. These diagrams show what happens inside a Wankel engine. How is the Wankel engine like a piston engine? How is it like a turbine?

ber. Because the rotor turns instead of moving back and forth, the Wankel engine is sometimes called a rotary engine. See Figure 14–7.

As a tip of the rotor passes the intake pipe opening, a mixture of fuel and air enters the chamber. The rotor keeps turning. Because of the shapes of the rotor and of the chamber, the space between the rotor and the chamber wall becomes smaller. This compresses the fuel and air. An electric spark starts the fuel burning. Gases from the burning fuel push on the rotor and keep it turning. In a way, this is like the power stroke of a piston engine. As the rotor turns, the tip passes the exhaust pipe opening. The turning rotor pushes the used gases through the opening. Then, the turning rotor passes the intake opening again, letting in more fuel and air. The cycle starts again.

Reaction engines

Have you ever heard of a reaction engine? Perhaps you don't think you have. Yet you see reaction engines in use every time you see a jet airplane or a rocket taking off. Both jet engines and rocket engines are reaction engines. They get this name because they use the third law of motion in doing work. This law of motion states that for every action there is an equal and opposite reaction.

Jet engines and rocket engines are alike in some ways. Their fuel is burned inside of the engines. So both are internal-combustion engines. Both kinds of engine have openings in one end for the exhaust gases to leave the engine. Because the exhaust gases of these engines are very hot, these gases leave the engine at a very high speed. Gases leaving the engine cause the action force. The engine moves forward as a reaction to this force.

The main difference between jet engines and rocket engines has to do with the burning of the fuel. Before a fuel will burn, *oxygen* [AHK-sih-juhn] must be mixed with the fuel. Oxygen is one of the gases in air. A jet engine has a large opening in the front of the engine. Air is pulled into the engine through this opening. The air supplies the oxygen needed to burn the fuel.

A rocket does not take in air to mix oxygen with the fuel. Instead, a rocket carries its own supply of oxygen. In some rockets, the oxygen is carried as liquid oxygen, or LOX. In others, the fuel is mixed with chemicals that give off oxygen as the fuel burns.

★ **Why are rocket engines used instead of jet engines for space travel?**

Find Out More

Rockets were first used thousands of years ago in China. What were they used for in those times? How are rockets used today? What kinds of fuels are used in rockets today? What is meant by the term "multistage" rocket? How many stages are used in rockets going to the moon? What kinds of rockets are being developed for use in the future?

DO IT YOURSELF

Use a balloon as a reaction engine

Fill a balloon with air. Hold one hand behind the opening of the balloon. Let go of the balloon. What do you feel in your hand? What happens to the balloon? Using one or more of the laws of motion, explain what you see and feel.

Bruce Anspach/Editorial Photocolor Archives, Inc.

The job of a mechanic is only one kind of job that has to do with engines. What other jobs involve working with engines?

Working with Engines

Today people need and use engines more than ever. In some jobs, such as truck driving, engines are used to move goods from one end of the country to the other. Since truck drivers often drive through places where there are few people, many truck drivers learn how to make simple repairs.

Many people work in jobs having to do with repairing engines and keeping them running properly. These people are called *mechanics* [mih-KAN-ihks]. Usually mechanics specialize—that is, they know more about one special kind of engine than they know about others. For example, some work only on automobile engines. Others work on airplane engines. There are also mechanics who are trained to repair truck engines, large factory engines, and the steam turbines in electric power plants. Some high schools have classes in automobile repair. But most mechanics have taken special classes to learn how to repair the kind of engine they work on.

There is always a need for more powerful and more efficient engines. Designing and improving engines is the job of a mechanical engineer. People who design new engines usually study this kind of engineering in college. Perhaps some day you will be one of the many people who work with engines.

Reviewing and Extending

SUMMING UP

1. If the fuel for an engine is burned outside the engine, the engine is an external-combustion engine.
2. If the fuel for an engine is burned inside the engine, the engine is an internal-combustion engine.
3. Before engines were invented, the energy to do work came from people, animals, wind, and moving water.
4. In a reciprocating steam engine, a piston is pushed back and forth inside a cylinder.
5. In steam turbines, the steam causes parts of the engine to have a turning motion.
6. Internal-combustion engines include gasoline-fueled piston engines, diesel piston engines, rotary engines, and reaction engines.
7. Piston engines may have either a two-stroke cycle or a four-stroke cycle.
8. Gasoline engines start fuel burning with an electric spark. Diesel engines use heat from compressed air to start fuel burning.
9. The Wankel engine has a continuously turning triangular-shaped rotor instead of pistons that move back and forth inside a cylinder.
10. Jet engines and rocket engines use the third law of motion to make airplanes and rockets move.

CHECKING UP

Vocabulary   Write the numerals *1–5* on your paper. Each numbered phrase describes a term from the following list. On your paper, write the term next to the numeral of the phrase that describes it.

internal-combustion	cylinder	piston
external-combustion	reciprocating	valve

1. type of engine in which the fuel is burned inside the engine
2. thick metal plate that moves back and forth
3. moving part that opens to let gases into or out of the engine
4. part inside of which a metal plate moves back and forth
5. back-and-forth motion

Knowledge and Understanding   Write the numerals *6–10* on your paper. Beside each numeral, write the word or words that best complete the sentence having that numeral.

6. Engines in which the fuel is burned outside the engine are _____ engines.

7. The force of expanding _____ was made to do useful work in the first engines that were invented.
8. The used gases leaving an engine are called _____.
9. When a gas is squeezed into a smaller space, the gas is said to be _____.
10. The moving parts have a turning motion in a steam _____.

Concepts   Beside each of the numerals *11–15* on your paper, write the word or words that best complete the sentence having that numeral.

11. Jet engines make airplanes fly because of the (*first, second, third*) law of motion.
12. Gases, such as steam, tend to (*become compressed, expand, do no work*).
13. Heat given off by compressed air is used to start fuel burning in a (*gasoline, Wankel, diesel*) engine.
14. In a reciprocating engine the piston has (*back-and-forth, turning, slow*) motion.
15. Wankel engines are sometimes called (*piston, turbine, rotary*) engines.

Application and Critical Thinking   Answer the following questions as briefly as you can without leaving out any important ideas.

16. How are a reciprocating steam engine and an automobile engine alike? How are they different?
17. In what ways do turbine engines differ from reciprocating engines? Which kind would be most useful in running wheel-like machines? Why do you think so?
18. How is a Wankel engine like a piston engine with a four-stroke cycle? How is it like a turbine engine?

DOING MORE

1. Take apart a small model airplane engine. Mount the parts on a board and label them. Draw a diagram to show how the parts fit together in the engine. What type of engine—internal-combustion or external-combustion—is this model airplane engine? How is the fuel burned to get energy?
2. Perhaps you have built a model of an automobile piston engine, a Wankel engine, or some other kind of engine from a kit. If so, bring your model engine to school and explain to the others in your class how this kind of engine operates.

Pros and Cons

Farmers today can grow more food than was ever possible before. One reason is that engines help do much of the hard work.

Engines—For Better or For Worse?

The first engine was invented about 300 years ago. Since then, the use of engines has caused many changes in the way people live. But have the changes been for the better or for the worse? If you think about some of these changes, you can probably think of many ways in which the use of engines has been helpful.

Today, with the help of engines (and several kinds of chemicals), a farmer can grow much more food than a farmer could years ago using only animals to help do the work. This is important because the number of people living in the world today keeps increasing. Engines also make it possible to ship goods much farther and faster than they could be shipped before the use of engines. People can go places much faster and more comfortably now than they could before engines were invented.

Engines and electricity made by using engines are used in factories to make work easier to do. Furthermore, engine-driven machines can make a large amount of goods in a short time. Therefore, many things cost far less than if they were made by a person using hand tools.

You have read about some good effects from using engines. But there have been some bad effects from using engines, too. For example, using engines causes several kinds of pollution. The exhaust gases contain several different chemicals. So far, no way has yet been found to keep all of these chemicals from getting into the air. Air pollution from engine exhausts has become a major problem in large cities because so many engines are found in a limited area.

Because more and more engines are being used, more and more land is being used for highways, streets, parking lots, and airports. In some places, this has been shown to be harmful to plants, animals, and even people living on nearby land. In fact, the building of an airport in Florida was halted because people were convinced that the airport would harm the environment of the region.

Another problem caused by engines is noise pollution. People who live or work near airports, busy highways, or factories are often affected by the amount of noise in these places.

Another harmful effect of using engines is that many people are badly hurt or killed in accidents resulting from the use of engines. In the United States alone, more than

What problems caused by the use of engines are shown here? What might be done to help solve these problems?

50,000 people are killed each year in automobile accidents. Others are hurt or killed in train accidents, in airplane crashes, and in factory accidents.

Indirectly, the use of engines causes oil spills that kill fish and ruin beaches. If there weren't so many engines in use, the need for oil would be much less. There would be no need to drill for oil in the oceans or to move oil across the oceans by ship.

The use of engines has good and bad effects. Do the good outweigh the bad? Should people keep using engines in spite of the bad effects? Or should the use of engines be limited in some way? Are there ways that the problems caused by using engines can be solved so that we can keep the good effects and get rid of the bad effects? How do you think people, such as yourself, will solve these problems in the future?

Investigate On Your Own

1. An easy way to estimate the mechanical advantage of pulleys is to count the number of ropes holding up the resistance. The part of the rope on each side of the pulley is counted as a separate rope. Draw diagrams of (a) one fixed pulley, (b) one movable pulley, (c) one fixed and one movable pulley together, and (d) two fixed and two movable pulleys together. Figure out the mechanical advantage of each of these pulley systems. Where fixed and movable pulleys are used together, does it matter whether the rope is fastened to the movable pulley or the fixed pulley?

Using real pulleys, set up each of the pulley systems you diagramed. Measure the distance the resistance moves and the distance the effort moves for each system. Calculate the mechanical advantage using the following formula:

$$\frac{\text{Effort Distance}}{\text{Resistance Distance}} = \text{Mechanical Advantage}$$

How does the calculated mechanical advantage of

the real pulleys compare to what you thought their mechanical advantages would be from the diagrams?

2. Find out what you can about the pollution caused by automobiles. Find answers to questions such as these: What pollutants do automobiles give off? How do the different kinds of pollution affect living things? Does pollution also affect nonliving things such as buildings and clothing? If so, how? What are considered safe levels for each kind of pollution? What is being done to reduce pollution in your state or city?

Read On Your Own

Ahnstrom, D. N., *The Complete Book of Jets and Rockets,* New York: The World Publishing Company, 1970.

The principles and uses of jet propulsion are discussed. This book also includes information on the requirements for becoming a jet pilot.

Butterworth, W. E., *Wheels and Pistons—The Story of the Automobile,* New York: Four Winds Press, A Division of Scholastic Magazine, Inc., 1971.

This book presents a lively, well-illustrated history of the automobile from the first steam-powered carriages to models now being developed.

Rosenfeld, Sam, *Science Experiments for the Space Age,* Irvington, New York: Harvey House, Inc., Publishers, 1972.

Many interesting and easy-to-do experiments on motion and energy conversions are described. There is also a discussion of each experiment and how it applies to space travel.

Woodburn, John H., *The Whole Earth Energy Crisis,* New York: G. P. Putnam's Sons, 1973.

Current problems concerning energy crises and why they occur are examined. The advantages and disadvantages of energy sources are discussed.

UNIT 4

Grant Heilman

ELECTRICITY

A Useful Kind of Energy

Have you ever wondered what your life would be like without electricity? Would you be able to control the temperature of your house? Would you be able to watch television? Would you be able to listen to a radio or to a record player? You might get some idea of how much you depend on electricity by making a list of all the electric devices that are used in homes. If you were to include in your list ways of using electricity outside the home, the list would be almost endless.

Chapters

CHAPTER 15

Charging with Electricity

Push your hands together and rub them back and forth rapidly. What do you feel? You probably feel heat. Rubbing causes a change. Your hands get warm. Rubbing can also cause other kinds of change. For example, did you ever slide across the seat of a car and then get a shock when you touched the door handle? The rubbing of your clothing on the seat as you slid across the seat caused a change. You became charged with electricity.

Becoming charged with electricity happens often in everyday life. You can get charged by walking across a carpet. But you can't tell you are charged until you touch someone or something else. A comb may become charged when you comb your hair. But you can't tell it is charged unless you hold it near something such as small bits of paper. Another example of electric charging is lightning. In a way, it is lucky that examples of charging happen so often. By studying these examples, a lot can be learned about that much-used form of energy called electricity.

A. Devaney, Inc.

Scientists can study some effects of lightning in the laboratory. What are some advantages of studying lightning in a laboratory? Do you think scientists ever try to study "real" lightning in a thunderstorm?

CHARGED OBJECTS

[1] In science, what is a property?
What causes some objects to become charged
*   with electricity when they are rubbed?*
[3] What is a conductor? An insulator?
[4] In electricity, what is a ground?

Charging a comb

Joan made a small pile of tiny pieces of paper. Then she held a plastic comb near the pieces of paper. Nothing happened.

Next, Joan looked carefully at her comb. Then she ran the comb through her hair several times. She looked carefully at the comb again. It looked the same as it did before. She again held the comb near the pieces of paper. The pieces of paper moved toward the comb. Some of them touched the comb and stayed on it. After a little while, these pieces of paper seemed to fly off the comb.

Running the plastic comb through Joan's hair gave the comb a *property* [PRAHP-urt-ee] it didn't have before. In science, a property is something special about a material that makes the material what it is. Just after a comb has been used, it has this property: It will pull tiny pieces of paper to it. That is, it will *attract* [uh-TRAKT] the paper. The pieces of paper stick to the comb for a while. Then, the comb will push away, or *repel* [rih-PEHL], some of them. The comb will do this because it has electric properties after being used. Whenever a comb or any other object has electric properties, it is said to be charged with electricity. Or, it is called a charged object.

Try doing what Joan did. But, before you start, you should know one thing: Experiments with charged objects work best when the air is dry.

A charging model

Why do some objects become charged? Why does the charged comb affect the pieces of paper the way it does?

Find Out More

Materials have many different kinds of properties. Being charged with electricity is a property a material may have. Using references, find out more about other kinds of properties. What properties seem to be common to all materials? What properties seem to vary from one material to another?

To answer questions like these, scientists have formed an interesting *model* [MAHD-uhl] of electricity.

Scientists often use models to explain what they see. In science, a model isn't just a small copy of some larger thing. Instead, a model is a way of explaining observations. The model used in explaining charging with electricity is partly described by the following list:

1. There are two different kinds of electric charges—*positive* [PAHZ-uht-ihv] and *negative* [NEHG-uht-ihv].
2. When an object has more positive than negative charges, it is positively charged. If it has more negative than positive charges, it is negatively charged. If it has equal numbers of positive and negative charges, it is *neutral* [N(Y)OO-truhl], or not charged.
3. Rubbing can cause negative charges to move from one solid object to another solid object. Positive charges do not move from one solid object to another.
4. Two negatively charged objects or two positively charged objects repel each other. But a negatively charged object and a positively charged object attract each other. Sometimes, this is stated as "like charges repel and unlike charges attract."
5. Materials in which negative charges move about easily are called conductors. Metals are good conductors. Materials in which negative charges do not move about easily are poor conductors, or *insulators* [IN(T)-suh-LAYT-urz]. Rubber is an insulator.

★ **A glass rod that is rubbed with silk becomes positively charged. According to the model, what happens to cause the glass rod to become positively charged?**

It's grounded

The model of electricity helps explain how rubbing can cause an object to become charged. But charged objects do not stay charged for very long. Can the model also explain how charged objects become neutral?

A neutral object has the same number of positive and negative charges. A negatively charged object has more

(*Text continues on page 294.*)

Investigate

How do charged objects behave?

You Will Need

plastic comb, glass rod, silk cloth, thread, 2 pith balls, 2 ring stands and rings

Background

You might be familiar with all the materials except the pith balls. Pith is the soft, spongy material found in certain plant stems. Because pith balls are very light in weight, they are noticeably affected by charged objects.

What to Do

Tie a piece of thread on a pith ball. Then tie the other end of the thread to the ring of a ring stand so that the pith ball hangs freely. Run the comb through your hair several times to charge the comb. Hold the charged comb near the pith ball. Observe and record what happens.

Tie a piece of thread to another pith ball and to another ring stand, and allow this pith ball to hang freely next to the first pith ball. The 2 pith balls should be at the same height and about 2 or 3 centimetres apart. Then run the comb through your hair several times again. Touch the charged comb to each of the pith balls. Observe and record how the pith balls affect each other. Then touch each pith ball with your finger. Observe and record what happens.

Run the comb through your hair once more. Have someone else rub the glass rod with the silk cloth. Touch one pith ball with the comb. Touch the other ball with the glass rod. Observe and record how the pith balls affect each other.

Now That You Have Done the Investigation

—When using 1 pith ball, what happened when the charged comb was brought near the suspended pith ball?

—When using 2 pith balls, what happened to the pith balls after each one had been touched with the charged comb? How did the balls behave after they were touched with your finger?

—How did the 2 pith balls behave when one was touched with the charged comb and the other with the charged glass rod?

—Would you say that the charged comb and the charged glass rod were both charged negatively? Why or why not?

negative than positive charges. To become neutral, it must either lose negative charges or gain positive charges. A positively charged object has more positive than negative charges. To become neutral, it must gain negative charges or lose positive charges.

According to the model, negative charges can move from one solid object to another. Positive charges cannot. Therefore, negative charges leave a negatively charged object when it becomes neutral. Negative charges come onto a positively charged object when it becomes neutral. But where do the negative charges go to or come from when an object that has been charged becomes neutral?

Negative charges often go to the earth or come from the earth when an object becomes neutral. The earth is so big and has so much matter that adding or taking away some negative charges makes hardly any change in its being neutral. It is like adding a drop of water to a bucket of water. No change is noticed.

In electricity, any object large enough to remain almost neutral when negative charges are added or taken away is called a ground. An object that is connected to the earth by means of a conductor is said to be grounded.

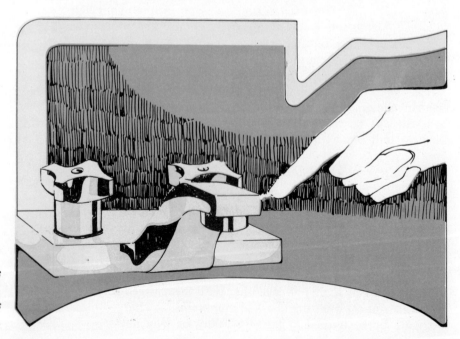

Figure 15–1. Has this ever happened to you? You touch a faucet, and a tiny spark jumps. Where did the charges that caused the spark come from? Where did they go? Is the faucet grounded? Explain.

THE ELECTROSCOPE

1 How do charged objects affect electroscopes?
2 Can an electroscope become charged by touching it with a charged object?
3 What happens when you touch your finger to a charged electroscope?

Is it charged?

You may have noticed that a comb or a glass rod looks no different after being charged than it did before. How, then, can you find out if an object is charged? One way is by means of a *leaf electroscope* [ih-LEHK-truh-sкoнp].

A glass jar may be used to make an electroscope. But the most important parts of the leaf electroscope are the charge collector and the leaves. The charge collector is a metal ball open to the air. The leaves are very thin sheets of metal foil which are inside the glass jar. The charge collector and the leaves are connected by a conducting rod which passes through the top of the jar.

DO IT YOURSELF

Make an electroscope

You will need a jar or a flask, a stopper to fit the jar or flask, a heavy copper wire, and some aluminum foil from a gum wrapper. Use these things to make an electroscope like the one at the left.

Push the wire through the stopper. Then make a loop at each end of the wire. One end will serve as the charge collector. The leaves will be at the other end. To make the leaves, separate the foil from its paper backing. Then cut a strip as shown in the diagram. The leaves are formed by hanging the narrow part of the strip over the wire loop. Then place the stopper in the jar so the leaves are inside. Be sure that no metal parts touch the glass. Now find out if your electroscope works by placing charged objects near the charge collector.

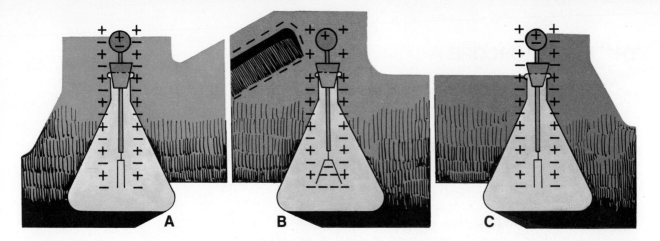

Figure 15–2. These diagrams show the effect of a negatively charged comb on a nearby electroscope. How would you describe what happens?

For You to Think About

What happens if you bring a charged comb near the hair on your arm? How would you explain what happens? Could you use the hair on your arm as a sort of electroscope to detect electrically charged objects?

Watch the leaves

The leaves of an electroscope usually hang straight down. This might be called the rest position. When a charged object is moved near the charge collector, the leaves move apart. If the charged object is then moved away without touching the charge collector, the leaves return to the rest position.

What happens to cause the leaves to move when a charged object is moved near the electroscope? Suppose the object is a negatively charged comb. Before the charged comb comes close to the electroscope, the electroscope has an equal number of positive charges and negative charges. The charges are spread out evenly through the whole electroscope, as in A of Figure 15–2.

But then the negatively charged comb is moved near the charge collector. Some negative charges in the electroscope are repelled by the negatively charged comb. They cannot get out of the electroscope, but they are pushed down to the leaves. Overall, the electroscope still has equal numbers of positive and negative charges. Each of the leaves, however, is negatively charged. So they repel each other and move apart, as in B.

When the comb is moved away, the charges become spread out evenly again. Then the leaves return to a rest position, as in C.

★ **When the negatively charged comb is near the electroscope, is the charge collector negatively charged or positively charged? Explain.**

Charge it negatively

When a negatively charged comb touches the charge collector, the leaves of the electroscope move apart. When the charged comb is moved away, the leaves remain apart.

What happens to cause the leaves to stay apart after the charged comb is moved away? See Figure 15–3. The leaves spread apart as the comb comes near, as in A. When the charged comb touches the charge collector, some of the excess negative charges in the comb move to the electroscope, as in B. The leaves stay apart even when the comb is moved away, as in C, because the whole electroscope is now negatively charged.

★ **Would an electroscope become charged if it were touched by a positively charged object? Explain.**

Spoil the charge

Suppose that you were to touch your finger to the charge collector of the electroscope when the leaves are apart. Would you receive a shock? Not at all. But something would happen. The leaves of the electroscope would return to a rest position. The leaves would remain in the rest position even after your finger was moved away.

Why would the leaves return to a rest position? The answer is that you would be acting as a ground. That is, you would receive the excess negative charges from a negatively charged electroscope so that the electroscope

(*Text continues on page 299.*)

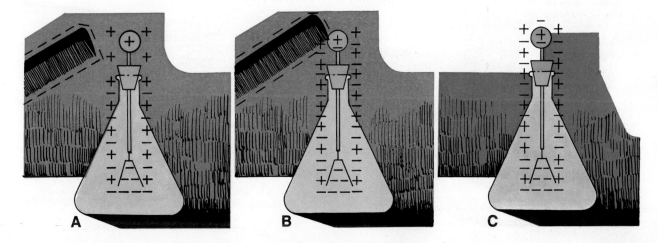

Figure 15–3. These diagrams show the effect of touching a negatively charged comb to an electroscope. How would you describe what happens?

A   B   C

Investigate

What are some effects of a charged object on an electroscope?

You Will Need

electroscope, comb

Background

Part of the investigation involves charging a comb by combing your hair. Then you use the charged comb to charge an electroscope in two different ways. As you do these things you can observe how a charged comb affects the charged electroscope.

What to Do

Charge the comb by running it through your hair. Bring the comb near an uncharged electroscope. Then move the comb away. Observe and record what happens to the electroscope.

Charge the comb as before. Touch it to the charge collector of the electroscope, and then move it away. Observe and record what, if anything, happens to the leaves. Bring the charged comb back to a position near, but not touching, the collector. Observe and record what happens. Touch the collector with your finger. Observe and record what happens.

Charge the comb as before. Hold the comb near, but not touching, the charge collector of the electroscope. While the charged comb is near the collector, touch the collector with your finger. Move your finger away. Then move the charged comb away. Observe and record what happens to the leaves of the electroscope. Then bring the charged comb close to the collector again. Observe and record what happens.

Now That You Have Done the Investigation

—Did bringing the charged comb near the electroscope affect the electroscope? Was any charge left on the electroscope when the charged comb was removed? How do you know?

—Did touching the electroscope with a charged comb affect the electroscope? Was any charge left on the electroscope? Was the charge on the electroscope the same as the charge on the comb? How do you know?

—Were you able to charge the electroscope by the second method? Was the charge on the electroscope the same as the charge on the comb? How do you know?

would become neutral. If the electroscope were positively charged, you would supply negative charges to it so that it would become neutral. However, the number of charges that would move between you and the electroscope would not be great enough to give you a shock.

VOLTAGE AND ELECTRIC ENERGY

What causes shocks and sparks?
What is the name for the "push" that causes negative charges to move?
3 What are two kinds of electrostatic generators?

What's voltage?

One way to understand what *voltage* [VOHL-tihj] means is to think about what happens when something becomes charged. Suppose you shuffled your feet along a wool or nylon rug on a dry day. You would become negatively charged. If you touched another person or a doorknob, you would feel a shock. Your might even see a spark.

The shock and the spark are caused by negative charges moving between you and whatever you touch. But what caused the negative charges to move? They must have been given some kind of "push."

When you shuffle your feet on a rug, negative charges move from the rug to you. Work must be done in order to move each negative charge from the rug to you. You do the work by shuffling your feet.

In doing the work to move the negative charges from the rug to you, you use *energy* [EHN-ur-jee]. Energy is the ability to do work. The energy you use goes to the negative charges. The negative charges, with the extra energy, are stored up on you. The amount of energy stored up is equal to the amount of work done in moving the negative charges onto you. This energy is the "push" that can cause negative charges to move. That "push" is sometimes called voltage.

★ **Would electric sparks from an object be more likely to happen on a dry or on a wet day? Why?**

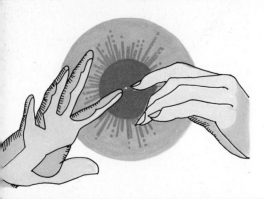

DO IT YOURSELF

Produce a voltage

With another person, go someplace where there is a carpet on the floor. Shuffle your feet as you walk across the carpet. Then touch the hand of the other person. Did both of you get a shock? If so, you must have produced a voltage to cause the shock. If only you were charged, why did you both get a shock?

Machines for charging

Shuffling on a rug, using a comb, or rubbing a glass rod are not the only ways to charge objects, or produce voltages. Machines called *electrostatic generators* [ih-LEHK-truh-STAT-ihk JEHN-uh-RAYT-urz] have been in use for many years. Some of these machines can produce high voltages and very large sparks.

The kind of electrostatic generator used in some schools is called a Wimshurst machine. See Figure 15–4. When you turn the crank on the Wimshurst machine, a movable disk turns next to another disk and rubs against some flexible metal strips. Because of friction, a high voltage is built up as the wheel turns.

Courtesy of Museum of Science and Industry, Chicago

Figure 15–4. This large Wimshurst machine is on display in a museum. Perhaps your school has a smaller model of this machine. How are machines like this used to study electricity?

Wide World Photos

Figure 15–5. An early model of a Van de Graaff generator is shown at the left. The newer model at the right was built to help scientists study the atomic nature of matter.

Courtesy of Brookhaven National Laboratory

Another kind of electrostatic generator is the Van de Graaff generator. See Figure 15–5. This kind of generator was invented more recently than the Wimshurst machine. With this kind of generator, very great voltages can be produced. In fact, sparks that look like lightning can be produced with it.

LIGHTNING AND ELECTRICITY

What did Benjamin Franklin learn by flying a kite in a thunderstorm?

Who invented the first lightning rod?

In what two ways do lightning rods protect buildings?

A shocking experiment

Most people are fascinated by lightning. Sometimes lightning is spectacular and very beautiful. But many people are afraid of lightning. There is good reason for them to be afraid of lightning. Lightning is dangerous. People can be killed or seriously injured by lightning. It can also do a lot of damage to buildings and trees.

One famous American decided to find out more about lightning. This person was Benjamin Franklin. During many experiments with electricity, Franklin had noticed that lightning looked like a big electric spark. He wondered if lightning had something to do with electricity. He decided to try to find out by doing an experiment.

The experiment may seem a little strange. Here's how the experiment was described in a letter to a friend: Fly a kite during a thunderstorm. A piece of wire should be attached to the upper part of the kite. On the string near the person's hand, a silk ribbon with a key attached should be tied. In order to keep the silk ribbon and the key dry, the person who holds the string must stand under some sort of cover. See Figure 15–6.

While Franklin's kite was in the cloud, the wire and the kite string allowed electricity in the cloud to travel down to the key. Franklin described the strands of the string as standing out and being attracted by his finger as he moved it near the string. But then the electricity jumped over to Franklin! He was lucky he wasn't killed.

★ **How did the kite-flying experiment show that lightning and electricity are related?**

Figure 15–6. What did Franklin hope to learn from his famous kite experiment?

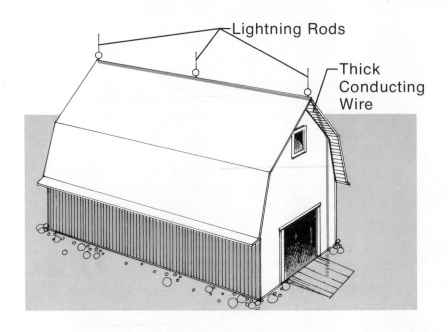

Lightning Rods

Thick Conducting Wire

Figure 15–7. Are the lightning rods on this building grounded? How can you tell?

Controlled lightning

From the kite experiment and other studies, Franklin had some understanding of electricity. For example, he had studied charged objects that were round and smooth. He had also studied charged objects with sharp edges and corners. Charged objects with sharp edges and corners became neutral faster than charged objects that were round and smooth.

Franklin used this knowledge about electricity to design the first lightning rod. The lightning rod was not designed by guesswork. The design was based on the way electric charges behave.

The lightning rod was designed to have a sharp point. In fact, some rods had more than one point. The rod was mounted on the top of a building and connected to the earth with a conducting wire. See Figure 15–7. Charges could move up the wire and easily escape from the pointed rod into the air. Charges could also move from the air to the rod and then to the earth.

★ **How would you explain why lightning rods have points, rather than smooth, rounded knobs, on the end?**

Photos from Artstreet

Figure 15–8. Lightning can cause severe damage when it strikes a building. Are these buildings likely to be damaged by lightning? Explain.

How does it work?

A lightning rod does two things. First, it reduces the chance of lightning striking the building it is protecting. Second, it reduces the chance that the building will be damaged by lightning if lightning does strike.

How does a lightning rod reduce the chances of lightning striking and damaging a building? Remember that the lightning rod has one or more sharp points, and that it is connected to the ground by a wire. The points allow charges to leak into the air. The wire allows charges to move between the rod and the ground. Therefore, lightning is less likely to strike because a very high voltage does not build up.

If lightning does strike, it strikes the rod, not the building. The electricity travels through the conducting wire to the ground. In this way, lightning does not damage the building or things inside the building.

Find Out More

Benjamin Franklin was one of the most important scientists that ever lived. Using references, find out more about Franklin's life, discoveries, and inventions. Discuss each discovery and invention with other members of your class. Which discovery do you think was the most important? Which invention? Why?

Lightning—Something to Think About

Many people are interested in how lightning behaves. Some people are simply curious. But did you ever stop to think that knowing about lightning is important in many kinds of work?

You probably know what a *meteorologist* [MEET-ee-uh-RAHL-uh-juhst] is. A meteorologist is a person who studies weather. Lightning is an important part of the weather. Meteorologists, then, are interested in learning about lightning. But what other kinds of workers are interested in knowing about lightning?

Some people who work for the U.S. Forest Service are very interested in lightning. They want to learn about lightning so they can try to control it. In fact, the Forest Service has been trying to conrol lightning for many years. After all, lightning causes many forest fires. If the amount of lightning can be reduced, so can the number of forest fires.

People who design and build high structures and people who manufacture electrical equipment, such as transformers, to be used outdoors are interested in how lightning behaves. They do not want lightning to damage whatever they have built. So they must build in some means of lightning protection. To do this, they must know about lightning.

Before long, you will be preparing for a career of some kind. Maybe you already are. Do you think that knowing about lightning will be useful in the career you choose?

Radar and pictures from orbiting satellites are two tools meteorologists use to study weather. How is lightning related to the work of meteorologists?

Reviewing and Extending

SUMMING UP

1. Sometimes an object has electric properties, or is charged with electricity, after being rubbed.
2. There are two kinds of electric charges—positive and negative.
3. An object may be positively charged (have excess positive charges), negatively charged (have excess negative charges), or neutral (have equal numbers of positive and negative charges).
4. Rubbing can cause negative charges to move from one solid object to another.
5. Like charges repel and unlike charges attract.
6. In a conductor, negative charges move about easily.
7. Grounded means connected to the earth by means of a conductor.
8. Electroscopes can be used to tell whether or not an object is charged.
9. The "push" that can cause negative charges to move is called voltage.
10. Some knowledge of lightning and of charged objects enabled Franklin to design a lightning rod that worked.

CHECKING UP

Vocabulary   Write the numbers *1–5* on your paper. Each numbered phrase describes a term from the following list. On your paper, write the term next to the numeral of the phrase that describes it.

5 attract	4 property	2 insulator
3 repel	1 voltage	conductor

1. "push" that moves negative charges
2. material in which negative charges do not move about easily
3. word that means to push away
4. something special about a material that makes the material what it is
5. word that means to pull things to itself

Knowledge and Understanding   Write the numerals *6–11* on your paper. Beside each numeral, write the word or words that best complete the sentence having that numeral.

6. The person who experimented with lightning and invented the lightning rod was (*Van de Graaff, Wimshurst, Franklin*).
7. When the leaves of an electroscope are not charged, they are (*spread apart, in a rest position, good insulators*).

306

8. A positively charged object and a negatively charged object will (*attract, repel, not affect*) each other.
9. Lightning is a big electric _____ . spark
10. The way a charged comb behaves is due to its _____ properties.
11. In science, a _model_ is a way of explaining observations, rather than just being a small copy of some larger thing.

Concepts   Beside each of the numerals *12–16* on your paper, write the word or words that best complete the sentence having that numeral.

12. An object having more positive charges than negative charges is (*positively charged, negatively charged, neutral*).
13. A (*smooth, rough, pointed*) object will remain charged for a longer period of time than any other object.
14. To become neutral, positively charged objects must (*gain, lose, keep the same number of*) negative charges.
15. Because the earth is so big, negative charges can be moved to or taken from the earth, and it will stay (*neutral, charged positively, charged negatively*).
16. If two pith balls are charged positively, the pith balls will (*attract, repel, not affect*) each other.

Application and Critical Thinking   Answer the following questions as briefly as you can without leaving out any important ideas.

17. Is it possible for the leaves of an electroscope to be spread apart even though, overall, the electroscope has the same number of positive charges and negative charges? Explain.
18. One day a class did some experiments with charging that were successful. The next day the same experiments were not successful. What might have caused the lack of success?

DOING MORE

1. Turn on the water faucet so that a small, steady stream flows from it. Move a charged comb slowly toward the stream of water. Explain what you see.
2. The Empire State Building, like many other skyscrapers, has been struck by lightning hundreds of times. But lightning has not damaged it. Prepare a report explaining (1) why the Empire State Building is struck so often, (2) why the people inside are not hurt when lightning strikes the building, and (3) why the building is not damaged when lightning strikes.

CHAPTER **16**

Electric Currents and Circuits

How many times a day do you use electricity? Turn a knob, and a radio or television starts to play. Flip a switch, and an electric light or perhaps a fan is turned on. You use electricity every day. And you use it a lot. But the electricity you use every day is somehow different from the electricity you studied in the last chapter. The electric charges you studied in the last chapter did not move around very much. In our everyday uses of electricity, negative electric charges move through wires. The movement of negative charges in a wire is called an electric *current* [KUR-uhnt]. The wire, or the path the current follows, is called a *circuit* [SUR-kuht].

Electric currents and circuits are what this chapter is all about. Maybe knowing more about electric currents and circuits will help you understand a little more about the world around you. You might even like to have a job that involves working with electricity.

What are towers and wires like those in the left-hand picture used for? Is a lot of electricity being used in the city shown at the right? How do you know?

Artstreet

Artstreet

SIMPLE CIRCUITS

*What may be used to keep a current moving in
   a circuit?*
What is measured with a voltmeter? An ammeter?
*How can you find out the amounts of resistance
   and power in an electric circuit?*

A model

The light that comes from light bulbs is caused by an
electric current in a wire. You can see the light. But you
cannot see the electric current in the wire. In order to
study something that cannot be seen, scientists sometimes
use a model.

One way to better understand electric currents is to
use a water model. In other words, the way an electric
current, which we cannot see, behaves is compared with
the way water, which we can see, behaves.

Think about the water behind a dam. The water is not
moving. It is not doing any work. It could do work, but
as long as it is behind the dam its ability to do work—
that is, its energy—is just being stored. When the stored
water begins moving, it can do work. It might turn a
waterwheel or wash out a bridge. Then the stored energy
of the water becomes moving energy.

The excess negative charges on a negatively charged
object are like the water behind the dam. The negative
charges have some energy, but the energy is just being
stored. If the charges were moving, they would form an
electric current. They could do useful work. But how can
negative charges be made to move?

Negative charges move if there is (1) a path, or circuit,
for the charges to follow and (2) an excess of negative
charges in one part of the circuit and a shortage in another part.

To better understand how negative charges are made
to move, think about water again. Suppose you have two
empty water tanks that are connected by a pipe near the
bottom of the tanks. There is a valve in the pipe. Now
suppose that the valve is closed and that one tank is filled

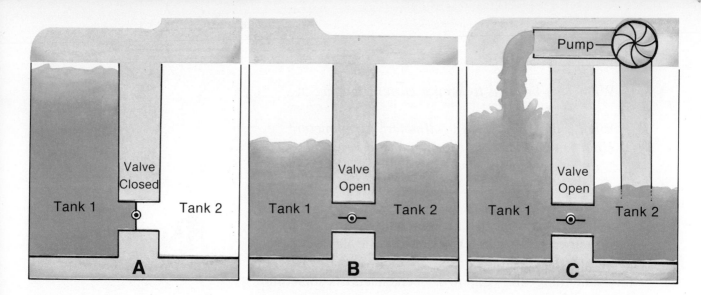

Figure 16–1. When will water stop flowing through the valve in B? In C? Why doesn't Tank 2 fill up in C?

with water. This tank has an "excess" of water. See A of Figure 16–1. What do you suppose will happen when the valve is opened? Will all the water flow from *Tank 1* to *Tank 2?* See B of Figure 16–1.

Now suppose we change one part of the example, but leave everything else the same. *Tank 1* has an excess of water and the valve is open. But now there is a pump in *Tank 2.* The pump is used to move water from *Tank 2* back into *Tank 1.* The water is pumped out of *Tank 2* just as fast as it flows in. See C of Figure 16–1. By using the pump, an excess of water can be kept in *Tank 1.*

Now, use the water model to help you think about how negative charges move. Two charged objects—one with an excess of negative charges and one with a shortage—can be connected by a conductor and a switch. The conductor is like the pipe in the water model. The switch is like the valve. When the switch is closed, negative charges move from one object to the other until the excess and the shortage no longer exist. This takes only a very short time. See Figure 16–2.

Keep it moving

What could be done to keep negative charges moving between the two charged objects? Remember how the water was made to keep flowing? A pump was used to put water back as fast as it flowed out. What is needed

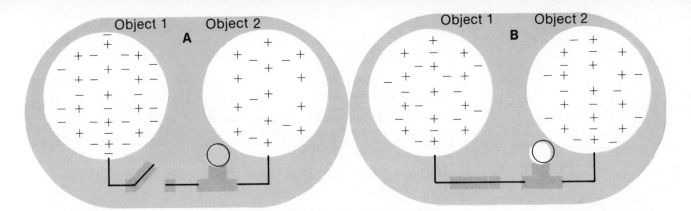

Object 1   Object 2   **A**

Object 1   Object 2   **B**

to keep negative charges moving is some sort of "pump" for negative charges.

One kind of "pump" that does this is called a dry cell. One important point to remember is that the posts of a cell are similar to the charged objects. The post marked + is positively charged. That is, it has a shortage of negative charges. The post marked — is negatively charged. It has an excess of negative charges. However, the cell is different from the two charged objects in a very important way. In the cell, when the negative charges move from the negative post through the wire to the positive post, something in the cell "pumps" the charges through the cell and back to the negative post. This keeps the negative post negatively charged. The cell can keep negative charges moving in a circuit for a long time. See Figure 16–3.

★ **Would the bulb in Figure 16–3 light up if the wires were interchanged? If both wires were connected to the same post? Explain.**

Figure 16–2. How is the object with excess negative charges like Tank 1 of Figure 16–1? What happens when the switch is closed? How would you compare B of this diagram with B of Figure 16–1?

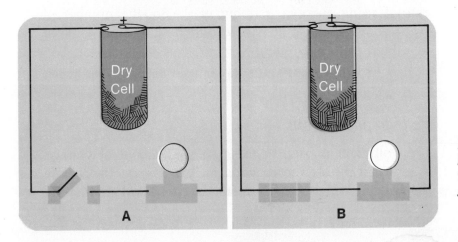

Dry Cell

Dry Cell

A   B

Figure 16–3. In this setup, charges keep flowing through the circuit. The bulb stays lighted. How is this setup like C of Figure 16–1?

How much?

You already have some understanding of electric circuits. You know that when an electric current is in a circuit, the negative charges move as if they are being pushed by some kind of "pump." You might also know that some things allow fewer charges to move than others. Or, you might say that these things offer more *resistance* [rih-ZIHS-tuhn(t)s] than others. For example, a light bulb offers more resistance to a flow of negative charges than the wire in the circuit.

In order to better understand circuits, it is important to know how much "push" the negative charges in a circuit have. It is also important to know how much current there is and to know how much resistance there is to the current. For these reasons, you need to measure electric currents and circuits in several different ways.

You may not have heard of the terms used in measuring electric currents. The term "volt" is used in describing the amount of "push" the negative charges have. Probably the voltage in your home is about 120 volts.

The term used in describing an amount of current is *ampere* [AM-PIH(UH)R]. This is sometimes shortened to amp. The amount of current a toaster uses is about five amps.

In describing resistance, *ohm* [OHM] is the term that is used. The light bulb in a flashlight causes a resistance of about twelve ohms.

Another term which is important is *watt* [WAHT]. A watt is a certain amount of electric power. Power is the rate of using energy, or doing work. So, the number of watts shows the rate at which something such as a motor or a light bulb uses energy.

★ **How many watts do the light bulbs in your home use?**

Voltage and current

A voltmeter is used to measure the amount of voltage in a circuit. Study the drawing in *A* of Figure 16–4. Note the way in which the voltmeter is connected in the circuit. The voltmeter must be connected that way because it offers a great deal of resistance to the current. Thus, the wires from the voltmeter must be connected one on each side of the light bulb. When the wires are connected this way, most of the current moves through the bulb. Notice, too, that the positive side of the voltmeter is connected by the wire in the circuit to the positive side of the cell.

An ammeter is used to measure the current in a circuit. Look at *B* of Figure 16–4. Note that the ammeter is not connected the way the voltmeter is connected. An ammeter must be connected so that all the current going through the ammeter also goes through the part of the circuit that is being studied. It must be connected like this because it has very little resistance to the current. When connected the right way, an ammeter causes very little change in the current in a circuit.

Resistance and power

As you have read, the resistance in an electric circuit is measured in ohms. To find out how many ohms of resistance are in a circuit, you must first know the amperage and the voltage in that circuit. You can measure amperage and voltage at the same time. Connect the ammeter and the voltmeter as shown in *C* of Figure 16–4.

Once the amperage and the voltage have been measured, the resistance may be found by using division. You simply divide the measure of the voltage by the measure of the amperage, as in the following formula:

$$\text{Voltage} \div \text{Amperage} = \text{Resistance (in ohms)}$$

For You to Think About

An ammeter has very little resistance. A voltmeter has a lot of resistance. Yet when they are connected properly in a circuit, the amount of current flowing in the circuit is not affected very much. Does the fact that each is connected in a different way cause the current to be unchanged? Explain.

Figure 16–4. Does all the current that goes through the light bulb also go through the voltmeter? Does it all go through the ammeter?

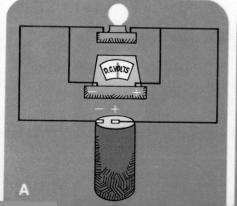

A

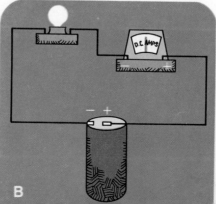

B

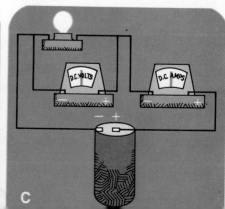

C

The power, or rate of doing work, in an electric circuit is measured in watts. A watt is the rate at which work is done when the current is one ampere and the voltage is one volt. So, to find the wattage being used in a circuit, you simply multiply the measure of the voltage times the measure of the current, as in the following formula:

$$\text{Voltage} \times \text{Amperage} = \text{Power (in watts)}$$

★ Suppose a toaster uses 5 amperes of current at 120 volts. What is the resistance offered by the toaster? How many watts of power does it use?

DO IT YOURSELF

Connect a voltmeter and an ammeter in a simple circuit

Use number 18 bell wire to connect a dry cell, bulb and socket, switch, direct-current ammeter, and direct-current voltmeter as shown in the diagram. The meters must be the kind that are used only in direct-current circuits. You will read about this kind of circuit later in this chapter. Now close the switch. Do you have a complete circuit? How do you know? What is the voltage of the dry cell? What is the amperage in the circuit? What is the resistance in the circuit?

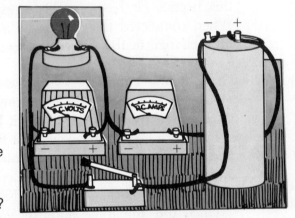

SERIES AND PARALLEL

How does a series circuit differ from a parallel circuit?

How is the total resistance in a circuit changed by adding light bulbs in series? In parallel?

How is the total voltage in a circuit changed by adding cells in series? In parallel?

Bulbs in series

Suppose you set up a circuit containing a cell, an ammeter, and a light bulb. You would probably set up the circuit as shown in A of Figure 16–5. Now suppose you

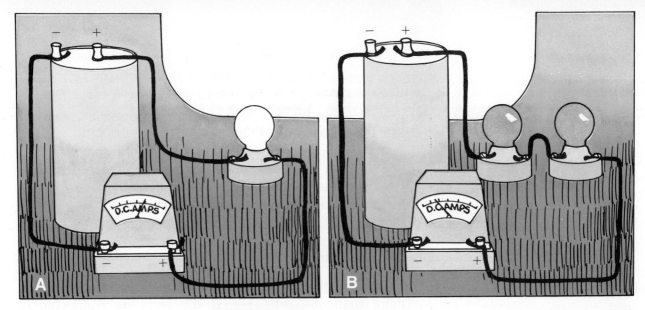

Figure 16–5. How does the amount of current in a circuit change as light bulbs are added in series to that circuit?

added another bulb just like the first one to the circuit. And you put it in the circuit as in B of Figure 16–5. Notice that all the current that goes through one bulb also goes through the other. The bulbs are said to be in *series* [SIH(UH)R-eez].

The two bulbs in B would be equally bright. But they would not be as bright as the one bulb in A. You can understand why if you trace the current in each circuit. In B, all the current that goes through one bulb must also go through the other. Thus, the bulbs have the same brightness.

But why are the bulbs in B dimmer than the one in A? Look at the ammeter reading in each circuit. More current is in A than in B. In fact, the current in A is twice the current in B. The greater amount of current is causing the bulb in A to be brighter than those in B. What could be causing the difference in the amount of current?

Each of the circuits in A and B has only one cell to supply voltage. So the voltage is the same—1.5 volts—in each circuit. But the current is twice as great in A as in B. For example, the meter might read 0.1 amp in A and 0.05 amp in B.

Put these values in the formula for resistance.

Voltage ÷ Amperage = Resistance

For the circuit in *A*, the resistance is fifteen ohms.

1.5 volts ÷ 0.1 amp = 15 ohms

For the circuit in *B*, the resistance is thirty ohms.

1.5 volts ÷ 0.05 amp = 30 ohms

According to the formula, then, the resistance in *B* is twice as great as in *A*. Thus, when light bulbs are placed in series, the total resistance is equal to the sum of the separate resistances.

Cells in series

Can the voltage in a circuit be made greater by using more than one cell? Yes, if the cells are connected in series. To connect cells in series, connect the positive post of one cell to the negative post of another. See Figure 16–6. When cells are in series, the total voltage is equal to the sum of the voltages.

For You to Think About

Suppose several lights were connected in series, and one light burned out. Would all the lights go out? If so, how would you find out which bulb had burned out?

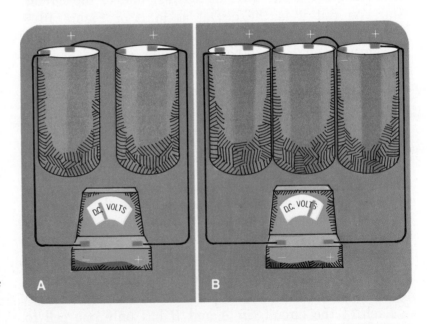

Figure 16–6. In this diagram, dry cells are connected in series to form a battery. How does the voltage of the battery compare with the voltage of each individual cell?

When cells are connected together, the combination is called a battery. A good example of a battery can be seen in a car. Each cell in a car's battery produces about two volts. Since the cells are connected in series, the total

(*Text continues on page 318.*)

Investigate

How does connecting bulbs and cells in series affect the current in a circuit? How does it affect the voltage?

You Will Need

direct-current ammeter, direct-current voltmeter, number 18 bell wire, three 1.5-volt dry cells, three 1.5-volt light bulbs and sockets

Background

This investigation involves connecting bulbs in series to study the effect of current in a circuit. It also involves connecting cells in series to study the effect of voltage in a circuit.

What to Do

Set up a circuit like the one in A of Figure 16–5. Record the readings of the ammeter and the voltmeter. Observe the brightness of the bulb so you can compare its brightness with that of the bulbs in the next 2 tests.

Add a second bulb, as in B of Figure 16–5. Record the readings of the ammeter and the voltmeter. Observe the brightness of the bulbs.

Then add a third bulb in series. Record the readings of the meters and observe the brightness of the bulbs.

Now connect a voltmeter to the posts of one dry cell. See the diagram. Record the reading of the voltmeter.

Connect 2 cells in series and record the voltage. Then connect a third cell in series and record the voltage.

Now That You Have Done the Investigation

—How did increasing the number of bulbs in a series circuit affect the current in the circuit?

—How did increasing the number of bulbs in a series circuit affect the voltage in the circuit?

—How did increasing the number of bulbs in a series circuit affect the brightness of the bulbs?

—How did increasing the number of cells in a series circuit affect the voltage in the circuit?

voltage of the battery is equal to the number of cells multiplied by two, the voltage of each cell.

★ **Today, most car batteries are 12-volt batteries. If each cell in these batteries produces 2 volts, how many cells are needed in each battery to produce the 12 volts?**

Bulbs in parallel

Suppose that you have just set up a circuit containing a cell, an ammeter, and a light bulb. The circuit would probably be like the circuit shown in *A* of Figure 16–7. A second light bulb could be added as shown in *B* of Figure 16–7. Notice that this circuit is a little different from the one in *B* of Figure 16–5. There is more than one path for the current to follow in this circuit. That is, current can go through either bulb without going through the other. Such a circuit is called a parallel circuit. The bulbs are said to be connected in parallel.

The two bulbs in *B* would be equally bright, and they would be as bright as the single bulb in *A*. Compare the ammeter readings in *A* and *B* to learn why the bulbs are equal in brightness.

Figure 16–7. How does the amount of current in a circuit change as light bulbs are added in parallel to that circuit?

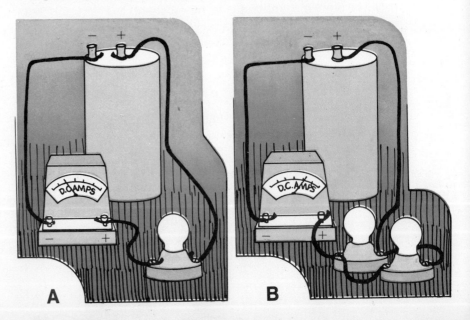

A   B

The ammeter readings show that twice as much current is in B as in A. But in B, the current has two paths to follow. So the current is divided equally between the two paths. Each of the bulbs in B, then, has the same amount of current as the one bulb in A. That is why the bulbs are all equally bright.

Do you know what would happen if more bulbs were added to the circuit in parallel with the first two bulbs? The circuit still has only one cell, so the voltage in the circuit would be the same—1.5 volts. However, the current in the circuit with three bulbs would be greater than that of the circuit having the two bulbs. Look at the formula for resistance.

$$\text{Voltage} \div \text{Amperage} = \text{Resistance}$$

According to the formula, in the circuit with one bulb, the resistance is fifteen ohms.

$$1.5 \text{ volts} \div 0.1 \text{ amp} = 15 \text{ ohms}$$

For two bulbs, the current is twice as great. According to the formula, the resistance is half as much as in the circuit having only one bulb.

$$1.5 \text{ volts} \div 0.2 \text{ amp} = 7.5 \text{ ohms}$$

For three bulbs, the current would be three times as great as with one bulb. The resistance, then, is one-third that of the circuit having only one bulb.

$$1.5 \text{ volts} \div 0.3 \text{ amp} = 5 \text{ ohms}$$

Thus, when light bulbs are placed in parallel, the total resistance of the circuit becomes less. That is because the current has more paths to follow. So, the current becomes greater.

Cells in parallel

Suppose a dry cell had to supply electricity to ten light bulbs connected in parallel. The cell would use up its power quickly because ten light bulbs use a lot of current. Is there any way to keep a dry cell from using up its power quickly when a lot of current is being used?

Connecting other dry cells in parallel with the one cell is a way to keep the cell from using up its power quickly. How are cells connected in parallel? Simply connect all

(*Text continues on page 321.*)

Investigate

How does connecting bulbs and cells in parallel affect the current in a circuit? How does it affect the voltage?

You Will Need

direct-current ammeter, direct-current voltmeter, number 18 bell wire, three 1.5-volt dry cells, three 1.5-volt light bulbs and sockets

Background

This investigation involves connecting bulbs in parallel to study the effect of current in a circuit. It also involves connecting cells in parallel to study the effect of voltage in a circuit.

What to Do

Set up a circuit like the one in A of Figure 16–7. Record the readings of the meters. Observe the brightness of the bulb so you can compare its brightness with that of the bulbs in the next 2 tests.

Add a second bulb, as in B of Figure 16–7. Record the readings of the meters and observe the brightness of the bulbs.

Now add a third bulb in parallel. Record the readings of the meters and observe the brightness of the bulbs.

Now connect a voltmeter to the posts of one dry cell. See the diagram. Record the reading of the voltmeter.

Connect 2 cells in parallel and record the reading of the voltmeter.

Connect 3 cells in parallel and record the reading of the voltmeter.

Now That You Have Done the Investigation

—How did increasing the number of bulbs in a parallel circuit affect the current in the circuit?

—How did increasing the number of bulbs in a parallel circuit affect the voltage in the circuit?

—How did increasing the number of bulbs in a parallel circuit affect the brightness of the bulbs?

—How did increasing the number of cells in a parallel circuit affect the voltage in the circuit?

Figure 16–8. In this diagram, dry cells are connected in parallel to form a battery. How does the voltage of the battery compare with the voltage of each individual cell?

the negative posts to one another. Also, connect all the positive posts to one another. See Figure 16–8.

When cells or batteries are connected in parallel, the voltage is the same as that from one cell or one battery. The advantage of having cells or batteries in parallel is that electric current can be supplied for a longer time.

★ **Look at B of Figure 16–7. Suppose that another dry cell is added in parallel with the one already in the circuit. How might this affect the length of time current is in the light bulbs? Explain.**

DIRECT AND ALTERNATING CURRENT

How does direct current differ from alternating current?

Which is most widely used in homes, businesses, and factories today, a. c. or d. c.? Why?

Direct current

Each of the circuits described so far has had a cell or a battery as its source of voltage. The negative charges in these kinds of circuits always go in the same direction. They go from the negative post of the cell to the positive post of the cell. Such a current is called direct current. The abbreviation d. c. is sometimes used.

Why do the negative charges in direct current always go in the same direction? One post of a cell or battery is always positive. The other post is always negative. Therefore, in a circuit containing a cell or a battery, the negative charges always go in the same direction.

Cells and batteries produce direct current. Some generators, or machines used to produce electric current, also produce direct current. The first power plants that made electricity for public use were planned and built to make direct current. However, today another kind of current is widely used.

Courtesy of Commonwealth Edison

Figure 16–9. At the left is a generator that was used many years ago. At the right is one that is used today. How are they different? How are they alike?

Courtesy of Tennessee Valley Authority

While these first power plants were being built, an inventor named Nikola Tesla was working with a different kind of electric current. Tesla was able to show that this current could be sent through wires for long distances.

Figure 16–10. Nikola Tesla, shown here in his laboratory, was one of the first people to suggest using alternating current instead of direct current. What are some advantages of alternating current?

Also it could be sent more safely and for less money than direct current. For these reasons, this different kind of current became widely used.

Alternating current

How is the kind of current that is widely used today different from direct current? The difference is in the way the current is made. The kind of generators used today do not have one post that is always positive and one that is always negative. Instead, each post changes from positive to negative very rapidly. When one post is positive, the other is negative.

Since first one post and then the other is negative, the negative charges move first in one direction and then in the other. This kind of current is called alternating current. The abbreviation a. c. is sometimes used.

★ **Does a flashlight use direct current or alternating current?**

An advantage of a. c.

The electricity used in your home and school is most likely alternating current. One reason that this kind of current has become widely used is that the voltage of alternating-current electricity can be changed easily by using a *transformer* [tran(t)s-FAWR-mur].

Figure 16–11. Transformers are necessary to decrease the voltage in power lines. They are familiar sights along streets near homes and factories. Where is the transformer near your home?

Alternating-current electricity can be changed easily from one voltage to another by using transformers. For example, in factories, there may be some 480-volt circuits. In homes, there may be both 120-volt and 240-volt circuits. Because the voltage of alternating-current electricity can be changed easily, one generator can supply electricity to all these circuits.

What if several different voltages of direct-current electricity were needed? The electricity from a direct-current generator is not changed easily from one voltage to another. There would have to be a separate generator for each voltage needed.

★ **Does your home have 120-volt circuits? Does it also have 240-volt circuits? Why do some homes need both 120-volt and 240-volt circuits?**

DO IT YOURSELF

Visit a power company

Visit the power company in your community. Find out the voltage of the electricity coming into your community. Ask to see different transformers. Find answers to questions such as these: Where are the transformers located that decrease the voltage before it is used in homes? Why are transformers of different sizes? Why must some transformers be cooled?

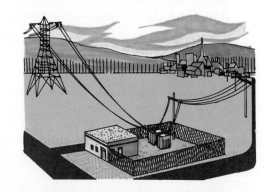

Courtesy of Commonwealth Edison

Repairing and replacing transformers is only one of many kinds of jobs done by the men and women who work for a power company.

Who Repairs Transformers?

My name is Cooper. I work for the power company. I'm in the department that takes care of the transformers. They need to be repaired once in a while, and that's my job. I repair transformers that do not work properly. Sometimes I take them back to the shop to be repaired.

I first became interested in electricity when I was in high school. That's when I tried to fix my mother's electric iron. When I had a question about how to fix it, I went to see my science teacher. She helped me learn a lot about electricity.

After I graduated from high school, I got a job with the power company. They sent me to classes where I learned more about electricity. I studied about motors, types of wire, circuit breakers, and other things as well. After my training classes, I worked as a helper with a crew. As a helper, I was being trained as I worked. I learned a lot about electricity from my boss. Now I am a crew leader and I am in charge of two other workers. They help me with my job.

The power company hires many men and women to make and repair electric equipment. Perhaps someday you might like to work for the power company, too.

Reviewing and Extending

SUMMING UP

1. The movement of negative charges in a wire is an electric current. A current must have a path, or circuit, to follow.
2. A cell is a sort of "pump" that keeps negative charges moving through a circuit.
3. Some terms used in describing currents and circuits are volt (force that pushes negative charges), ampere (amount of current), ohm (resistance), and watt (electric power).
4. Voltmeters have high resistance and are connected in parallel. Ammeters have low resistance and are connected in series.
5. Resistance and power can be determined if the voltage and the amperage are known.
6. In a series circuit there is only one path for the current to follow.
7. In a parallel circuit there is more than one path for the current to follow.
8. Putting cells in series increases voltage. Putting cells in parallel increases the length of time current can be used.
9. The voltage of alternating current can be changed easily by using a transformer.

CHECKING UP

Vocabulary Write the numerals *1–5* on your paper. Each numbered phrase describes a term from the following list. On your paper, write the term next to the numeral of the phrase that describes it.

ohm 5	current 1	ampere 3
watt	circuit 2	volt 4

1. movement of negative charges in a circuit
2. path that an electric current follows
3. term used in describing the amount of electric current
4. term used in describing the amount of "push" the negative charges have
5. term used in describing the amount of resistance to the movement of negative charges

Knowledge and Understanding Write the numerals *6–10* on your paper. Beside each of the numerals, write the word or words that best complete the sentence having that numeral.

6. A transformer is a device used for changing the voltage of _____-current electricity.
7. A circuit that has more than one path for current to follow is called a _____ circuit.

8. An electric current in which negative charges go first one way and then the other is called _alternating_ current.

9. A circuit that has only one path for current to follow is called a _____ circuit.

10. An electric current in which negative charges go in only one direction is called _direct_ current.

Concepts   Beside each of the numerals *11–13* on your paper, write the word or words that best complete the sentence having that numeral.

11. An important advantage that a. c. has over d. c. is that the (*voltage, amperage, wattage*) of a. c. can be changed easily.

12. A light bulb uses 1.2 amps of current when the voltage is 120 volts. The resistance of the bulb is (*120, 100, 12*) ohms.

13. A voltmeter must be connected in parallel to a light bulb in a simple circuit because the voltmeter offers a great deal of (*voltage, resistance, wattage*) to the current.

Application and Critical Thinking   Questions *14–17* refer to the circuit shown in the margin.

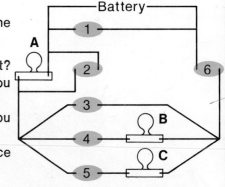

14. Which light bulb—*A, B,* or *C* —has the greatest amount of current?

15. If you wanted to measure the voltage of the battery, would you place the voltmeter at *1,* at *2,* or at *3?*

16. If you wanted to measure the total current in the circuit, would you place the ammeter at *4,* at *5,* or at *6?*

17. If you wanted to measure the current in bulb *B,* would you place the ammeter at *4,* at *5,* or at *6.*

DOING MORE

1. Set up the following circuit: Connect four 1.5-volt cells in series. Then, using this battery as a source of voltage, connect 3 light bulbs in series. Measure the voltage across each bulb and then across all the bulbs together. Explain your findings. Measure the current in each bulb and the total current in the circuit. Explain your findings. Draw a picture of the circuit.

2. Set up the following circuit: Connect two 1.5-volt cells in parallel. Use this battery as a source of voltage, and connect to it 3 flashlight bulbs in parallel. Measure the current in each bulb and the total current in the circuit. Explain your findings. Draw a picture of the circuit.

CHAPTER 17

Magnetism

Have you ever played with magnets? If you have, you know that when you put two magnets close together, one of two things will happen. The magnets will either attract each other or repel each other. In this way, magnets are like objects that are charged with electricity. Sometimes they attract each other. Sometimes they repel each other. Could it be that electricity and magnetism are somehow related? If so, how are they related?

Scientists have found that electricity and magnetism are, indeed, related. In fact, one of the great discoveries of the nineteenth century was that a magnetic field could be made by electricity. Another discovery was that electricity could be made by using magnetic fields. So, knowing about magnets helps in finding out how electricity is made and used. That's what this chapter is all about—some of the ways in which magnetism and electricity are related.

Courtesy of Interlake, Inc.

The uses of magnetic properties range from lifting tons of steel to doing rapid calculations with a computer. What other uses of magnetic properties do you know of?

Photo Research International

MAGNETIC PROPERTIES

How would you describe a magnet?
What are some properties of magnets?

What are magnets?

A certain kind of rock has some strange properties. For one thing, it attracts things that contain iron. The second property is that, if the rock is hanging on a string so it can turn in any direction, the same part of the rock always faces in the same direction.

Long ago, sailors used the second property to find direction. The stone always seemed to point toward a certain star. This star was one that did not seem to move about in the sky. It always appeared in the north. Today we call this star the North Star. The ancients called it the lodestar, or leading star. It is not surprising, then, that a rock that always pointed to this star would be called a *lodestone* [LOHD-stohn].

Today, properties like those of lodestone—the abilities to attract iron and to face toward the same direction—are called *magnetic* [mag-NEHT-ihk] *properties*. Things that have these properties are called *magnets* [MAG-nuhts]. A lodestone, then, is a natural magnet.

Artstreet

Figure 17–1. The lodestone, just like the compass needle, always faces the same way when it is free to turn in any direction. How is this behavior related to magnetic properties?

329

Figure 17–2. Bar magnets have magnetic properties. How could a bar magnet be used to learn if other materials have magnetic properties?

Photos from Larry P. Trone

Scientists have learned how to cause iron, steel, and other metals to have magnetic properties. Such "artificial" magnets are often much stronger than natural magnets. Besides, they can be made in many different shapes. Some are flat disks. Some are long and needlelike. In school labs, the shape often used in studying magnetism is that of a bar magnet. See Figure 17–2.

★ **When would a lodestone be most helpful to sailors in a ship far from shore—during the day or during the night? Explain your answer.**

Properties of magnets

What happens when a bar magnet is free to turn? It does just what a lodestone does. It lines up in a north-south direction. You may know that the ends of a bar magnet are called *poles* [POHLZ]. The end of a bar magnet that always points toward the north is the north-seeking pole. The other end is the south-seeking pole. Most of the time these names are shortened to north pole and south pole. All magnets have a north pole and a south pole.

Suppose you hang two bar magnets near each other. One pole of one magnet will attract one pole of the other. But the same pole of the first magnet will repel the other pole of the second magnet. The north pole of one magnet

For You to Think About

Think back to the description of the way electric charges attract and repel each other. Does the description of the way magnets attract and repel sound familiar? How are the descriptions similar? How are they different?

330

attracts the south pole of the other. The two north poles or the two south poles repel each other. The amount of attracting and repelling between two magnets is greatest at the poles.

Other interesting properties

Besides attracting and repelling, magnets have other properties. Some of these properties are very interesting. Suppose a magnet is broken into many pieces. Each piece will still be magnetic. Another interesting thing has to do with making magnets. A long piece of iron such as an iron pipe can be made slightly magnetic in the following way: Hold the piece of iron in a north-south direction, parallel to the earth's surface. Then hit one end of the iron sharply with a hammer. The piece of iron will become slightly magnetic. See Figure 17–3.

Now, hold the piece of iron in an east-west direction. Hit it sharply with the hammer. When you do this, the iron will lose much of its magnetism.

A magnet can be used to magnetize other pieces of iron. If one pole of a magnet is rubbed across a piece of iron several times, the iron will become magnetized.

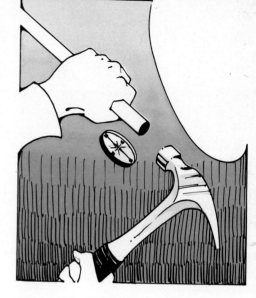

Figure 17–3. *A piece of iron pipe may be made magnetic if it is struck with a hammer while the pipe is held in a north-south direction. Why must the pipe be held in a north-south direction?*

★ **Two steel needles are each suspended by thread. One needle is magnetized and the other is not. How can you find out which is magnetic?**

DO IT YOURSELF

Make a compass

Find a cork and a needle. Magnetize the needle by rubbing it with the north pole of a magnet. Rub the needle from the blunt end toward the pointed end. Place the cork in a glass bowl or dish filled with water, to which a small amount of soap has been added. Place the magnetized needle on top of the cork so that it is balanced. In which direction does the needle point? Move an iron or magnetic object near the side of the needle. What happens? Why?

Investigate

What are some effects of one magnet on another?

You Will Need

string, ring stand, 2 bar magnets

Background

One way to find out how one magnet affects another would be to use 2 magnets having poles that are labeled. One magnet would have to be free to move in any direction, and the other magnet would have to be controlled by you.

What to Do

Using the string and the ring stand, hang a magnet so it is parallel to the tabletop and free to turn in any direction. Hold the other magnet in your hand, and move this magnet near the hanging magnet so that the like poles of the magnets are near each other. Observe and record what happens. Then, move the unlike poles of the magnets near each other. Observe and record what happens.

Now, move the magnet in your hand so that a pole of the magnet is near the center of the hanging magnet. Observe and record what happens.

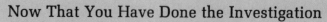

Now That You Have Done the Investigation

—What happened when you moved the like poles of the 2 magnets near each other?
—What happened when unlike poles were moved near each other?
—What happened when the pole of the magnet in your hand was moved near the center of the suspended magnet?

MAGNETIC FIELDS

What are magnetic lines of force?

*What is the typical pattern formed by iron
filings when two magnets attract each other?
Repel each other?*

*What are some ways of producing magnetism
in an iron object?*

*What idea is used to explain some properties
of magnets?*

Fields and lines of force

There are many ways to study magnetism. One way is
to use iron filings. Suppose you place a sheet of glass on
top of a bar magnet. Then you sprinkle iron filings on
top of the glass. What happens?

If you do this, the first thing you might notice is that
the magnet attracts the filings, even through the glass.
You might also notice that the iron filings line up in a
certain pattern on the glass. By tapping the glass, the
pattern becomes clearer. See Figure 17–4.

You can see only the pattern that is on the glass. But
iron filings would be affected in the space all around the
magnet. The space in which the iron filings would be
affected is known as the magnetic field of the magnet.

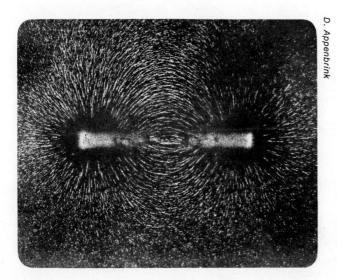

D. Appenbrink

*Figure 17–4. If a piece of glass were placed on a
bar magnet and sprinkled with iron filings, the
filings would form a pattern much like the one
shown here. What kind of pattern would be formed
if the magnet were shaped like a "U"?*

Every magnet has a magnetic field around it. The magnetic field is the area in which magnetic effects are noticeable.

In order to describe a magnetic field, lines are often drawn. The lines are called magnetic lines of force. These lines are a kind of picture of the magnetic field. Magnetic lines of force drawn to describe the field around a bar magnet would look very much like the pattern of iron filings shown in Figure 17–4.

Remember that a magnetic field is not really made up of lines like those in Figure 17–4. Magnetic lines of force are imaginary. In a way, lines of force are like lines drawn on maps. You know that the equator is not really a line around the earth. But a line is often put on a globe to show the location of the equator.

Magnetic lines of force are used for the same reason that lines, such as the equator, are used on globes. They help us "see" something that is not really visible.

★ **How do you think you could show that there is a magnetic field around a lodestone?**

DO IT YOURSELF

Observe magnetic fields

Get several magnets of different shapes. Cover each magnet with a sheet of glass or a sheet of cardboard. Sprinkle iron filings on the sheet of glass or cardboard and gently tap the sheet. Look at the patterns made by the iron filings. Are the patterns similar for each magnet? If so, try to explain why. If not, try to explain why not.

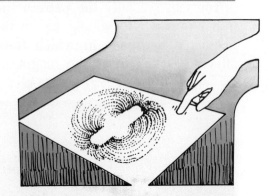

Magnetic fields between magnets

What happens when two magnets are moved near each other? You already know that like poles repel each other and unlike poles attract. But what does the pattern of the magnetic lines of force look like when magnets are placed near each other?

Suppose that two bar magnets are placed side by side. The north pole of one is near the south pole of the other. A sheet of glass is placed over the magnets. Iron filings are sprinkled on the glass. As before, a pattern of iron filings forms.

The pattern of filings represents magnetic lines of force in the magnetic fields of the magnets. Look at A of Figure 17–5. This pattern shows what happens to the magnetic fields of two magnets that attract each other. The magnetic lines of force go from one magnet to the other.

What is the pattern when magnets repel each other? Suppose that two bar magnets are placed side by side. This time, though, the north pole of one magnet is opposite the north pole of the other magnet. The south poles would then be opposite each other too. Look at B of Figure 17–5.

The pattern of iron filings shows what happens to the magnetic fields of two magnets that repel each other. The magnetic lines of force do not go from one magnet to the other. In fact, the lines curve so that those from one magnet are alongside those from the other magnet.

★ **How could you use a compass to find out if two magnets were either attracting or repelling?**

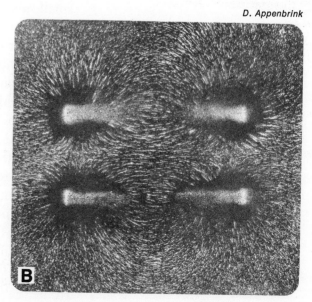

Figure 17–5. What do you think caused the pattern shown in A? In B? In which picture, A or B, are the magnets attracting each other?

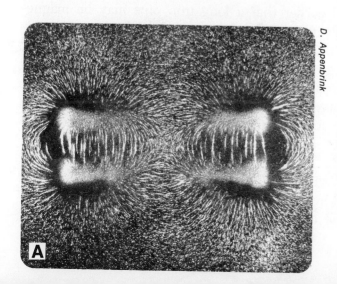

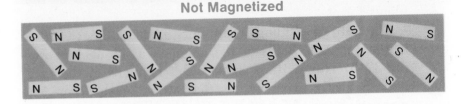

Figure 17–6. How does the model for magnets shown here explain the difference between iron that is magnetized and iron that is not magnetized?

A model for magnetism

Some magnets are called *permanent* [PURM(-uh)-nuhnt] *magnets*. However, they are not really permanent. All magnets lose most of their magnetic properties over a long period of time. They become just pieces of iron.

But losing its magnetic properties does not seem to change a magnet in any visible way. This brings up a question. How is a magnet different from a piece of iron that has no magnetic properties?

To answer this question, a model for magnets has been suggested. The model suggests that a piece of iron can be thought of as being made up of many small magnets. In a piece of iron that is a strong magnet, most of the small magnets are lined up in a certain way. That is, their north poles are pointed in the same direction. In a piece of iron that has no magnetic properties, the small magnets are not lined up in any special way. See Figure 17–6.

You read earlier that a long iron pipe may be magnetized by hitting it with a hammer while the pipe is pointing north and south. How does the model explain this?

According to the model, the hitting probably causes some of the small magnets to line up along the magnetic lines of force of the earth's magnetic field. The more small magnets that line up, the stronger the magnetism of the pipe.

When the pipe is hit as it points east and west, it loses its magnetism. The small magnets are knocked out of line. They get out of line because the iron pipe is crossing the earth's magnetic lines of force.

Find Out More

One bit of evidence for the magnetism model is the fact that when magnets are heated they lose their magnetic properties. Use references to find out more about the domain theory of magnetism that was first proposed in the nineteenth century. How may the domain theory be used to explain a magnet's loss of magnetic properties during heating?

The model is not perfect, though. It does not explain why only certain metals can become magnetic. Nor does the model explain why the small magnets exist at all. So the model does not explain magnetism. It is useful, though, because it does explain some properties of magnets.

★ **When a magnet is broken, each piece is magnetic. Can the model be used to explain this? If so, how?**

ELECTRICITY AND MAGNETISM

How did Oersted find out that electricity forms a magnetic field?
How did scientists make magnetic fields that were stronger than those made by a single wire?
What is an electromagnet?
How did Faraday use magnets to make electricity? What is a transformer?

Oersted's discovery

Does electricity cause a magnetic field to form? A scientist named Hans Christian Oersted was the first person to find out that it does. One day in 1819, Oersted was teaching a lesson about electricity to a science class. On the desk were a battery, some wire, and some other parts of a circuit. Near this was a large compass. The compass needle, of course, was free to point in any direction.

Because of the earth's magnetic field, the compass needle was lined up in a north-south direction when the lesson began. During the lesson a wire was connected to the battery, closing the circuit. Suddenly the compass needle swung away from its north-south direction. When the circuit was opened, the needle went back to its north-south direction.

After more tests with the wire and battery, Oersted decided that electricity moving in a wire caused the wire to become a magnet. Today, we say that a magnetic field forms around a wire in which there is electricity.

Figure 17–7. Oersted's discovery led to the invention of the electric motor. The device below shows that electricity plus magnetism can produce motion.

Photo Research International

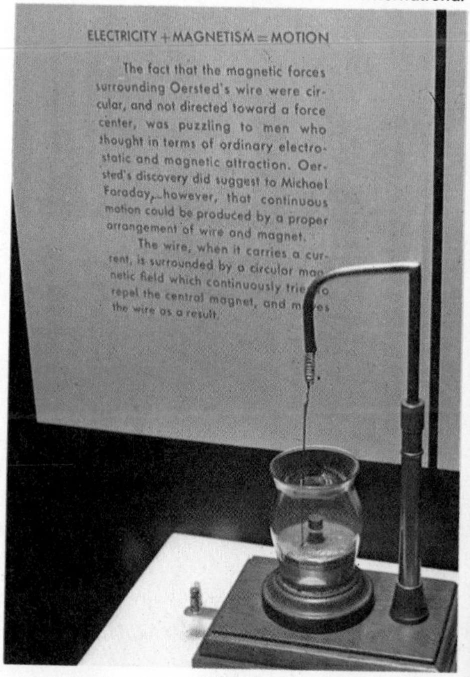

ELECTRICITY + MAGNETISM = MOTION

The fact that the magnetic forces surrounding Oersted's wire were circular, and not directed toward a force center, was puzzling to men who thought in terms of ordinary electrostatic and magnetic attraction. Oersted's discovery did suggest to Michael Faraday, however, that continuous motion could be produced by a proper arrangement of wire and magnet.
The wire, when it carries a current, is surrounded by a circular magnetic field which continuously tries to repel the central magnet, and moves the wire as a result.

Investigate

Does electricity in a wire cause a magnetic field to form around the wire?

You Will Need

sheet of cardboard, number 18 insulated copper wire, dry cell, 4 small compasses

Background

Usually a compass needle points in a north-south direction because that is the direction of the earth's magnetic field. A compass needle in a magnetic field that is stronger than the earth's field points in the direction of the stronger field. So, compasses can be used to find out if there is a magnetic field around a wire in which electricity is moving.

What to Do

Make a small hole in the center of the cardboard. Insert the wire through the hole. Place 4 small compasses on the cardboard around the wire at equal distances from the wire. Note the direction in which each compass is pointing.

Connect an end of the wire to one post of a dry cell. Then, while holding the cardboard away from any metal objects, touch the other end of the wire to the other post of the dry cell. As you touch the wire to the dry cell look at the compasses. Record what happens to the compasses. *CAUTION: Touch the wire to the dry cell for only a few seconds, otherwise you may cause the cell to go dead.*

Repeat what you have done. This time, however, touch the wires to the opposite posts so the electricity flows in the opposite direction. As you touch the wire to the dry cell look at the compasses. Record what happens to the compasses.

Now That You Have Done the Investigation

—Did the electricity in the wire affect the compass? If so, how?

—Did reversing the direction of the electricity in the wire change the way the compasses were affected? If so, what was the change?

—Do you think there is or is not a magnetic field around a wire in which electricity is moving?

Electromagnets

Electricity can be used to make very strong magnets. Scientists discovered that using a loop of wire causes the magnetic field inside the loop to be stronger than the field around a wire. Having many loops together makes the magnetic field inside the loops stronger, because the field of each loop is added to that of the other loops.

To make an even stronger magnet, a piece of iron can be placed inside the loops of wire. When electricity flows in the loops of wire, the iron becomes a strong magnet. Such a magnet is called an *electromagnet* [ih-LEHK-troh-MAG-nuht]. By the use of more loops of wire or more electricity, very strong electromagnets can be made. Besides, this kind of magnet can be turned off and on by stopping or starting the flow of electricity. Ordinary magnets cannot be turned off and on.

★ **Why is it an advantage to be able to turn a magnet off and on?**

Faraday's discovery

After the discovery that electricity in a wire made a magnetic field, scientists began to look for the opposite effect. That is, they tried to use the magnetic field around a magnet to make electricity.

The first person to do this was Michael Faraday. All he did was move a wire through a magnetic field. You can cause electricity to move in a wire by doing the same thing. Wind several loops of insulated wire around a small jar. Then remove the jar. When the loops of wire are moved in a magnetic field, electricity moves in the wire.

To show that electricity is moving in the wire, the ends of the wire that form the loops should be connected to a *galvanometer* [GAL-vuh-NAHM-uht-ur]. A galvanometer is used for detecting and measuring small amounts of electricity. The pointer on a galvanometer moves to one side when electricity flows in one direction and then moves to the other side when electricity flows in the other direction.

(*Text continues on page 341.*)

Find Out More

Michael Faraday was a great scientist. Among his discoveries were the first electric motor and the first electric generator. Using references, find out more about these discoveries and inventions. Discuss the importance of each discovery and invention with other members of your class.

Investigate

How does the magnetic strength of an electromagnet compare with that of a coil of wire?

You Will Need

dry cell, iron nail or bolt, number 18 insulated copper wire, 30 paper clips

Background

Electricity in a conductor causes a magnetic field to form around the conductor. Later, this discovery was used to produce a useful kind of magnet. In this investigation you can find out how the magnetic effects of electricity in a conductor can be increased and made more noticeable.

What to Do

Wind some of the wire around a pencil to form a coil. Remove the pencil. Connect an end of the wire to one post of the dry cell. Then while holding the coil of wire near a pile of paper clips, touch the other end of the wire to the other post of the dry cell for a few seconds. Observe and record how the clips are affected. Try to lift the clips with the coil. Take away the wire you were touching to the post of the dry cell. Observe and record what happens to the clips.

Insert an iron nail or bolt into the coil. Touch the wire to the post of the dry cell again. Hold the nail near the pile of clips. Observe and record how the clips are affected.

Take away the wire you were touching to the post of the dry cell. Observe and record what happens to the clips.

Now That You Have Done the Investigation

—How were the clips affected by the coil of wire?

—What happened to the clips when the wire touching the post of the dry cell was taken away?

—How were the clips affected when the iron nail was inside the coil?

—Did all the clips fall off when the wire was taken away?

—How would you compare the strength of a magnetic field formed by a coil and iron nail with that of a magnetic field formed by a coil of wire without the nail?

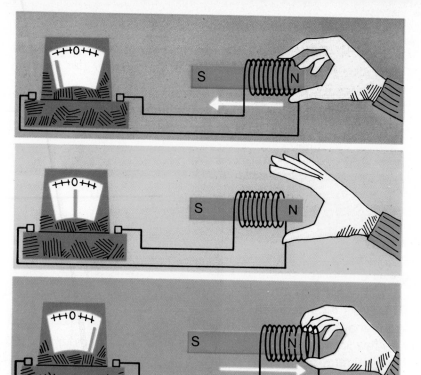

Figure 17–8. Is current produced when the coil is moving onto or off of the magnet? When the coil is on the magnet but not moving? Does the direction the coil is moved seem to affect the direction the electricity flows? How can you tell?

Quickly move the loops of wire so that they slip over one pole of the magnet. The needle moves to one side, indicating that electricity flows. When the loops of wire stop moving, the needle returns to the center, indicating that electricity is not flowing. See Figure 17–8.

When the loops of wire are quickly removed from the magnet, the needle again moves, indicating a flow of electricity. This time, however, the needle moves to the other side of the center. The electricity is flowing in the opposite direction when the loops are slipped off the magnet.

What causes electricity to flow in the wire? Remember the magnetic lines of force that are used to describe a magnetic field? When the loops are slipped over the magnet, the loops of wire cut across these lines of force. Somehow, moving the loops of wire in a magnetic field so that the wire cuts across these imaginary lines causes electricity to flow in the wire. Electricity also flows in the wire when the magnet is moved and the wire is

341

held still. Either way, the more magnetic lines of force that are cut across in a given time, the greater the amount of electricity produced.

★ **What are some ways to increase the number of magnetic lines of force cut in a given amount of time?**

Induction

Michael Faraday performed many experiments with magnets and electricity. In one of them, two pieces of wire were wound around an iron ring. The pieces of wire were not touching. Look at Figure 17–9.

By doing such experiments, something very important was discovered. A changing flow of electricity in one wire can cause electricity to flow in a second wire, even though the wires are not connected. This is called *induction* [ihn-DUHK-shuhn].

How can electricity flowing in one wire cause electricity to flow in a second wire if the wires are not touching? Remember that both wires are wrapped around the same piece of iron. When electricity flows through the first wire, the whole iron ring becomes an elecromagnet. That is, a magnetic field builds up around the iron ring.

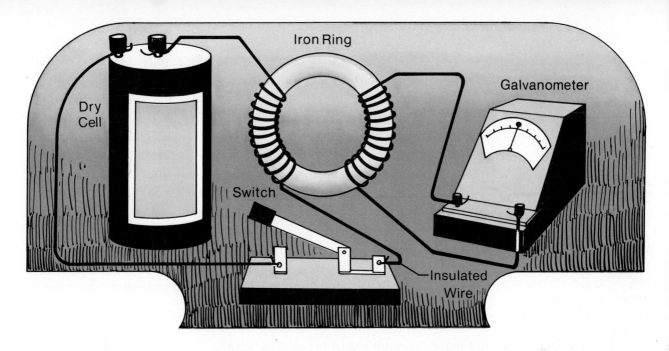

Figure 17–9. Why does current flow through the meter as the switch is closed, and again (in the opposite direction) as the switch is opened? Why does no current flow in the meter when the switch is closed?

As the field builds up, lines of force cut across the loops in the second wire. As you know, whenever lines of force are cutting across a wire, electricity flows in the wire.

The second wire has electricity only when the flow of electricity in the first wire is changing. A steady flow of electricity in the first wire does not cause a changing magnetic field around the iron. If the magnetic field is not changing, lines of force are not cutting across the second wire. Then, no electricity will flow through the second wire.

Stepping up and stepping down

Something else about induction was discovered. If the second wire on the iron ring had a different number of loops than the first wire, the voltage in the second wire would be different from that in the first. For example, the second wire might have fewer loops than the first wire. Then, the voltage in the second wire would be

343

less than the voltage in the first wire. If the second wire had more loops than the first wire, the voltage would be greater in the second wire than in the first.

A device that uses induction to change the voltage of a. c. electricity is called a transformer. If the transformer increases the amount of voltage, the transformer is called a step-up transformer. If the transformer causes the voltage to decrease, the transformer is called a step-down transformer. Look at Figure 17–10.

★ **The transformer for operating a toy electric train is plugged into a circuit having 120 volts. But the train is running on only 12 volts. What kind of transformer is being used, a step-up or a step-down transformer?**

Figure 17–10. Two diagrams of transformers are shown below. How does the number of turns on each side of the iron ring affect the change in voltage for each transformer?

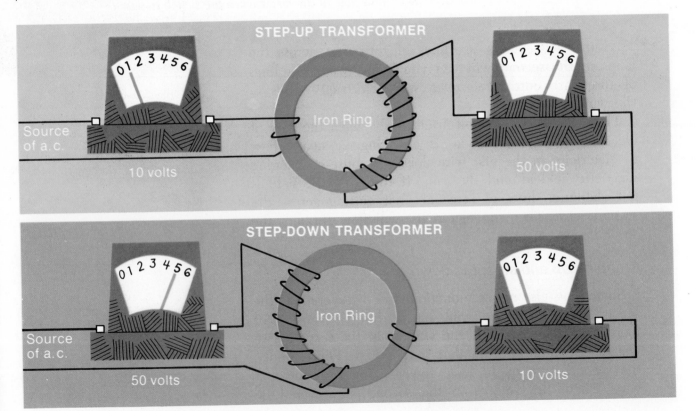

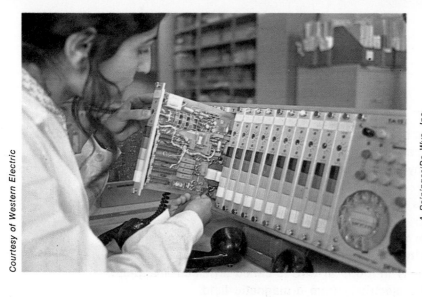

Courtesy of Western Electric

A Reininger/De Wys, Inc.

Electromagnets for Many Jobs

Many people would probably say that science has nothing to do with their job. Chances are, they are wrong. They probably mean that they do not need to know anything about science principles to do their job. But that is not the same thing as saying that science has nothing to do with their job. A person who sells cars, for example, does not need to know anything about electromagnets to sell a car. But every time that person starts a car, that person is using an electromagnet.

Even people who know how they use electromagnets do not have to know anything about the principles that cause electromagnets to work. A crane operator may use an electromagnet to lift heavy pieces of iron and steel. This person must be skilled in using the crane, but the person need not know much about an electromagnet in order to use one.

But in order to do their job, some people do have to know about science principles involving electricity and magnetism. Some people design and build electric and magnetic equipment. These people are usually electrical engineers. Other people have to repair and install equipment and machines that use electromagnets, transformers, and other electric devices. They must know something about electricity and magnetism in order to do their job.

Soon you will be thinking about a career of some kind. Do you think that knowing about electromagnets or science principles of electricity will be useful in the career you might choose?

For jobs like those shown here, knowing about electricity and magnetism is important. What other jobs do you know of that require a knowledge of electricity and magnetism?

Reviewing and Extending

SUMMING UP

1. A lodestone is a kind of rock that has special properties called magnetic properties. Objects having these special properties are called magnets.
2. A magnet that is free to turn in any direction will always line up so that one end, or pole, is pointed in a northerly direction.
3. The pole of a magnet that points toward the north is called a north-seeking, or north, pole. The other pole is a south-seeking, or south, pole.
4. One model for magnets suggests that a magnet is made up of many small magnets.
5. Oersted discovered that electricity produces a magnetic field.
6. A magnet made by using electricity in loops of wire is called an electromagnet.
7. Faraday discovered how to make electricity from a magnetic field.
8. Transformers are used for changing the voltage of alternating-current electricity.

CHECKING UP

Vocabulary   Write the numerals *1–5* on your paper. Each numbered phrase describes a term from the following list. On your paper, write the term next to the numeral of the phrase that describes it.

5 pole	3 lodestone	4 transformer
1 model	magnetic	2 North Star

1. used to explain certain observations
2. star called the leading star
3. rock with part that always faces the same direction
4. used to change the voltage of alternating-current electricity
5. end of a magnet

Knowledge and Understanding   Write the numerals *6–9* on your paper. Beside each numeral, write the word or words that best complete the sentence having that numeral.

6. A transformer that puts out a greater voltage than is put into it is called a _____ transformer.
7. The end of a magnet that always points toward the north is called the *north* Pole.
8. The process of _____ is what makes alternating-current transformers possible.
9. The person who discovered how to use magnets to produce electricity was *Oersted*

346

Concepts   Beside each of the numerals *10–13* on your paper, write the word or words that best complete the sentence having that numeral.

10. The reason sailors used lodestones was that lodestones (*attracted iron filings, pointed north, stopped sudden storms*).
11. The amount of attracting and repelling between magnets is greatest at the (*centers, coils, poles*) of the magnets.
12. An electromagnet uses (*electricity to make magnetism, magnetism to make electricity, electricity to make voltage*).
13. Iron filings may be used with a magnet to show that there is a (*model, magnetic field, loop of wire*) all around a magnet.

Application and Critical Thinking   Answer the following questions as briefly as you can without leaving out any important ideas.

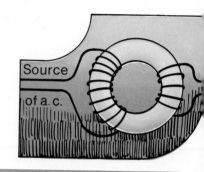

14. Look at the transformer pictured on the right. Is it a step-up or a step-down transformer? What effect does it have on the voltage in a circuit?
15. In what ways are electromagnets like other magnets? In what ways are they different?

DOING MORE

1. Use the following materials to demonstrate induction. Wind 25 loops of wire around the end of a metal rod. Wind 50 loops of another wire around the other end, and connect the wire to a galvanometer. Touch the first wire to a dry cell. What happens each time you touch this wire to the cell? How would you explain why electricity flows in the coil that is not attached to the dry cell? Expain how induction is related to transformers.

2. Make an electric buzzer by arranging materials as shown in the illustration. After connecting the 2 wires to a dry cell, use a screwdriver to raise or lower the long screw in order to adjust the distance between the head of the metal "T" and the heads of the wrapped nails. Make sure the head of the metal "T" is touching the underneath part of the head of the long screw.

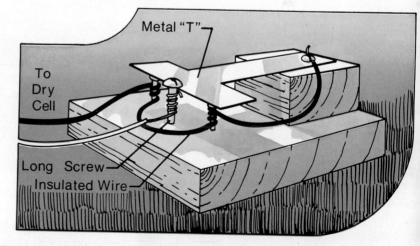

CHAPTER 18

Electricity and Chemistry

Did you ever wonder where the electricity comes from that starts a car or lights the bulb in a flashlight? This electricity is the result of a *chemical* [KEHM-ih-kuhl] change. The discovery that chemical changes, or changes in matter, can be used to make electricity has been very useful. Another useful discovery that has been made is that the reverse is true. That is, electricity can be used to cause certain chemical changes.

As you study this chapter you will discover some ways in which chemical changes are used to make electricity. You will also find out about some ways in which electricity is used to cause chemical changes. Finally, you will see how the knowledge of matter has been used to make electricity in new and different ways.

A. Devaney, Inc.

Alfa Studio

Electricity and chemistry are closely related. Electricity can cause certain chemical changes. Some chemical changes make electricity. What uses of the relationship between chemistry and electricity can you think of?

ELECTRICITY FROM CHEMICALS

What kind of electricity did Galvani believe he had discovered?

What did Volta say about animal electricity?

What does a chemical cell need in order to make electricity?

Animal electricity

The study of electricity from chemicals had a very interesting beginning. It all started with frogs. In 1770, an Italian biologist, Luigi Galvani, was studying the muscles in frogs. The muscles were studied by hanging the hind legs of freshly killed frogs on copper hooks. Whenever these copper hooks were put on an iron rod, the legs of the frogs moved as if the legs were alive.

Galvani already knew that electric charges could cause muscles to move. So he thought that hanging the frog legs on the metal hooks somehow let out the electricity from inside the frog legs. Letting out the electricity caused the legs to move. Galvani thought that he had discovered a new kind of electricity. He called it animal electricity. See Figure 18–1.

Later it was learned that when frog legs on copper hooks were placed on a copper rod, the legs did not move. It seemed as though two different metals had to touch the frog legs in order to let out the animal electricity.

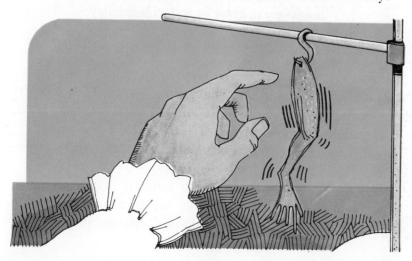

Figure 18–1. How did Galvani explain the twitching of the frog leg? Is the same explanation still used today?

Another scientist, Alessandro Volta, did not agree with Galvani. Volta did not believe there was such a thing as animal electricity.

Contact electricity

Volta showed that frog legs were not needed to make electricity. Two different metals and salt water were all that seemed to be needed to make electricity. Since the electricity was formed when the metals touched, the electricity was called contact electricity.

From this idea, the first chemical cell was made. For the first time, a device could be used to make electricity flow for a period of time. The device was a pile of disks. The disks were probably made of zinc, silver, and paper. They were arranged as shown in Figure 18–2. The paper disks were kept wet with salt water.

Because the disks were piled one on top of another, the device was called a pile. Later, the pile was placed on its side in a pan of salt water so the paper disks would not dry out. Without moisture, the pile would not make electricity. Today the word "pile" is not used. Cell is the more common term. A chemical cell is made of two different metals called *electrodes* [ih-LEHK-TROHDZ] that are placed in a liquid or paste called an *electrolyte* [ih-LEHK-truh-LYT]. The liquid or paste is a conductor of electricity.

★ **How was it shown that frog legs were not necessary in order to make electricity?**

Chemical electricity

After the discovery of the chemical cell became known, scientists tried to find out what made it work. They learned that many different metals could be used to make electricity. For example, strips of lead and copper placed in an acid produced electricity. Strips of zinc and copper in an acid also produced electricity.

It was Michael Faraday who noticed that a chemical change always took place when electricity was made in a chemical cell. When the chemical change stopped, the

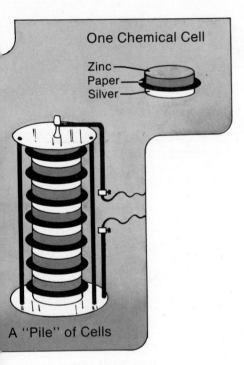

Figure 18–2. One type of early chemical cell is shown here. A pile of these cells made up the first electric battery.

One Chemical Cell

Zinc
Paper
Silver

A "Pile" of Cells

DO IT YOURSELF

Use a lemon to study electricity

Wash a copper penny and a zinc-coated washer with soap and water. Next, make 2 small cuts in the skin of a lemon. The cuts should be side by side and about a centimetre (⅜ of an inch) apart. Push the penny halfway into a cut. Push the washer halfway into the other cut. Now hold the lemon close to your mouth so your tongue touches the penny and the washer at the same time. Does touching the penny and the washer with your tongue cause any unusual sensation? Try using other kinds of metals. Also try using other kinds of fruits and vegetables. Do you get the same results?

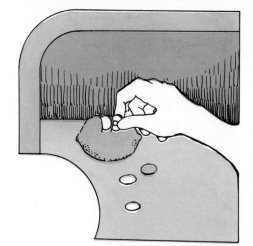

electricity stopped. Faraday said that the electricity was made because of the chemical change. Electricity made in this way was called chemical electricity.

Electrodes are the places where chemical changes take place in a chemical cell. The chemical changes are what make the electricity. During the chemical changes, one electrode becomes positively charged. The other becomes negatively charged. When the two electrodes are connected by a wire, electricity flows from the negatively charged electrode, through the wire, to the positively charged electrode. See Figure 18–3. If there is a bulb in the circuit, it lights up as the electricity flows through the circuit.

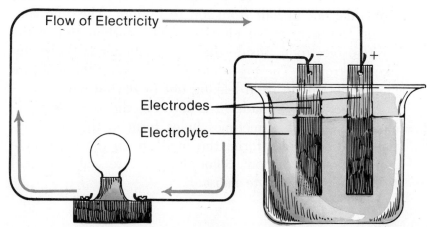

Figure 18–3. Chemical changes make the electricity that lights the bulb in this circuit. Where are the chemical changes taking place?

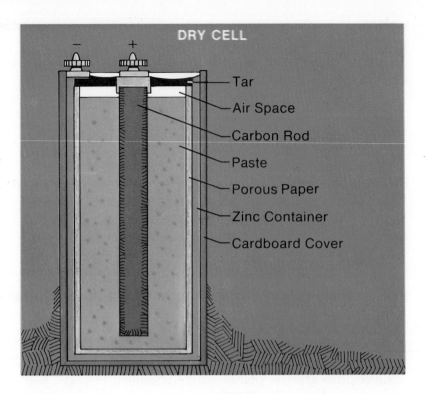

DRY CELL

- Tar
- Air Space
- Carbon Rod
- Paste
- Porous Paper
- Zinc Container
- Cardboard Cover

Figure 18–4. A dry cell is one kind of chemical cell. What parts of the dry cell are the electrodes? What part is the electrolyte? Is a dry cell really dry?

Find Out More

The most common chemical cell is the dry cell. It is the kind most often used in flashlights and transistor radios. However, wet cells are used in automobiles. Use reference materials to find out more about wet cells and the ways they differ from dry cells.

Dry cells

The kind of chemical cell you have probably seen most often is a dry cell. However, a dry cell is not really dry. The inside of the cell is moist. If the inside of the cell becomes dry, it will not make electricity.

The most common dry cell is the zinc-carbon cell. It is the kind most often used in flashlights and transistor radios. You can see what the main parts of a dry cell are by looking at Figure 18–4. There you see what a dry cell looks like cut in half from top to bottom. The zinc container is the negative electrode. The carbon rod is the positive electrode. Inside the zinc container is the paste-like electrolyte. The top is closed up to keep the moisture in the electrolyte from leaking out or drying out.

As electricity is made in a dry cell, the zinc electrode changes. In fact, sometimes holes form in the zinc container. When holes form, the moisture in the electrolyte can leak out or dry out. Some dry cells are sealed in steel to keep the electrolyte moist.

ELECTROCHEMISTRY

What does electrolysis do to water?
What metal may be obtained by using
electrolysis?
What process may be used to coat an object with
metal?

Chemical changes by using electricity

In dry cells and batteries, chemical changes make electricity. Can the reverse also happen? That is, can electricity be used to cause a chemical change? The answer is Yes. A good example of using electricity to cause a chemical change is in recharging a battery like the one in a car. During recharging, electricity is sent through the battery. The chemicals that changed to make the electricity are changed back to what they were. The study of ways to use electricity to cause a chemical change is called *electrochemistry* [ih-LEHK-troh-KEHM-uh-stree].

Electrolysis

One chemical change caused by electricity is the breakdown of water by using a direct current. This change is called *electrolysis* [ih-LEHK-TRAHL-uh-suhs] of water. During electrolysis, water is broken down, or separated, into two gases—hydrogen and oxygen.

One set of equipment that could be used to separate water is shown in Figure 18–5. It consists of two electrodes, water (mixed with some chemical), and a source of direct-current electricity such as a battery.

Figure 18–5. The equipment shown here is being used to separate water into two gases. What two gases are being produced? Why is there more gas in one tube than in the other?

You may be wondering why the water must contain some other chemical. Electrolysis cannot take place unless the water is able to conduct electricity. Pure water will not conduct electricity. A chemical, such as sodium sulfate, is added to make water conduct electricity.

As soon as the electrodes are connected to a battery and placed in the electrolyte, bubbles begin to form at the electrodes. Bubbles of hydrogen gas form at the electrode connected to the negative post of the battery. Bubbles of oxygen gas form at the other electrode.

Obtaining metals by electrolysis

You probably know what aluminum is. Aluminum is a metal. Aluminum is used to make cans for soft drinks. It is used to make window frames and doors. Some car engines have aluminum parts. Many pots and pans are made from aluminum. What other uses for aluminum can you name?

Today, aluminum is used a great deal. But before 1886 it was used very little because separating aluminum from its ore cost a lot of money. At that time, in fact, objects made of aluminum cost more than similar objects made of gold!

Then, in 1886 a way to separate aluminum from its ore by using electricity was discovered. It was found that the mineral *cryolite* [KRY-uh-LYT], when melted, dissolved aluminum ore. Aluminum ore is not pure aluminum. The ore contains other materials. Pure aluminum can be obtained by passing electricity through the solution of cryolite and aluminum ore. See Figure 18–6.

Figure 18–6. Plants that produce aluminum by the process shown here are usually located near hydroelectric power plants. Why?

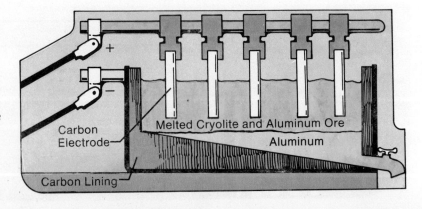

Carbon Electrode

Melted Cryolite and Aluminum Ore

Aluminum

Carbon Lining

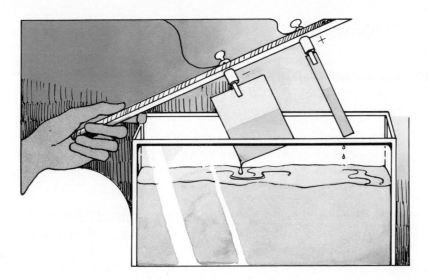

Figure 18–7. A simple electroplating cell is shown here. On which electrode, positive or negative, is the pure metal deposited? Where does the metal come from?

This way of obtaining aluminum is an example of electrolysis. That is, electricity is passed through the molten ore. The electricity separates aluminum from the other materials in the ore. This process is similar to the separating of oxygen from hydrogen during the electrolysis of water.

Electroplating metals

The *electroplating* [ih-LEHK-truh-PLAYT-ihng] process covers a material, most often a metal, with another kind of metal. Electroplating is another form of electrolysis. Some of the metals used in electroplating are copper, nickel, silver, and gold.

The object to be electroplated, or covered with metal, is usually connected to the negative post of a source of direct current. The positive post is a piece of the metal that is to be plated onto the object. The two posts are placed in an electrolyte that contains a compound of the metal that is to be plated onto the object. When the electricity is turned on, a layer of metal is deposited on the object connected to the negative post. See Figure 18–7.

There are different reasons for electroplating one metal onto another. Suppose you wanted a table setting made out of solid silver. A set of knives, forks, and spoons made

(*Text continues on page 357.*)

For You to Think About

Enough energy to keep a 100-watt light bulb burning for about 10 days is needed to make 1 kilogram (2.2 pounds) of aluminum metal. This amounts to about 24 kilowatt-hours of electric energy. Suppose that 1 kilowatt-hour of energy costs 0.3 cents. What would it cost for the electricity needed to make 1 kilogram of aluminum metal?

Investigate

How are metals electroplated?

You Will Need

copper strip, carbon rod, beaker or jar, insulated copper wire, cup of copper sulfate solution, four 1.5-volt dry cells

Background

Whenever a metal is to be electroplated onto another object, you need a source of direct-current electricity. You also need an electrolyte and a container. Dry cells may be connected in series to provide the source of electricity. To do this, copper wire is used to connect the positive post of one cell to the negative post of the next, and so on. Dry cells connected together are called a battery.

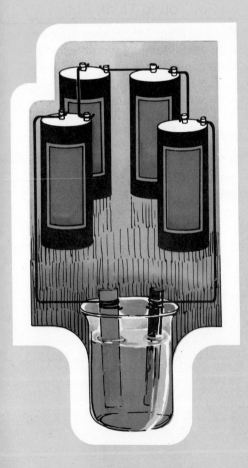

What to Do

Connect the 4 dry cells in series. Then connect the strip of copper to the wire from the positive side of the battery. The copper strip supplies the metal to be plated. Connect the carbon rod to the wire from the negative side of the battery. The carbon rod is the object to be plated. Then place the copper strip and the carbon rod in the solution of copper sulfate. The copper sulfate solution is the electrolyte. In a few minutes, remove the carbon rod. Observe and record what changes, if any, have occurred on the carbon rod, in the copper sulfate solution, and on the copper strip.

Reverse the flow of electricity. Observe and record what changes, if any, have occurred on the carbon rod, in the copper sulfate solution, and on the copper strip.

Now That You Have Done the Investigation

—In the first part of the investigation, how did the carbon rod change?

—In the first part of the investigation, how did the solution of copper sulfate change?

—In the first part of the investigation, how did the copper strip change?

—After the flow of electricity was reversed, what changes occurred?

of solid silver would be very pretty, but it would cost a lot of money. By electroplating silver onto a cheaper metal, a pretty table setting can be made for a lot less money.

★ **Why, do you suppose, are the steel bumpers on cars often plated with chromium?**

NEW SOURCES OF ELECTRICITY

Where have fuel cells been used to make electricity?
What device uses sunlight to make electricity?
What device uses a difference in temperature to make electricity?

Fuel cells

The electricity used in some spaceflights comes from what is called a fuel cell. A fuel cell uses a chemical reaction to make electricity.

Because fuel cells are used in spaceflights, many people think that the fuel cell is a new discovery. It is not. The first fuel cell was made around 1830. However, the early fuel cells were not widely used. One reason was that hydrogen and oxygen gases were needed. At that time, these gases were not easy to get, so they cost a lot. Another reason was that these two gases were very dangerous when mixed together because they exploded easily. Also, the first fuel cells did not make much electricity.

It was not until the space age that major improvements were made in fuel cells. For spaceflights, a source of electricity that could be depended upon was needed. Also, the source had to be able to make quite a bit of electricity. The fuel cells that are used now meet these needs.

Solar cells

Another space-age source of electricity is the *solar* [SOH-lur] *cell*. A solar cell is a very simple device. A single cell consists of a thin disk of silicon to which other

---

Find Out More

During the operation of a fuel cell, electricity and pure water are made. Inside a spaceship, such as those used in the Apollo flights, the electricity and the water are both important. Use reference materials to find out what kinds of chemical changes take place inside a fuel cell.

chemicals have been added. When sunlight strikes the disk, electric charges move from one side of the disk to the other.

The voltage of a single solar cell is very small. To be useful, therefore, hundreds of cells are connected in series. On some spaceships, solar cells are placed on the surface of the spaceship. On others, the solar cells cover winglike arms that stick out from the spaceship. See Figure 18–8.

★ **If you could set up solar cells anywhere in the United States, what place would you choose as the best? Explain.**

Courtesy of NASA

Figure 18–8. Hundreds of solar cells (on the "wings") are used to produce electricity for the radio and the television camera in this satellite.

Thermoelectric energy

A difference in temperature can be used to make electricity. Suppose, for example, that each end of an iron wire is connected to a separate piece of copper wire. Then

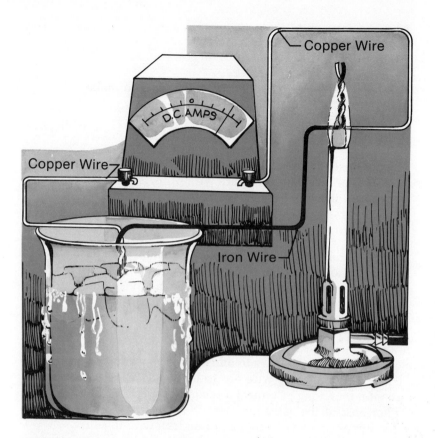

Figure 18–9. *This device, consisting of two different kinds of metal wire twisted together, is capable of producing electricity from a difference in temperature. What is such a device called?*

suppose the free ends of the copper wires are connected to a very sensitive ammeter. One copper-iron connection is placed in ice water. The other is placed in a flame. See Figure 18–9. The ammeter will show a current in the circuit. Usually, the greater the difference in temperature, the greater the amount of current produced.

A device that uses a difference in temperature to make electricity is called a *thermocouple* [THUR-muh-KUHP-uhl]. Thermocouples have been put to practical use. In a car, for example, one end of a thermocouple is placed inside the engine. The other end is kept outside the engine. As the engine warms up, a difference in temperature between the two ends produces a current. The warmer the engine, the greater the difference in temperature and the greater the amount of current. The current is used to operate a gauge that shows the engine temperature.

Find Out More

Find out how thermocouples are used in furnaces or water heaters to keep gas from escaping if the pilot light goes out.

Investigate

How may a temperature difference be used to make electricity?

You Will Need

> ice, Bunsen burner, galvanometer or very sensitive ammeter, beaker or jar, lengths of bare wire (iron, nickel, and manganese), insulated copper wire

Background

Wires and a difference in temperature may be used to make a small amount of electricity. The amount of electricity is small, so a galvanometer or a very sensitive ammeter must be used to detect the current in a wire.

What to Do

Connect a copper wire to one post of a galvanometer. (Hint: All lengths of wire are to be 30 centimetres, or about a foot, long.) Connect a second copper wire to the other post of the galvanometer. Twist the open end of one of the copper wires and one end of an iron wire together. Then twist the end of the second copper wire and the other end of the iron wire together. Heat one copper-iron connection by placing it in a Bunsen-burner flame, and place the other copper-iron connection in a beaker of ice water. Continue the heating and cooling for at least 10 minutes. Observe and record any changes indicated by the galvanometer.

Repeat the investigation using the nickel wire in place of the iron wire. Observe and record any changes indicated by the galvanometer.

Now repeat the investigation using the manganese wire in place of the nickel wire. Observe and record any changes indicated by the galvanometer.

Now That You Have Done the Investigation

—In the first part of the investigation, did the galvanometer reading show that current was produced? If so, did the current continue as long as you continued the heating and cooling?

—Did using the nickel wire or manganese wire have any effect on the amount of electricity being made?

Batteries—Part of Today's World

As you have read, batteries are used in many different ways. Suppose you were making a list of all the ways that batteries are used. You probably know that they are used in cars, transistor radios, and some toys. You could probably make a long list of ways in which batteries are used.

Suppose, too, you were making a list of jobs that have something to do with batteries. What kinds of jobs might you list? You might list working in an auto shop and putting new batteries in cars. People doing this work find out a lot about batteries. They learn what the electrodes are and what the electrolyte is. They also learn how long batteries may be used in cars before they must be replaced.

Perhaps you might list the work done by engineers and scientists. Certain engineers and scientists work with batteries. They work with batteries in special ways. Some test new materials to be used as electrodes. Others test new chemicals to be used as electrolytes. Still others try to build new kinds of batteries.

Someday you will choose a career. Will the career you choose have something to do with batteries? At this time, you probably don't know. Chances are you may never have to design or build a battery. But no matter what career you choose, whether you are a scientist or not, you will use batteries in many ways. You might use them in your job. You surely will use them in your daily life. Knowing something about batteries may help you use them wisely.

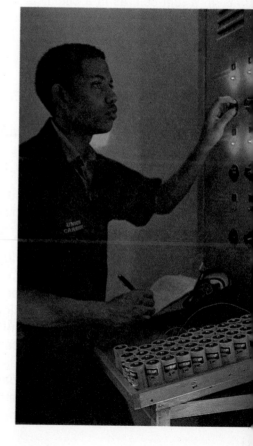

Photos courtesy of Union Carbide

Not everyone has a job involving the use of batteries, as these people do. But everyone uses batteries and should know something about them.

Reviewing and Extending

SUMMING UP

1. Early ideas about electricity included animal electricity and contact electricity. Later, chemical changes were shown to cause these kinds of electricity.
2. All chemical cells are similar in certain ways. All have two electrodes in an electrolyte.
3. In all chemical cells, electricity is made as a result of a chemical change.
4. Electrolysis is the breakdown, or separation, of a substance by means of a direct current.
5. Electroplating is the process of covering a material, most often a metal, with a layer of another kind of metal.
6. In a fuel cell, as in a chemical cell, electricity is made as a result of a chemical change.
7. In a solar cell, the energy of sunlight is changed to electric energy.
8. In a thermocouple, a difference in temperature is used to make electricity.

CHECKING UP

Vocabulary Write the numerals *1–7* on your paper. Each numbered phrase describes a term from the following list. On your paper, write the term next to the numeral of the phrase that describes it.

cryolite	thermocouple	pile
electrode	solar cell	electrolysis
electrolyte	fuel cell	electroplating

1. liquid that is a good conductor of electricity
2. mineral used to dissolve aluminum ore
3. earliest type of chemical cell that could be used to make electricity flow for a period of time
4. chemical change in which materials are broken down, or separated, by using electricity
5. device able to make electricity from a difference in temperature
6. part of a chemical cell on which the chemical changes that make electricity take place
7. process which covers a material with metal

Knowledge and Understanding Write the numerals *8–11* on your paper. Beside each numeral, write the word or words that best complete the sentence having that numeral.

8. The electricity supposedly caused by frog legs was called _____ electricity.

362

9. Electricity caused by a chemical reaction between two different metals in an acid solution became known as _____ electricity.
10. The first chemical cell consisting of two different metals and salt water was made by _____.
11. A metal that is separated from its ore by electrolysis is (*iron, lead, aluminum*).

Concepts Beside each of the numerals *12–14* on your paper, write the word or words that best complete the sentence having that numeral.

12. In order to make electricity, a dry cell must not be allowed to become (*dry, wet, pure*).
13. All chemical cells must contain (*one electrode and one electrolyte, two electrodes and one electrolyte, one electrode and two electrolytes*).
14. To make water an electrolyte, something must be added to the water to make it (*a conductor of electricity, melt aluminum powder, cover a material with metal*).

Application and Critical Thinking Answer the following questions as briefly as you can without leaving out any important ideas.

15. Is a dry cell really dry? Explain.
16. In what ways is a dry cell an improvement over a pile?

DOING MORE

1. Make several different kinds of chemical cells, using different combinations of metal strips as electrodes and different chemicals as electrolytes. Keep a record of the voltage made by each combination. Report your findings to the class.
2. Fill a glass about ¾ full of dilute sulfuric acid. *CAUTION: Handle the sulfuric acid with care.* Connect an end of a copper wire to a strip of copper and an end of another copper wire to a strip of zinc. Connect the free ends of the wires to a single-cell flashlight bulb. Place the 2 metal strips in the glass of acid, making sure that the strips do not touch. The bulb should light. Look carefully at the metal strips. After a little while, the bulb will be less bright. Again, look closely at the metal strips. Then remove the metal strips from the glass of acid. Wash the metal strips with water and dry them. Return the metal strips to the acid. Does the light burn brightly again? From your observations, what might have caused the bulb to become dim?

CHAPTER 19

Electricity for the Home

In your home, when it gets dark you can turn on the lights. That is, you turn on the electricity to light the lights. If you would like some toast, you put some bread in the toaster. Electricity in the toaster heats the bread and makes it brown. Sometimes you turn on the TV so you can watch a program. Electricity makes the TV work.

The electricity you use is not free. Whatever electricity is used must be paid for. Perhaps you know that before electricity comes into your home, it first goes through a meter. As you study this chapter, you will discover how to read a meter to find out how much electricity you use.

Using electricity can be dangerous. Therefore, to help you use electricity safely, certain safety devices are put in your home. As you study this chapter you will find out something about these devices. You will also discover some simple rules you can follow to help you use electricity safely.

The electricity that comes into your home is used in many different ways. How is the amount of electricity used in your home measured?

Zimmerman/FPG

De Wys, Inc.

ELECTRICITY IN YOUR HOME

*What are the voltages of the two most common
kinds of electric service in homes today?*

*Where is the electric service usually separated
into different circuits?*

*Why are electric appliances connected in par-
allel in a circuit?*

Electric service

The electricity that comes to your home is called electric service. In the past, most homes received 60-amp,
120-volt service. Over the years, the amount of electricity
used in the home has increased. Today, almost all new
homes have at least 100-amp, 240-volt service. With 100-
amp, 240-volt service, individual circuits in the house can
be connected so they are 120-volt circuits or so they are
240-volt circuits.

An electric *appliance* [uh-PLY-uhn(t)s] is a device that
uses electricity to do a certain job. Most electric appliances
use 120 volts. So, most circuits are 120-volt circuits. However, 240-volt circuits are needed for some electric appliances. Some electric appliances that use 240 volts are
electric stoves, electric water heaters, electric clothes dryers,
and large air conditioners.

Electric service comes into your home through large
wires. If your home has only 120-volt circuits, there are

*Figure 19–1. The amount of voltage
an appliance uses is usually shown
somewhere on the appliance. Why
is it important to know how much
voltage an appliance uses?*

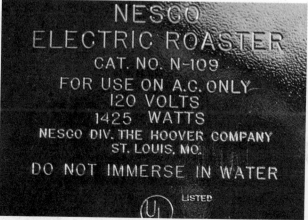

NESCO
ELECTRIC ROASTER
CAT. NO. N-109
FOR USE ON A.C. ONLY
120 VOLTS
1425 WATTS
NESCO DIV. THE HOOVER COMPANY
ST. LOUIS, MO.

DO NOT IMMERSE IN WATER

LISTED

two wires. If your home has 120-volt and 240-volt circuits, there are three wires. Sometimes these wires are buried underground so that you cannot see them.

★ **What advantages are there in having the electric service wires underground?**

Separate circuits

The wires that bring electric service into your home go into a service panel. See Figure 19–2. In the service panel, the electricity is separated into different circuits. Each circuit supplies electricity to a certain part of the house. There is a good reason for having different circuits in a house. Suppose your home has 100-amp service. The wires coming into the house must be able to carry 100 amps. So, these wires are large. But the appliances used on any one circuit do not use that much current. Each circuit needs to carry only fifteen or twenty amps. It would be a waste to use wires that could carry 100 amps in all parts of the house. The wires would cost a lot and be hard to install.

If you look at the service panel in your home or in Figure 19–2, you might see why it is often called a fuse box or a circuit-breaker box. In the service panel is a fuse or a circuit breaker to protect each circuit in the home.

For You to Think About

Most circuits in the home carry 120 volts. These circuits are connected to the outlets in the home. Circuits that carry 240 volts have special outlets. Appliances which use 120 volts cannot be plugged into them. What might happen if a 120-volt appliance were connected to such a circuit? Explain.

Figure 19–2. Every home has an electric service panel similar to the one shown here. Where is the service panel located in your home?

Investigate

How do fuses protect electric circuits?

You Will Need

electric bell, number 18 bell wire, block of wood, paper with aluminum foil from gum wrapper (to act as a fuse), knife switch, piece of metal, 2 thumbtacks, two 1.5-volt dry cells

Background

A fuse is connected in series in a circuit. A simple fuse consists of a thin piece of metal which will melt if the metal gets too hot. When too great a current moves through the fuse, the thin piece of metal gets hot and melts. When the fuse melts, the circuit is opened. The fuse will melt before the wiring in the circuit gets hot enough to do any damage to the wiring.

What to Do

Make a complete circuit by using the number 18 bell wire to connect the dry cells, electric bell, knife switch, and fuse. The drawing shows one possible plan for the circuit. The fuse is made by cutting a thin strip of foil from the gum wrapper. Use the block of wood, tacks, and foil strip in making the fuse. You may have to try using different widths of foil strips until you can cut a fuse which will allow the current to move through the circuit when connected properly, but will melt when there is a short circuit.

Remove some insulation from each of the two wires near the bell. The bell should ring when the knife switch is closed. Observe and record what happens to the bell and the fuse.

While the bell is ringing place a piece of metal across the two bared wires. Observe and record what happens to the bell and the fuse.

Now That You Have Done the Investigation

—Did the electric bell ring when you closed the switch?

—Did the fuse melt when the piece of metal was placed across the two bared wires? Explain.

—How do fuses protect the circuits in a house? How do they prevent a possible fire?

Plugs and outlets

Have you ever wondered how plugging in an appliance allows electricity to flow through that appliance? As you know, there is an electric plug at the end of the wire connected to every appliance. The plug is attached to what looks like one thick wire. But the thick wire, or cord, really has two wires in it. These wires are insulated so they do not touch each other.

Look carefully at an electric plug. The plug has two flat pieces of metal sticking out of it. Each flat piece of metal is connected to one of the wires in the cord. Each of these wires is connected to the appliance. The plug is used to connect the appliance to the wiring in the wall. See Figure 19–3.

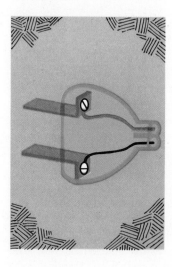
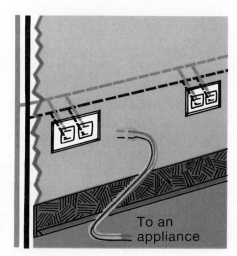

To an appliance

Figure 19–3. Notice that each of the flat pieces of metal on the plug touches a different wire when the plug is put into the outlet. What difference, if any, does it make if the plug is turned over? Explain.

Look closely at an electric outlet. Every outlet is connected to wiring that carries electricity. Do not place any metal thing such as a screwdriver, a hairpin, or anything else except an electric plug into the openings of an outlet.

Whenever you push the plug of an appliance into an electric outlet, the flat pieces of metal on the plug touch the wires that carry electricity. This connects the appliance to the electric circuit, so that when the appliance is switched on, the appliance will begin to work. The out-

Figure 19–4. These appliances are
all connected on the same circuit.
Can each appliance work separately?
How can you tell?

lets in a circuit are all connected in parallel. Therefore, any appliance plugged into the circuit can be used whether or not the other appliances plugged into that circuit are being used. See Figure 19–4.

★ **Why do appliances have an on-off switch instead of starting as soon as they are plugged into the circuit?**

THE COST OF ELECTRICITY

*What term is used to describe the rate at
    which electric energy is used?*
*What does the electric meter for your home
    measure?*

Measuring electricity

Electricity that comes into your home is used to do many things. It might be used to light up a light bulb or to make heat in a toaster. It might also be used to make sound in a radio or to move clothes and water in a washing machine. Although electricity does all these things, the number of electric charges that come into your home is the same as the number that leave. This may make you wonder just what is being used to do all these things. What is a person paying for when paying an electric bill?

369

The electric charges that move in the wires in your home have energy. Some of this energy is used by the electric appliances in doing different kinds of work. It is the energy that is paid for whenever an electric bill is paid.

Every electric appliance uses energy at a certain rate. The term that describes the rate at which electric energy is used by an appliance—that is, the power used by the appliance—is "watt." Most appliances are labeled to show how many watts they use. For example, light bulbs are labeled 60 watts, 75 watts, and so on. An electric iron might be labeled 600 watts. See Figure 19-5 for a list of examples of electric ratings of some home appliances.

Figure 19-5. Look at the labels on the appliances in your home. How do the numbers of watts used by the appliances in your home compare with the ratings shown here?

ELECTRIC RATINGS OF SOME HOME APPLIANCES	
Appliance	Watts
Light bulbs	7½ to 300
Radio	75 to 100
Television	200 to 300
Refrigerator	200 to 275
Electric iron	600 to 1 000
Toaster	500 to 1 000
Clock	1 to 3
Vacuum cleaner	150 to 500
Electric water heater	1 500 to 3 000

Terms used in measuring

The total amount of electric energy used in your home may be determined by knowing two things: the total number of watts for all the appliances being used and how long (the number of hours) the appliances are used. To figure out the total amount of electric energy used over a period of time, multiply the power (watts) by the time (hours). The term for electric energy being used is "watt-hour." One watt-hour is the amount of energy used when an appliance uses one watt for one hour.

The watt-hour is a very small amount of energy. Thus, the amount of electric energy used is usually measured in thousands of watt-hours. One thousand watt-hours is called a kilowatt-hour. This amount is easier to use when figuring electric bills. For example, if you use a 1 000-watt electric oven for one hour, you pay for one kilowatt-hour of energy.

★ **If a person uses a 500-watt vacuum cleaner for four hours, how many kilowatt-hours does the person pay for?**

Reading the meter

The electric power company uses an electric meter to measure the number of kilowatt-hours of electric energy used in a home. The meter is attached to the outside of the home. A person who works for the electric power company comes to read the meter every month or two. The number of kilowatt-hours used since the last reading of the meter is found by subtracting the last reading of the meter from the present reading of the meter.

You can learn to read an electric meter. Look at Figure 19–6. Notice the pointer on the first (left-hand) dial. Read the number passed last by the pointer. The pointer on the first dial is between the 2 and the 3, so you read 2. The pointer on the next dial is between the 4 and the 5, so you read 4. Doing the same thing for the next two dials, you find that the reading on the meter is 2 481.

★ **Suppose that last month the meter reading was 1 783. This month the reading is 2 481. How many kilowatt-hours of electricity were used during the month?**

Figure 19–6. Most electric meters have dials similar to those shown here. Look at the meter for your home. Does it have dials like these? What is the purpose of the meter?

DO IT YOURSELF

Study the electric meter for your home

Find the electric meter for your home. Look at the spinning disk. Notice that the disk has a black mark on it. You can use the mark to help you count the number of turns it makes. First, turn off as many electric appliances as possible. Observe and record the number of turns a minute as each appliance is turned on. Compare the number of turns made when a high-wattage appliance (air conditioner or heater) is being used with the number of turns made when a low-wattage appliance (light bulb or clock) is being used. What happens to the number of turns when both appliances are being used at the same time?

SAFETY WITH ELECTRICITY

When might electricity be dangerous?
How might grounded circuits protect you from electric shocks?
What can you do to keep safe with electricity?

Electric shock

Have you ever wondered why electric wires in your home must be covered with insulation? One reason is that a person touching an uncovered wire can get a shock. A shock is felt when electricity goes through a person.

You could get shocked if you touched an electric appliance such as a radio while you were taking a bath. As you know, an electric appliance is connected to the wiring in the home. There is electricity in the wiring. If you touch the appliance while you are wet, the electricity might flow into your wet hand, through your body, and through the water pipes to the ground.

Perhaps you do not know why being shocked is dangerous. Of course, not all electric shocks are dangerous. You probably have been shocked many times. Do you ever remember walking on a rug and then getting a shock when you touched someone or some metal object? This kind of shock might have surprised you, but it certainly was not dangerous.

If a lot of electricity flows through your body, however, the shock can be very dangerous. The danger is that a strong electric shock causes a person's muscles to become tight. If the shock is strong enough, the muscles become so tight that the person has no control over them. He or she may not be able to move away from the electricity that is causing the shock. The electricity may also stop the beating of a person's heart.

Short circuits and fires

To keep people from being shocked is not the only reason why the wires that carry electricity must be covered with insulation. Without insulation, two bare wires could touch each other. Two bare wires touching each other cause a short circuit. The term "short circuit" is used because the electricity does not go through the entire circuit. You might say that the electricity takes a shortcut. See Figure 19–7.

If a short circuit happens, the wires could get very hot. Sparks could occur. The very hot wires and/or the sparks could start a fire. Another cause of fires that are started by electricity is using one extension cord for several appliances. Using only one cord is dangerous because the

For You to Think About

Which would be more dangerous: touching an electric appliance while you are standing on a wet basement floor or touching the appliance while you are standing on a dry basement floor? Explain.

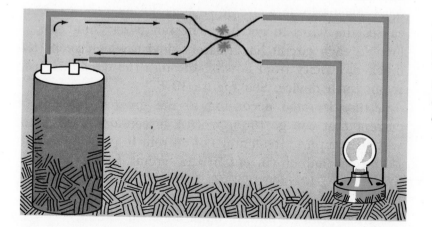

Figure 19–7. A short circuit could occur when the covering on electric wiring becomes worn or damaged. What happens to the flow of electricity when the two wires in the circuit touch each other? How could a short circuit be dangerous?

wires in the extension cord are much smaller than the wires in the rest of the circuit. The wiring in most circuits can safely carry fifteen amperes of current. However, an ordinary extension cord can safely carry only seven amperes. The wire in the extension cord could become overheated if too many appliances were connected to it all at the same time. The overheated wire could start a fire.

Grounded circuits

Today, when a home is wired for electricity, all the circuits are grounded. Usually the wiring that makes up the circuits is put inside metal pipes. The metal pipes are grounded by connecting them to the earth in some way. The pipes may be connected to the earth by connecting them to a water pipe or to a copper rod that has been put in the earth.

Even though a circuit is grounded, you must be careful. A grounded circuit can keep you from getting a strong electric shock when you touch an electric appliance. But you would get a very strong shock if you touched the wiring in a grounded circuit.

Fuses and breakers

Electric circuits in homes and other buildings are made safe in ways other than being grounded. Remember, too much electricity in a circuit, such as during a short circuit, causes the wires to get hot. The hot wires could start a fire. So each circuit has a safety device which keeps too much electricity from flowing through the circuit. A fuse is one such device. See Figure 19–8.

A fuse is rated according to the greatest amount of current that can go through it. A fifteen-amp fuse, then, will allow up to fifteen amps of current to pass through it. If the amount of current in the circuit (and, therefore, in the fuse) becomes greater than the rating of the fuse, the thin metal inside the fuse melts and opens the circuit. Electricity cannot flow through an open circuit.

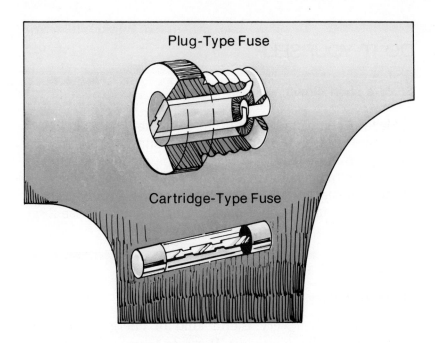

Plug-Type Fuse

Cartridge-Type Fuse

Figure 19–8. Two common types of fuses are shown above. How do fuses like these protect circuits? Which type is used in your home?

A circuit breaker is like a fuse in one way. That is, a circuit breaker opens the circuit if too much current is in the circuit. Because a circuit breaker is like a switch, it can be reset. But a burned-out fuse must be replaced with a new fuse.

Sometimes after a fuse is replaced or a circuit breaker is reset, it blows or opens again right away. If this keeps happening, something is wrong in the circuit. The wiring may have a short circuit. An electrician should be called to fix it. Perhaps an appliance being used has a short circuit. That appliance should be repaired or replaced. Perhaps too many appliances are being used on the same circuit at the same time. Then some appliances should be taken off the circuit.

★ **If a fuse or a circuit breaker is placed in a circuit, should it be wired into the circuit in parallel or in series? Explain.**

DO IT YOURSELF

Study a short circuit

Make a complete circuit using a dry cell, a small light bulb, and a fuse. The drawing shows one possible way for making up the circuit. The fuse may be made of a very thin strip of aluminum foil, such as that from a gum wrapper. Remove some insulation from each of the 2 wires connecting the bulb. Place a piece of metal across these 2 wires. What happens to the fuse? Explain.

Rules of safety

Electricity is a very useful kind of energy. However, electricity can be dangerous. It is safe to use only if certain rules of safety are closely followed. Here are some rules of safety that should be followed.

1. Never use an electric appliance when you are touching a water pipe, a gas pipe, a wet floor, a radiator, a sink, or a bathtub.
2. Never touch a light switch, a radio, or a TV set while taking a shower or a bath.
3. Never use an appliance that has a worn electric cord. Replace or repair such cords.
4. Never touch a wire that has fallen from a power line. Do not go near such a wire or anything touching the wire. Instead, call the police.
5. Never poke anything into an electric outlet or into an electric appliance that is plugged into an outlet.
6. Never climb a pole or a tree near electric wires.
7. Never put an extension cord under a rug or in a place where it could be cut.

If you follow these rules of safety, you are not likely to be hurt by electricity.

★ **What other rules can you think of that can help you be safe while using electricity?**

Using Electricity Safely

In this chapter you read about how you can use electricity safely in your home. But did you know that there are some people whose job it is to help make using electricity safer for you and for everyone else?

One person who is important in helping to make electricity safe to use is the electrician. Electricians put wires inside the walls of homes and other buildings. They connect the service panel to these wires. They also connect the outlets and the lights to wires. Electricians connect the wiring so that it will not shock people or start fires.

Another person who helps make electricity safe to use is the building inspector. While a building is being built the building inspector checks the work of the electrician. The inspector makes sure the correct wire size is being used. The inspector also checks to see whether the service panel has been put in correctly and whether the wires are connected correctly. When the right wires are used and connected correctly, a fire is not likely to start.

People who repair electric appliances also help make electricity safe to use. They repair electric appliances that could start a fire. They also repair appliances that could give you electric shocks. After being repaired, the appliances are safe to use again.

There are many other people who help make electricity safe to use. Perhaps someday you might choose a career that helps make electricity safe to use. But no matter what career you choose, it's good to know that there are many people who help make electricity safer for you to use.

Ronald Nielsen/Artstreet

Owen Franken/Stock, Boston

The work of electricians is very important in making electricity safe to use. What do you think these electricians are doing?

Reviewing and Extending

SUMMING UP

1. The electricity that comes into your home is called electric service.
2. At the service panel, the electric service is divided into different circuits. Fuses or circuit breakers that protect the circuits are located in the service panel.
3. As electric charges move through the wires in your home their energy may be used to do work.
4. The term that describes the rate at which an appliance uses electric energy is "watt."
5. The electric power company uses an electric meter to measure the amount of electric energy used in a home.
6. Wires that carry electricity must be covered with insulation because uncovered wires can cause shocks and can cause fires.
7. Electricity is safe to use if certain rules of safety are closely followed.

CHECKING UP

Vocabulary Write the numerals *1–7* on your paper. Each numbered phrase describes a term from the following list. On your paper, write the term next to the numeral of the phrase that describes it.

fuse	electric service	service panel
watt	electric outlet	appliance
shock	electric plug	electric meter

1. electricity that comes into a home
2. place where the electricity that comes into a home is separated into different circuits
3. measures the amount of electricity used in a home
4. has openings for electric plugs
5. term that describes the rate at which electricity is used by an appliance
6. opens a circuit if too much current is in the circuit
7. felt when electricity goes through a person

Knowledge and Understanding Write the numerals *8–12* on your paper. Beside each numeral, write the word or words that best complete the sentence having that numeral.

8. Today, almost all new homes have 120 _____-amp, 240-volt service.
9. All the circuits in a home are connected to the electricity coming into the home at the *service panel*

10. One difference between a circuit breaker and a fuse is that a *circuit breaker* can be reset, while the other must be replaced.

11. A (*service panel, meter, fuse*) measures the amount of electric energy used in a home.

12. All the outlets and lights in each circuit are connected (*in parallel, in series, to the same switch*).

Concepts Beside each of the numerals *13–16* on your paper, write the word or words that best complete the sentence having that numeral.

13. The electric service wires that come into your home need to be (*large, small, 7-amp*) wires.

14. Each circuit supplies electricity to (*all parts, a certain part, no part*) of the home.

15. Grounding a circuit protects you from (*fires, fuses, strong shocks*) while touching electric appliances on that circuit.

16. In paying an electric bill, a person is paying for (*all the electric charges flowing through the circuits, the use of the meter, the electric energy used in the home*).

Application and Critical Thinking Answer the following questions as briefly as you can without leaving out any important ideas.

17. What is the meaning of the rating "15 amps" on a fuse or circuit breaker?

18. This month's meter reading is shown at the right. Suppose that last month the meter reading was 2 473 kilowatt-hours. Also suppose that the average cost for electric energy is 4 cents a kilowatt-hour. What would be the cost of the electric energy used during the month?

KILOWATT-HOURS

DOING MORE

1. Find out the rate per kilowatt-hour for using electric energy where you live. The local electric power company can give you this information, or you can figure it out from your electric bill. Figure the cost of using all the light bulbs in your home. Figure how many kilowatt-hours would be used if all the bulbs were on for 3 hours.

2. Find out what kinds of fuses or circuit breakers are used in your home and in your school. What kind of metal is used in a fuse? Take apart an old fuse. Study all the different parts of the fuse. Make a drawing of all the parts you study.

Pros and Cons

Hold your speed under 50.

Lower your thermostat to 68.

Turn off all unused lights and appliances.

DON'T BE FUELISH

Posters like these help remind people not to waste electricity. How can you reduce your use of electricity?

Electric Energy—How Should We Meet Our Need?

Do you know what a brownout is? During a brownout, electric lights and electric appliances do not work properly. A brownout would happen if the supply of electricity could not meet the demand for electricity. For example, a brownout could happen during very hot weather. The use of many air conditioners might cause a demand for electricity that is greater than the supply. But, some people are saying that brownouts will happen even if we don't have very hot weather. They say that brownouts will happen because the population is increasing and because each person is using more and more electricity. For these two reasons, the demand for electricity is going to increase faster than the supply will increase.

One way to avoid brownouts would be for people to reduce the amount of electricity they use. However, no one knows if people would be willing to reduce their use of electricity. In fact, many people say that the best way to avoid brownouts is to build more plants for generating electricity.

If more electricity-generating plants are to be built, an important question must be answered. What source of energy will be used to produce the electricity? Today, most electricity is produced by burning fuels such as coal, oil, and natural gas. However, deciding which fuel is best is difficult. There are reasons for using or not using each kind. For example, using coal is good because there is plenty of it and its cost is low. But using coal causes air pollution, and the devices that could be used to keep the burning of coal from polluting the air cost a great deal of money.

Fuel oil and natural gas are used to produce electricity whenever extra electricity is needed for a short time. These fuels do not pollute the air as much as coal. However, the supply of oil and natural gas is limited and they cost much more than coal.

Perhaps the demand for more electricity could be met by building more nuclear power plants. Nuclear power plants do not pollute the air with smoke and gases. Nuclear fuel is not in short supply. To date, nuclear power plants have had excellent safety records. However, some people say that nuclear power plants are not safe. They claim that an accident could release deadly radiation. The accident could occur at the power plant or during transportation and storage of fuel or wastes. There is also the fear that nuclear power plants will cause pollution in the form of heat and radioactivity.

There are other kinds of energy which could be used to produce electricity. For example, the energy of the wind and of the tides could be used. Solar energy could be used, too. None of these would cause air pollution. However, the big problem with them is that they would not always be dependable. For example, solar energy

Pollution is one problem that may increase as we try to meet our need for electricity. What two types of pollution are suggested by these pictures? How might these types of pollution be kept under control?

could not be used during cloudy weather. Likewise, wind could not be used to produce electricity when the air was quiet. Tides are dependable in some places, but not all places have tides great enough to be useful.

There are many questions about meeting our need for electricity. Consider the increased population and the increased demand for electricity by each person. Can people reduce their use of electricity so new plants need not be built? If more plants are built, should these plants use coal, oil, or gas? Should more nuclear power plants be built? Should new plants use energy from wind, water, or sun? You can see that for each way to produce electricity, there are some pros and some cons. How do *you* think we should meet our need for more electricity?

Investigate On Your Own

1. Try making a galvanoscope. You will need a compass, a switch, a dry cell, a length of number 18 insulated copper wire, and a piece of cardboard. Cut a round hole in the center of the cardboard so that the compass may be fitted into it. Fit the compass into the cardboard so that the wire you wind around the compass and cardboard is wound over the north and south poles marked on the compass. Attach an end of the wire to the switch and the other end to a post of the dry cell. Use a short length of wire to connect the switch to the other post of the dry cell.

Close the switch for a few seconds to test the galvanoscope. Notice what happens to the position of the compass needle. Repeat your test after you reverse the connections on the dry cell. Again notice what happens to the position of the compass needle.

Try increasing and decreasing the number of turns of wire around the compass. How is the compass needle affected when more turns of wire are used? When fewer turns of wire are used? Test different sizes of wire and different combinations of dry cells. How is the needle affected?

2. Using insulated copper wire, a galvanometer (or very sensitive ammeter), a bolt, and a magnet, set up an arrangement of equipment as shown. Make sure the wire that is wound around the bolt and attached to the galvanometer does not touch the wire that is wound around the bolt and formed into an open coil. Move the magnet back and forth in the open coil. Observe the effect on the needle of the galvanometer. What happens if you move the magnet faster? What happens if the procedure is repeated with coils of various numbers of turns?

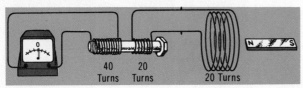

Read On Your Own

Asimov, Isaac, *How Did We Find Out About Electricity?* New York: Walker & Company, 1973.

This book contains an interesting, lively account of the history of electricity from the time of the early Greek philosophers to modern times.

Press, Hans Jurgen, *Science Projects for Young People.* New York: Van Nostrand Reinhold Company, 1971.

Here is a book with over 200 safe, easy-to-do, fun projects that require only household material for learning about basic concepts in all the major sciences, including electricity and magnetism.

Sootin, Harry, *Experiments with Electric Currents.* New York: Grosset & Dunlap, Inc., 1969.

This book is a collection of experiments and information about electromagnets, motors, and circuits.

Stone, A., and Siegel, B., *Turned On: A Look at Electricity.* Englewood Cliffs, New Jersey: Prentice-Hall, Inc., 1970.

This book about people and the ways they studied electricity and magnetism gives some ideas about what it means to be a scientist.

UNIT **5**

WAVES

Moving Energy from Place to Place

You have seen waves in water many times. But the waves you see in water are only one kind of wave. Scientists believe that there are many other kinds of waves. Many of these waves cannot be seen, but they are used by scientists to explain how energy moves from place to place. For example, have you ever seen radio, radar, or television waves? (You do not see television waves when you watch television.) And have you ever seen sound waves? No, you have not. And yet scientists tell us that many kinds of energy, including sound energy and light energy, move from place to place as waves.

Chapters

Photo Research International

CHAPTER 20

Moving Waves

Have you ever been to the beach on a windy day? If so, you may have seen waves traveling into the shore. How can the waves on the beach be described? You might say, for example, that the waves come into the shore in a regular pattern. One wave seems to be very much like another wave, and the waves seem to be evenly spaced.

What is causing the waves? The waves that you see at the beach on a certain day are all about the same height. But if you go to the beach on a day which is not as windy, the waves would not be as high. It seems that the waves are bigger on windy days than on calm days. The wind seems to be causing the waves.

But is wind the only thing that can cause waves? Can different kinds of waves be made in the same material? How do waves move from one place to another? In this chapter you will find answers to these and other questions about waves.

Water waves have energy as they move in toward the shore. Where do you think the waves get their energy?

William B. Finch/Stock, Boston

WHAT ARE WAVES?

How is the word "wave" defined?
How do waves travel from one place to another?
What does the amplitude of a wave have to do
with energy?
In what way are frequency, wave length, and
speed of waves related?

Can you define "wave"?

You have heard the word "wave" used in many different ways. For example, you can wave good-bye to someone. You might have a wave in your hair. You can make a wave by throwing a stone into water.

If you look in a dictionary, you will find even more ways to use the word "wave." One definition for wave is

a disturbance in a medium that transfers energy progressively from one point to another ...

There are two points to remember from this definition. (1) A wave is a *disturbance* [dihs-TUR-buhn(t)s] in a *medium* [MEED-ee-uhm]. (2) A wave moves *energy* [EHN-ur-jee] from place to place.

In this definition of "wave," the medium is some form of matter. The medium could be a pool of water, the air in a room, a piece of rope, a coiled spring, or any other material. A disturbance is any part of the medium that has been changed from its normal position. Energy is the ability to do work, or to cause activity.

How do waves travel?

Part of the definition of "wave" is that a wave moves energy from place to place. In order to move this energy, the wave must move *through* the medium. But the medium itself does not move. The following example will help you understand how waves travel.

Place a small piece of wood in a large pan of water. When the water is still, drop a small stone into the pan. The stone will make waves in the water. Watch the way the wood moves. The wood moves up and down. But it

For You to Think About

Try to remember some waves you have seen. In what materials have you seen these waves? What caused each of the different kinds of waves to be made? What kinds of waves have you seen most often? Do you think there may be some kinds of waves which you cannot see? If so, what kinds of waves do you think these are?

387

does not move along with the waves. The wood stays in about the same place it was before the waves passed.

Amplitude, frequency, and wave length

You can also watch a wave made in a long rope. Try this. Tie one end of a rope to a table or to any fixed object. What happens when you flip the free end up, then down, and then back to its first position? You can watch a wave move along the rope. See Figure 20–1.

In a wave like the one in the rope, the high point is called the *crest*. The low point is called the *trough* [TRAWF]. The *amplitude* [AM-pluh-T(Y)OOD] of a wave such as this is half the distance from the bottom of a trough to the top of a crest. Waves with a large amplitude transmit more energy as they travel than do waves with a smaller amplitude.

Waves are often made one right after another. Think again about the rope tied to the table. What would happen if you kept repeating the up-and-down motion of your hand? Then, as the first wave moves toward the table, another wave would be formed just behind it. A series of waves would be made.

The number of waves made in one second is called the *frequency* [FREE-kwuhn-see] of the waves. Scientists use the term *hertz* [HURTS] to describe frequency. One hertz means the same as one wave a second. Ten hertz would be ten waves a second, and so on. See Figure 20–2.

Suppose some waves are made one right after another in a series. A way to describe one wave in such a group of waves is by its length, called a *wave length*. A wave

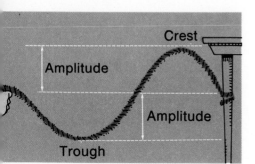

Figure 20–1. The crest, the trough, and the amplitude of a wave are shown in the diagram. After looking at the diagram, how would you describe each of these properties of a wave?

Figure 20–2. What is the frequency of the waves in the rope if one second has elapsed between the diagram in A and the diagram in B?

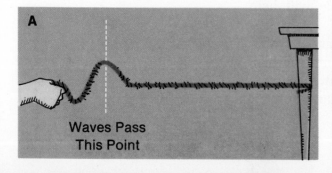
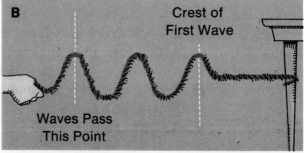

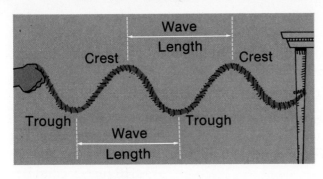

Figure 20–3. After looking at the diagram, how would you describe what the term "wave length" means?

length is the distance between any place on one wave and the same place on the next wave. So a wave length could be the distance between the crest of one wave and the crest of the next wave. It also could be the distance between the trough of one wave and the trough of the next wave. See Figure 20–3.

★ **Some kinds of waves in the ocean have a very large amplitude as they move into the shore. What can you say about the energy of these waves?**

Let's speed it up!

Waves travel at different speeds in different mediums. Think about the example of the rope again. If you used a heavy rope, waves would travel through it at a rate different from the rate of waves traveling through a lightweight rope.

In the same medium, however, waves travel at the same speed, regardless of the amplitude or the frequency of the waves. Because of the constant speed of waves through a particular medium, there is a relationship between frequency, wave length, and speed. This relationship is

$$\text{Frequency} \times \text{Wave Length} = \text{Speed}.$$

Scientists say that the speed of one wave in a series of waves is the product of the frequency and the wave length. This relationship is true for any series of waves. So knowing the frequency and wave length, you could find the speed.

Suppose that the frequency of a series of waves is 200 hertz (waves a second). Suppose the wave length of each wave is 2.0 metres (about 6½ feet). To find the speed, you would multiply the frequency by the wave length. The way to do it is given below.

$$\text{Frequency} \times \text{Wave Length} = \text{Speed}$$

200 waves/second $\times$ 2.0 metres/wave =
$$400 \text{ metres/second}$$
(200 waves/second $\times$ 6.56 feet/wave =
$$1{,}310 \text{ feet/second})$$

★ **Suppose you knew the speed and the frequency of a series of waves. Could you find the wave length? If so, how would you do it? Suppose you knew the speed and the wave length. Could you find the frequency? If so, how would you do it?**

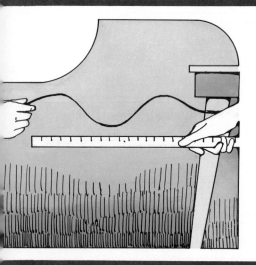

DO IT YOURSELF

Find the speed of waves that you make

Tie a long rope to some fixed object, such as a table. Make waves in the rope by flipping the free end up and then down. Repeat this motion at a steady rate. Count how many waves you make in thirty seconds. Divide this number by thirty to find the frequency of the waves in hertz.

Have another person use a metre stick to measure the wave length in metres as closely as possible. Then multiply the frequency by the wave length to find the speed of the waves you made.

SOME KINDS OF WAVES

What kind of wave can be made to travel in a piece of rope?
What kinds of waves can be made to travel in a stretched coil spring?
How are standing waves made?

What's a transverse wave?

The shape of the waves you can make in a piece of rope is much like the shape of water waves. Both kinds

390

have a crest and a trough. These two different waves—water waves and waves in a rope—are examples of one kind of wave. They are *transverse* [tran(t)s-VURS] *waves*.

Perhaps you know that the word "transverse" means across. If so, you may be wondering why this kind of wave is called transverse. Evidently something crosses something else as these waves travel.

Think again about the rope tied to the table. Suppose the rope is marked in one place with a piece of red yarn. Suppose, too, that a series of waves is made in the rope. The marked spot moves up and down as the waves move toward the table. See Figure 20–4.

There are two things to notice in the figure. (1) Each wave moves along the length of the rope. (2) The spot on the rope moves up and down. So, the direction any one spot on the rope moves is at right angles to, or across, the direction in which the wave moves. Now you can see why these waves are called transverse waves.

★ **Do you think the waves moving through a flag on a windy day are transverse waves? Why or why not?**

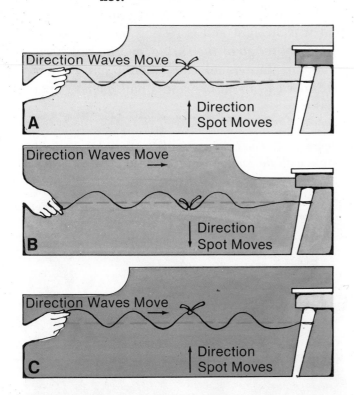

Figure 20–4. These diagrams show three stages in the motion of a transverse wave along a rope. In A, the marked spot moves up as a wave travels through. In B, the spot moves down as a wave travels through. In C, the spot moves up again. How does the direction the marked spot moves compare with the direction the waves move?

DO IT YOURSELF

Make transverse waves

Tie one end of a long piece of rope to a table or some other object. Tie a piece of yarn or wrap a piece of tape around the rope at one place. Make a series of waves in the rope. Notice how the place that is marked on the rope moves up and down. How is the moving of the place on the rope different from the moving of each wave?

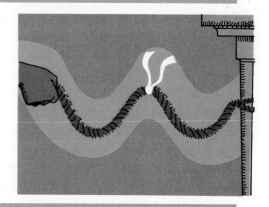

What's a longitudinal wave?

Another kind of wave is known as a *longitudinal* [LAHN-juh-T(Y)OOD-nuhl] *wave.* Longitudinal waves can be made in a stretched *coil* [KOY(UH)L] *spring.* A good coil spring for looking at longitudinal waves is a toy called a Slinky. See Figure 20–5.

If you have a Slinky, place it on a smooth floor. Have someone hold one end of the spring to keep it from moving. Now hold the other end of the spring and stretch the spring so that it is straight and is resting on the floor. *BE CAREFUL: Do not let go of the spring, and do not stretch the spring too far.* Individual coils should not be more than four centimetres (about one and a half inches) apart. See Figure 20–6.

Figure 20–5. Have you ever held a Slinky in your hands as the person in the picture is doing? If you have, you know how the spring behaves as you let the coils move from hand to hand.

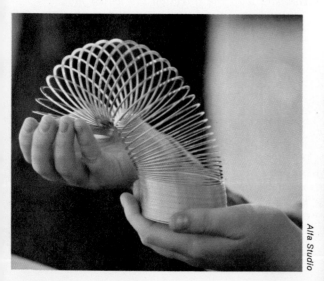

Alfa Studio

Figure 20–6. The boys are ready to make longitudinal waves with the spring. How will they make the waves?

John D. Firestone & Associates, Inc.

With the spring stretched and on the floor, quickly move the end of the spring you are holding a short distance toward the other end of the spring and then back to its first position. You will be able to see a wave move along the spring.

As the wave travels in the spring, there are places where the coils of the spring move close together. In other places the coils move far apart. The places where the coils move close together are called *compressions* [kuhm-PREHSH-uhnz]. The places where the coils move far apart are called *rarefactions* [RAR-uh-FAK-shuhnz]. See Figure 20–7.

Mark a spot on the spring with a piece of yarn. Then move your hand back and forth rapidly to cause a series of compressions and rarefactions to move through the spring. Look closely at the yarn as the waves move through the spring. You should see two things. (1) The waves move along the length of the spring. (2) The spot you marked on the spring moves back and forth in a direction parallel to the direction in which the waves move. See Figure 20–7 again.

The word "longitudinal" means related to length or to the lengthwise direction. Individual parts of the spring move back and forth in a direction parallel to the length of the spring. So waves that have a series of compressions and rarefactions are called longitudinal waves.

★ **What do you think would happen if you moved your hand back and forth a greater distance as you made the longitudinal waves? Why?**

Find Out More

You have learned that longitudinal waves can be made in a stretched coil spring. But longitudinal waves can be made in many other mediums too. Using references, find out in what mediums longitudinal waves can be made.

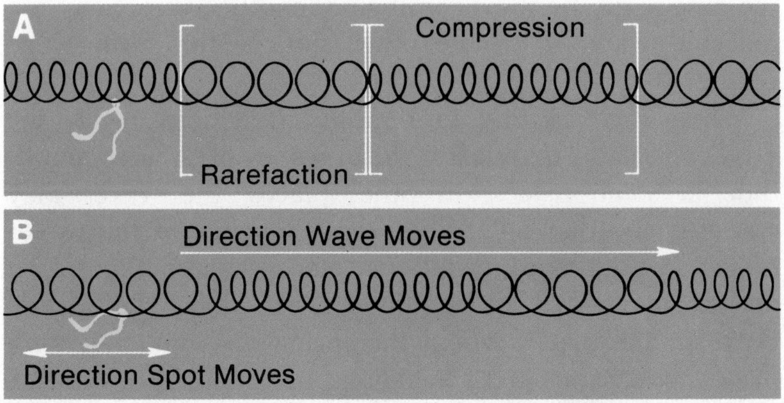

Figure 20–7. In the diagrams at the left, longitudinal waves are moving from left to right. What happens to the marked spot as the waves move through the spring?

393

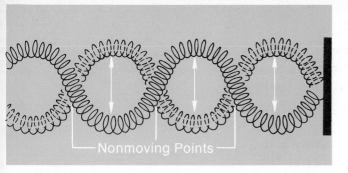

Figure 20–8. Standing waves may be made when incoming waves and reflected waves interact. In standing waves, parts of the spring do not move.

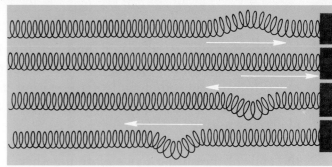

Figure 20–9. A transverse wave is shown being reflected from a fixed end of a spring. How is the reflected wave different from the incoming wave?

What are standing waves?

Suppose the spring is stretched out on the floor, as before. One end is tied to something, such as a table leg, so the end will not move. Suppose, too, that a series of transverse waves is made by moving the free end from side to side. If the waves are made at just the right rate, certain parts of the spring move back and forth rapidly while other parts of the spring do not move at all. When this happens, *standing waves* are being made. They are called standing waves because they do not seem to be moving along the spring. See Figure 20–8.

To understand how such waves are made, you should know what happens to just one wave. A wave made by moving the free end of the spring will move toward the fixed end. When it gets to the fixed end, it *reflects* [rih-FLEHKTS], or bounces back. The reflected wave then moves along the spring in the other direction, or toward the free end. Besides going in the other direction, the reflected wave is on the other side of the spring. See Figure 20–9.

When waves going in opposite directions meet, the waves may add together to form waves of greater amplitude in some places. In other places, the waves may cancel each other out. When the frequency of the waves is just right, the cancelled-out places—where the spring doesn't move—are all equally spaced along the spring. Between the places where the spring does not move are places where the spring is moving back and forth rapidly.

Investigate

How is the frequency of a standing wave on a spring related to the distance between places on the spring that do not move?

You Will Need

coiled spring, metre stick, watch

Background

You know how standing waves can be made in a stretched coil spring. By changing the rate at which you move the free end of the spring back and forth (the frequency), you can make standing waves of different lengths. In this investigation you will make standing waves of different frequencies to find out how the frequency is related to the distance between the places on the spring that do not move.

What to Do

Attach one end of the spring to a fixed object. Stretch the spring so that it is flexible enough to be stretched out farther, but still able to spring back if you let go.

Cause transverse waves to be formed in the spring by moving your hand from side to side at a regular rate. Try moving the spring at different rates until you can make standing waves. Then, using a watch, find out the number of waves made in one minute. This number is the frequency. Record this number. Have a partner use a metre stick to measure the distance between two places on the spring that are not moving. Record the distance.

Cause transverse waves to be formed faster in the spring by moving your hand from side to side at a faster rate. Make the frequency greater and greater until you find another frequency at which standing waves are formed. Then, using a watch, find out the number of waves made in one minute. Record this number. Again measure the distance between places that are not moving. Record the distance.

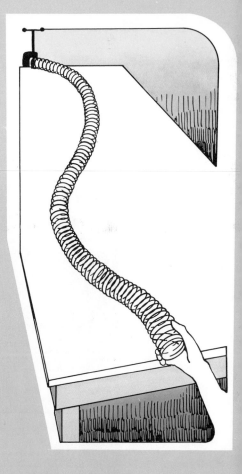

Now That You Have Done the Investigation

—Which distance was longer—the first distance measured or the distance measured when the frequency was greater?
—According to your results, how is the frequency related to the distance between places that are not moving on a standing wave?

WAVES IN WATER

*What kind of water wave can be made by dipping
  your finger into water?*
*What kind of water wave can be made by dipping
  the length of a long bar into water?*
*What is the difference between reflected waves
  and refracted waves?*

What's a ripple tank?

When most people think of waves, they think of water
waves. This is because people often see these waves. Keep
in mind as you study water waves that all water waves
are transverse waves. Also keep in mind that many of the
characteristics of water waves also hold true for other
kinds of waves, such as sound waves and light waves.

One way to study water waves is by using a tank in
which you can make waves. Such a tank is called a *ripple
tank* because ripples, or small waves, are made in it. In
this tank you can control many of the things that affect
water waves. See Figure 20–10.

In using a ripple tank, you do not look at the waves
directly. A piece of white paper is placed on the tabletop or on the floor beneath the tank. A clear light bulb

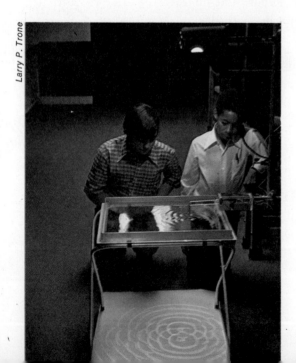

Larry P. Trone

*Figure 20–10. The boys in the picture
are working with a ripple tank. As you
can see, the pattern of ripples in the
tank can be seen on the paper below the
tank. How is the pattern made to appear
on the paper?*

is hung above the tank. The light shines through the water onto the white paper.

When the water is still, the paper is evenly lighted. But when waves are made in the tank, the paper is not evenly lighted. A pattern of light and dark places can be seen on the paper. The pattern of light and dark places makes it easy to study the way that waves, or ripples, move in the tank.

Making waves

Some of the ways that waves behave can be studied by looking at single waves. For example, what happens when your finger is dipped in and out of the water in a ripple tank? Your finger pushes down on the water, making a trough where it touches the water. At the same time that the trough is made, a crest forms all around the trough. Because of this, a *circular* [SUR-kyuh-lur] *wave* moves away from the place where you dipped your finger.

For some studies of waves, straight waves are wanted. But how can such waves be made? A straight wave can be made by dipping the length of a long bar into the water. The bar pushes down on the water and transfers energy to the water. Because of this, all along the length of the bar, water is pushed away from the bar. The crest of the wave and the trough of the wave then move away from the bar, forming a straight wave.

★ **What do you suppose you would have to do to make a series of circular waves or a series of straight waves?**

Water waves that are reflected

Using a ripple tank is a good way to study what happens when a wave is reflected. First, a *barrier* [BAR-ee-ur] is placed in the tank. A barrier is some hard object, like a board or a block of paraffin. When a wave hits the barrier, the wave bounces off. This bouncing off is called *reflection* [rih-FLEHK-shuhn].

What happens when a circular wave is reflected from a straight barrier? The reflected wave is also circular. But

Figure 20–11. *What kinds of waves are in the water? Which wave has the highest crest and the deepest trough? What do you think caused the waves?*

397

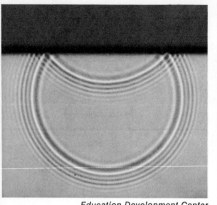

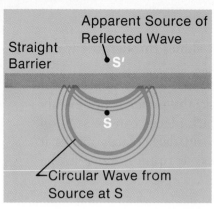

Straight Barrier

Apparent Source of Reflected Wave

S'

S

Circular Wave from Source at S

Education Development Center

Figure 20–12. A photograph and a diagram of a circular wave being reflected from a straight barrier are shown at the left. In what direction does the wave move after it is reflected?

the reflected wave appears to have started from a point behind the barrier. See Figure 20–12.

Now suppose that a straight barrier is placed in the ripple tank so that a straight wave will hit it at an angle. The straight wave hits the barrier and bounces off. See *A* of Figure 20–13.

The angle at which the straight wave hits the straight barrier determines the direction in which the wave will be reflected. Look at *B* of Figure 20–13. Black direction lines show the direction of the waves. A dashed line perpendicular to the barrier is shown at the place where the direction lines touch the barrier.

The angle between the dashed line and the direction line for the incoming wave is labeled *a*. The angle be-

Figure 20–13. The diagram in A shows a straight wave being reflected from a straight barrier which is at an angle to the wave source. In B, the wave is not shown; however, the arrows show the direction of the incoming wave and the reflected wave. How does angle a compare with angle b?

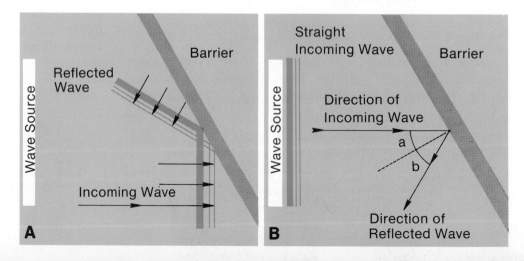

A
Wave Source
Reflected Wave
Barrier
Incoming Wave

B
Wave Source
Straight Incoming Wave
Barrier
Direction of Incoming Wave
a
b
Direction of Reflected Wave

tween the dashed line and the direction line of the reflected wave is labeled *b*. If you were to measure each angle in *B* of Figure 20–13, you would discover that angle *a* equals angle *b*. When waves are reflected from a straight barrier, angle *a* and angle *b* are always equal. Be sure to keep this in mind when you read about reflection in other chapters in this unit.

★ **How is the reflection of waves in a ripple tank like the reflection of a mirror?**

The crooked wave

The depth of the water in a ripple tank affects the speed of the waves. The waves travel slower in shallow water than they do in deep water.

Suppose a flat piece of glass is placed in the water at one end of the ripple tank. Then the water at one end of the tank will be shallower than it is at the other end. What happens when straight waves move from the deep end to the shallow end?

If the waves hit the shallow end at an angle, something interesting happens. The waves entering the shallow end are bent. The direction in which the waves travel is changed. Such a change in the direction in which waves travel is called *refraction* [rih-FRAK-shuhn]. The direction changes because the waves move slower in shallow water. The waves are said to be *refracted* [rih-FRAK-tuhd]. Look at Figure 20–14.

For You to Think About

When you look through eyeglasses, binoculars, or a magnifying glass, the light that comes to your eyes has been refracted, or bent. Why? What causes the light to be refracted? How is the refraction of light like the refraction of water waves?

Education Development Center

Figure 20–14. The photograph at the left shows the refraction of waves as they enter a shallow area in a ripple tank. What happens to cause waves to be refracted?

Investigate

What happens to waves you make with a medicine dropper in a pan of water?

You Will Need

flat pan, medicine dropper, water

Background

You have read about circular waves that are made in a ripple tank. The sides of the ripple tank usually stop the circular waves. In this investigation, however, the sides of the pan will not stop the waves.

What to Do

Fill the flat pan about half full of water. Then place the pan on the floor or on a tabletop. Fill a medicine dropper with water. Allow one drop of water to fall from the medicine dropper into the center of the pan of water. Notice what happens when the wave made by the drop of water hits the sides of the pan. Next, allow one drop of water to fall from the medicine dropper into the water near a corner of the pan. Notice what happens when the wave made by the drop of water hits the sides of the pan in this case.

Now allow drops of water to fall from the medicine dropper into the center of the pan at a regular rate. Make a sketch of the pattern of waves that you see. Then let drops of water fall at a regular rate into the water near a corner of the pan. Make a sketch of the pattern of waves that you see.

Now That You Have Done the Investigation

—What happened when a circular wave that started in the center of the pan hit the sides of the pan? Explain.

—What happened when a circular wave that started near a corner of the pan hit the sides of the pan? Explain.

—What caused the pattern of waves that you saw when drops of water fell into the center of the pan at a regular rate? Explain.

—What caused the pattern of waves that you saw when drops of water fell near a corner of the pan at a regular rate? Explain.

Courtesy of U.S. Geological Survey

Seismographs are able to detect waves made by earthquakes and nuclear explosions. Interpreting these waves is an important part of this seismologist's job.

Earthquakes and Seismologists

Do you know which water waves have the largest amplitude of all? They are the waves called *seismic* [SYZ-mihk] *sea waves,* or *tidal waves.* Even though these waves are sometimes called tidal waves, they really have nothing to do with tides. But seismic sea waves are closely related to earthquakes.

As you may know, earthquakes that happen near cities or towns may cause a great deal of damage. But earthquakes under the sea may also cause damage. Undersea earthquakes may cause seismic sea waves to move toward land. Such waves have damaged cities and towns near the ocean throughout history. But today something is being done to prevent the loss of life which used to happen when seismic sea waves hit these cities and towns. Today people are warned of the coming of these waves.

A system for predicting seismic sea waves is now being used. The system for predicting them is based on detecting waves in the earth made by earthquakes. At different places on the earth, scientists called *seismologists* [syz-MAHL-uh-juhsts] have set up recording stations to detect and measure earthquake waves. These recording stations have detectors called *seismographs* [SYZ-muh-GRAFS]. Seismographs help seismologists find out where and when undersea earthquakes have happened. Using this information, they can figure out how long it will take for a seismic sea wave to reach certain cities and towns. Then people can be warned in time.

Seismologists do many other things too. For example, they find out where earthquakes and nuclear explosions have happened anywhere in the world. As you can see, these scientists have an interesting job and one that sometimes saves lives.

Reviewing and Extending

SUMMING UP

1. A wave moves through matter without the matter itself changing its overall position.
2. There is a relationship between the frequency, wave length, and speed of waves in a series.
3. Transverse waves have crests and troughs as they move.
4. Longitudinal waves have compressions and rarefactions as they move.
5. Standing waves are made when transverse waves come together in just the right way with other transverse waves that have been reflected.
6. The angle at which straight water waves hit a straight barrier is equal to the angle at which the waves leave the barrier.
7. When water at one end of a ripple tank is shallower than it is at the other end, water waves are refracted. They are refracted because waves travel slower in shallower water.

CHECKING UP

Vocabulary   Write the numerals *1–7* on your paper. Each numbered phrase describes a term from the following list. On your paper, write the term next to the numeral of the phrase that describes it.

2 crest   amplitude   rarefaction
3 energy   frequency   refraction
  trough   reflection   compression

1. number of waves made in one second
2. high point of a wave
3. the ability to do work or to cause activity
4. place in a longitudinal wave where the medium is spread apart
5. distance from a middle line of a wave to either the crest or the trough
6. bouncing of a wave
7. bending of a wave

Knowledge and Understanding   Write the numerals *8–11* on your paper. Beside each numeral, write the word or words that best complete the sentence having that numeral.

8. A kind of wave which can be made in a stretched coil spring and which travels by a series of compressions and rarefactions is called a (*longitudinal, standing, transverse*) wave.
9. When a pointed object is dipped in water, a (*straight, circular, longitudinal*) wave is made.

402

10. If a flat piece of glass is placed in the water at one end of a ripple tank so that the water is shallower at that end, waves coming to it at an angle will be (*stopped, reflected, refracted*).

11. In a series of waves, the distance between any place on one wave and the same place on the next wave is called (*an amplitude, a hertz, a wave length*).

Concepts   Beside each of the numerals *12–14* on your paper, write the word or words that best complete the sentence having that numeral.

12. Transverse waves are waves in which individual points on the wave move across the direction in which (*the waves move, the amplitude moves, marked spots on the wave move*).

13. The angle between a straight barrier and a wave moving to the barrier is (*greater than, equal to, less than*) the angle between the barrier and the reflected wave.

14. Longitudinal waves are waves in which individual points on the wave move (*perpendicular, parallel, at right angles*) to the direction in which the waves move.

Application and Critical Thinking   Answer the following questions as briefly as you can without leaving out any important ideas.

15. Suppose that transverse waves are made in a piece of heavy rope that is tied to a tree. How are the waves that are reflected from the fixed end different from the incoming waves?

16. What is the relationship between frequency, wave length, and amplitude when waves move through a medium at a constant speed?

DOING MORE

1. Tie one end of each of two different sizes of coiled springs together. Place them on a smooth floor. Have a classmate hold one free end and you hold the other. Cause a transverse wave to travel from one spring to the other. Can your partner detect the wave? Then have your partner cause a wave. Can you detect it? Can your partner detect a reflected wave? What happens as the wave moves from one spring to the other? Where is the reflected wave coming from? How do you know?

2. Make straight waves in water. Allow the waves to hit some barriers that are curved inward and some that are curved outward. What happens to the reflected waves when they hit each kind of barrier? Explain.

CHAPTER 21

Sound Waves

From the time you wake up in the morning until you are asleep at night, you hear many sounds. You may hear the sound of wind, the chirping of crickets, the rumble of thunder, the screeching of car tires, and the sirens of fire engines and police cars. You also hear people talk—either directly or on a telephone. You probably also listen to a radio and record player. Sound, then, is a very important part of your life.

But what is sound? How is it detected and measured? What are some ways in which people have learned to control and use different sounds? In this chapter you will explore these and other questions as you investigate sound. You will read about sounds that are pleasing to hear, such as music. You will also read about unwanted sound, or noise. You will discover that sound can be controlled to some extent by using certain materials. You will discover many other things about sound too.

How does the band shell change sound?
How do the amplifiers change sound?

Artstreet

Photo Research International

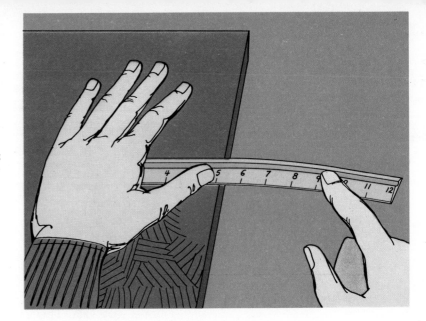

Figure 21–1. What happens when one end of a ruler is held down on a tabletop as shown, and the other end is pushed down and then released?

WHAT IS SOUND?

What kind of waves do sounds make?
How are longitudinal waves and transverse / waves different?
What materials can sound travel through?
What things are needed for making sound?

Matter vibrates!

For sound to be made, matter must *vibrate* [VY-BRAYT]. That is, matter must move back and forth. Every sound begins with a back-and-forth motion, or *vibration* [vy-BRAY-shuhn]. But if every sound begins with such a motion, why don't you hear a sound when you wave your hand back and forth? The reason is that you cannot wave your hand back and forth fast enough to make a sound you can hear.

To see a vibrating object that does make sound, try this. Hold one end of a ruler firmly against a tabletop, with the other end sticking out about fifteen centimetres (six inches) over the edge of the table. Push the free end of the ruler down and release it. As the ruler springs back, it will begin to vibrate. You will see the vibration and hear the sound made. See Figure 21–1.

405

Investigate

How can you find out whether or not a tuning fork is vibrating whenever it is making a sound?

You Will Need

tuning fork, table-tennis ball, pan of water, thread, transparent tape

Background

Sometimes a sound-producer, or source of sound, vibrates so fast that you cannot see the vibrations. In this investigation you will find out that one kind of sound-producer does indeed vibrate very fast. This kind of sound-producer vibrates so fast that you may not be able to see the vibrations themselves. But you will be able to see how the vibrations affect other objects.

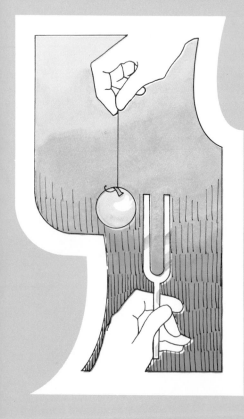

What to Do

Strike the tuning fork against the rubber heel of your shoe. Observe and record what happens.

Tape a piece of thread to the table-tennis ball. Again strike the tuning fork against the heel of your shoe. Holding the table-tennis ball by the thread, let the ball touch the forked end of the tuning fork. Observe and record what happens.

Strike the tuning fork again. Place the forked end of the tuning fork into the pan of water. Observe and record what happens.

Now That You Have Done the Investigation

—Could you hear the sound the tuning fork made? Could you see its vibrations? Could you feel its vibrations?

—What happened when the table-tennis ball was placed next to the prong of the just-struck tuning fork? Did the tuning fork vibrate or not? Explain your answer.

—What happened when the just-struck tuning fork was placed in a pan of water? Did the tuning fork vibrate or not? Explain your answer.

—From your observations, would you say that a tuning fork that produces sound is vibrating? Explain your answer.

406

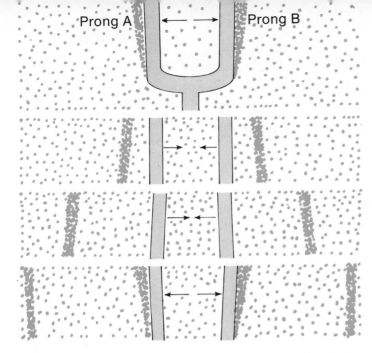

Figure 21–2. The diagrams represent what happens to the molecules of air around a vibrating tuning fork. Arrows show the direction in which the prongs of the tuning fork are moving. As the prongs move out, they crowd some molecules close together. What happens to air molecules when the prongs move inward?

Waves of sound

All sound begins when matter vibrates. But how can a vibrating object in one part of a room make a sound heard by someone in another part of the room? Energy from the vibrating matter must move through the air. How can the energy move?

One explanation is that the vibrating object disturbs the *molecules* [MAHL-ih-κγοο(υη)Lz], or tiny particles, of air around the object. The disturbance, or wave, that moves through the air is called a *sound wave*.

Sound waves are longitudinal waves. Longitudinal waves have compressions (places where the medium is squeezed together) and rarefactions (places where the medium is spread out). But how does sound travel in the form of longitudinal waves? In Figure 21–2, you see the prongs of a tuning fork. The dots represent molecules of gases that are all around the prongs. Molecules of gases are scattered evenly in the air, and they are always moving.

As they vibrate, molecules in the air push on everything they touch. When Prong B of the tuning fork moves to the right, it pushes the molecules nearest it and crowds these air molecules together, or compresses them. The

407

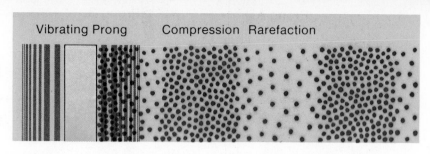

Figure 21–3. Molecules in the air next to a vibrating tuning fork will become crowded and then become less crowded as sound waves move outward from the tuning fork. What are the crowded areas called? What are the less crowded areas called?

crowded molecules against push their neighboring molecules. As they spread out into the space partly taken up by the neighboring air molecules, their own crowding becomes less. However, their neighbors become crowded. This crowding is passed along as the region of compression moves away from the prong.

After swinging to the right, the prong swings to the left, leaving a space in which the molecules in the air are not crowded. The air in this space has fewer molecules in it than it did before. This space is a rarefaction. The rarefaction follows the region of compression as it moves away from the tuning fork.

When the prong moves to the right again, it causes another compression. When it moves to the left, another rarefaction follows. As the prong moves back and forth, a series of compressions and rarefactions moves away from it through the air. See Figure 21–3. Soon the space around the tuning fork is filled with a series of compressions and rarefactions, or longitudinal waves. These waves carry energy away from the tuning fork. See Figure 21–4.

Figure 21–4. The drawing shows sound waves moving away from a vibrating tuning fork. If the tuning fork were real, do you think the sound waves would also move out toward you? Why or why not?

Traveling waves

When an object vibrates, sound waves travel through the air around it. The waves travel outward in all directions from the vibrating object. Sound waves travel outward in much the same way as water waves travel outward from the places where stones are dropped into water. Water waves travel outward only along the surface of the water—that is, in two dimensions. Sound waves travel outward in *all* directions—that is, in three dimensions.

Sound waves can travel through materials other than air. In fact, sound waves can travel through *any* material. But sound moves better through some materials than others. Remember this about sound waves. They must have some material, or medium, through which to travel.

★ **Do you think sound waves could travel through a vacuum? How would you explain your answer?**

Hearing sound

By now you know that two things are needed for making sound. (1) Vibrating matter is needed to make sound waves. (2) A medium is needed to carry sound waves. In addition, one definition of "sound" says that sound must also be heard by someone. According to this definition, if no sound is heard, no sound has been made.

★ **What organs of your body are used for hearing?**

SOME CHARACTERISTICS OF SOUND

What is the relationship between the speed of sound in air and air temperature?
In which kind of material—solid, liquid, or gas— does sound travel fastest? Slowest?
What do the numbers on tuning forks mean?

Speed of sound

When you see a flash of lightning, you usually hear thunder soon afterward. The farther away the lightning is, the longer it takes to hear the thunder. By knowing

---

Find Out More

Work with several classmates, and look up as many definitions of sound as you can find. Then think about this. A tree falls to the ground in a forest, but no one is there to hear it hit the ground. Based on the definitions you have looked up, answer these questions. Did anyone hear the tree hit the ground? Was any sound made by the tree when it hit the ground? Were any sound waves made by the falling tree when it hit the ground? Explain your answers.

409

SPEED OF SOUND IN VARIOUS MATERIALS	
Material	Speed (m/s)
Air (0°C)	331
Aluminum	5 000
Brick	3 650
Glass	3 720
Steel	5 200
Water	1 486
Wood (oak)	3 850

Figure 21–5. Which material listed above allows the sound to move the fastest? The slowest?

the time between seeing a lightning flash and hearing the thunder, you can figure out about how far away from you the lightning is.

Next time you see lightning, try this. Just after you see the flash, start to count slowly. Say "One thousand one, one thousand two, one thousand three, . . ." and so on. By doing this you will be counting time intervals of about one second each. For each three seconds you count before you hear the thunder, the lightning flash was about one kilometre (about 0.6 mile) away.

This method can be used because sound travels through air with a speed that can be measured. But the method is not very accurate. One reason is that the speed is different at different temperatures. For example, at 0°C, or 32°F (the temperature at which water freezes), the speed of sound in air is 331 metres (1,090 feet) a second. At 100°C (212°F) the speed is 390 metres (1,280 feet) a second.

★ **Based on the above sentence, how does an increase in temperature change the speed of sound?**

Look at the table in Figure 21–5 to find the speed of sound in some other materials.

DO IT YOURSELF

Hear how sound travels through matter

Hold the end of a long stick up against one ear, closing the ear to outside sounds. Have a classmate hold a ticking watch against the other end of the stick. Can you hear the ticking of the watch? Then, holding the watch the same distance away from your ear, remove the stick. Can you hear the ticking now? In which situation was it easier to hear the watch ticking?

Tap on a windowpane and listen to the sound. Then tap on the windowpane and put your ear next to the glass. Does the sound seem louder with your ear next to the glass? Tap two stones together in a pan of water. Can you hear the sound? Does sound travel through liquids? Through solids?

Frequency and pitch

If you have some tuning forks in your classroom, look at them. Notice that each fork has a number on it. One fork may be marked 256, another 288, another 320, and so on. Do you know what these numbers mean? The number is the frequency of that tuning fork. Frequency is the number of vibrations, or waves, the fork makes in one second.

At any one temperature, the sound from each fork travels at the same speed. In air at a temperature of 20°C, for example, sound from any tuning fork travels with a speed of 343 metres (about 1,100 feet) a second. The tuning fork marked 256 would send out 256 waves in one second. The first wave made would have traveled 343 metres when the 256th wave was just leaving the fork. In other words, 256 waves would be spread out over 343 metres. To find the wave length you would divide 343 by 256. That is, the wave length of sound from this fork at this temperature is 1.34 metres per wave.

343 metres ÷ 256 waves = 1.34 metres/wave
(1,130 feet ÷ 256 waves = 4.41 feet/wave)

★ **At a temperature of 20°C, what would be the wave length of the sound from the fork marked 320?**

By doing some figuring, you can see that sounds of different frequency have different wave lengths. But can you detect any difference in the sound from two different tuning forks just by listening? If you try it, you will find you can. You might say that the sound made by one fork is lower than the other. When you say a sound is lower, you mean that the pitch of the sound is lower. The frequency of a sound determines the pitch you hear.

How loud is loud?

Some sounds are louder than others. So another characteristic of sound is its *loudness* [LOWD-nuhs], or how loud the sound is. Loudness can be measured by a device called a *sound-level meter*. Sound waves are detected by a microphone on the meter and changed to an electric

(*Text continues on page 413.*)

Find Out More

Using references, find out more about the measurements of the speed of sound. When were the first measurements made? Who made the early measurements? How were the measurements made?

411

Investigate

How is the frequency of a tuning fork related to its pitch?

You Will Need

tuning forks of different frequencies

Background

You have learned that the frequency of a sound determines the pitch you hear. By striking two different tuning forks and comparing the different sounds, you can hear a difference in pitch. This is true no matter what two tuning forks you use, as long as they have different frequencies.

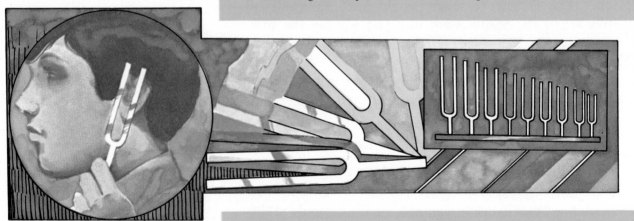

What to Do

Arrange your tuning forks in order from the highest number to the lowest number. In turn, hit each tuning fork on the rubber heel of your shoe. Hold each fork near your ear after you hit it on your shoe. Notice the difference in pitch from one fork to the next.

Now That You Have Done the Investigation

—Which tuning fork do you think had the highest pitch?
—Which tuning fork do you think had the lowest pitch?
—Did the numbers of the tuning forks with the highest and lowest pitch correspond to the tuning forks with the highest and lowest numbers? Why or why not?
—What can you say about the relationship between the frequency of a tuning fork and its pitch?

412

LOUDNESS OF COMMON SOUNDS

Sound	Decibels
Whisper	10–20
Quiet office	20–30
Classroom	30–40
Automobile	40–50
Conversation	50–60
Light street traffic	60–70
Heavy street traffic	70–80
Air hammer	90–100
Loud thunder	110

Figure 21–6. Based on the list at the left, how many decibels do you think the sound of rustling leaves would be? How many decibels do you think rock music would be?

current. The size of the current depends on how loud the sound is. The size of the current is shown on the meter. The meter is marked off in *decibels* [DEHS-uh-BEHLZ].

A decibel is the unit used to compare the loudness of sounds. Some examples of loudness, in decibels, for some sounds you have heard are shown in the table in Figure 21–6.

Hearing sound waves

You detect sounds with your ears. If your hearing is normal, you can probably hear sounds having frequencies from about 20 to 20 000 hertz. That is, you cannot hear sounds having frequencies less than 20 hertz.

Remember earlier the question was brought up, "Why don't you hear a sound when you wave your hand back and forth?" Now you know the answer. You would have to wave your hand back and forth twenty times in one second to make a sound you could hear.

Sounds that have a frequency above 20 000 hertz are too high pitched for you to hear. But some animals are able to hear very high-pitched sounds. For example, have you ever heard about a dog whistle? This whistle makes sound waves having a very high frequency. When the whistle is used, people cannot hear it, but dogs can.

★ **If dogs hear a whistle people cannot hear, what does this suggest about the hearing of dogs?**

413

MUSIC AND NOISE

What is the difference between music and noise?
How are sounds made with stringed instruments,
wind instruments, and percussion instruments?
What is the relationship between an overtone
and its fundamental tone?

What's the difference?

There is a difference between music and noise, even though music and noise are both sound. Noise is sometimes thought of as being unwanted sound. In general, the vibrations that cause noise do not follow a set pattern. In music, however, the vibrations are often in a series of regular patterns. See Figure 21–7.

Music has three things that are not found in noise. When you hear them, you know that you are hearing music. The three things that music has are *pitch, rhythm* [RIHTH-uhm], and *quality* [KWAHL-uht-ee].

Pitch has to do with the frequency of vibrations. Rhythm is a regular pattern of tones in a series or in groups. The quality of music depends on the different tones that are heard. See Figure 21–8.

★ **Can you think of any noises that are pleasant to hear? If so, what are they?**

Figure 21–7. A noise and a musical sound are shown below as they might look on the screen of an oscilloscope, a device used in studying sound. Which sound has a regular pattern?

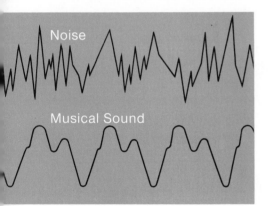

Noise

Musical Sound

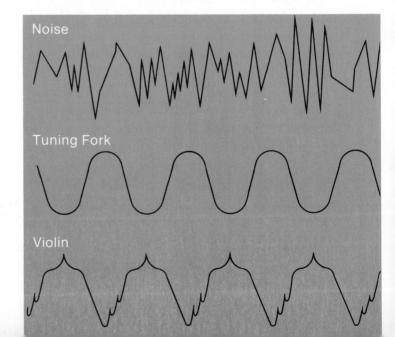

Noise

Tuning Fork

Violin

Figure 21–8. Noise does not make a regular wave pattern on an oscilloscope. But, as you can see, a tuning fork and violin do make regular patterns. How is the pattern of the tuning fork different from that of the violin?

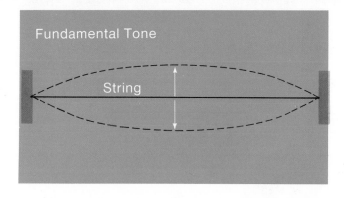

Figure 21–9. *When a plucked string vibrates in only one loop, the sound made is a fundamental tone.*

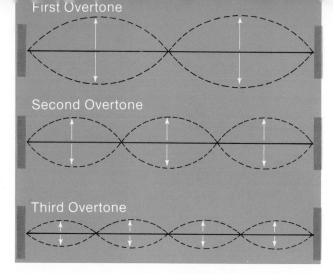

Figure 21–10. *If plucked strings vibrate so that more than one standing wave is in the string, the sounds made are called overtones. Three different overtones are shown. How does the length of the loops change as the number of overtones is increased?*

Stringed instruments

Guitars, harps, and violins are *stringed instruments* [IHN(T)-struh-muhnts]. Music is made by stringed instruments in several ways. When a string is plucked so that it vibrates as a whole, it makes a single standing wave. The wave length is equal to the length of the string. See Figure 21–9. The sound made by such a vibration is called the *fundamental* [FUHN-duh-MEHNT-uhl] *tone* of the string. It is the lowest tone that can be made by that length of string. However, the same string can make other tones that are higher than the fundamental tone.

When a string is plucked so that it vibrates in two places at the same time, two standing waves are made. Vibration in three places at the same time makes three standing waves, and so on. The greater the number of waves on a string, the shorter the length of the waves. The shortest waves make sounds of the highest pitch.

As you know, a sound that has a high frequency is a high-pitched tone. So the pitch of a sound is determined by the number of sound waves made by a vibrating object in one second. These higher-pitched tones are called *overtones*. The frequency of an overtone is a multiple of the frequency of the fundamental tone. See Figure 21–10.

When a string on a guitar or violin is stroked or plucked, it vibrates at several different frequencies. It is the combination of the fundamental tone and the overtones that gives a musical instrument its individual quality. So a guitar

415

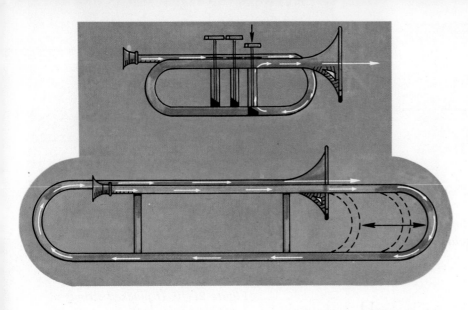

Figure 21–11. By looking at the diagram, can you tell how sounds of different pitch are made with the trumpet? With the trombone?

sounds different from a violin even though they are playing the same fundamental tone.

★ **If a guitar and a violin play the same fundamental tone, what causes them to sound different?**

Wind instruments

The trumpet, trombone, clarinet, and other *wind instruments* have vibrating columns of air which can make music. These instruments are called wind instruments because air is needed to make the sounds. In some wind instruments, the pitch is changed by covering or uncovering holes in the instruments. This changes the length of the column of vibrating air which, in turn, changes the pitch of the sound that is made. A long column makes a low pitch. A short column makes a high pitch.

In other wind instruments, such as the trumpet, the length of air columns is changed by valves. In a trombone, the length of the air column is changed by sliding a U-shaped tube in and out. See Figure 21–11.

The air starts to vibrate in some wind instruments due to the moving of the player's lips. Trumpets, trombones, and French horns are instruments of this kind. Other instruments, such as the clarinet, use the vibrations made by a wooden reed. The reed starts to vibrate when a person blows air against it.

416

DO IT YOURSELF

Make music with columns of air

Place a metal or glass tube that is open at both ends partway into a bottle about half full of water. Hold the tube steady, and blow across the top opening of the tube. Move the bottle up and down in order to change the length of the column of air. Does the pitch change when the length of the column of air in the tube is changed? Can you use this activity to explain how a trombone, tuba, or French horn makes sounds of different pitch?

Fill seven pop bottles with equal amounts of water. Blow across the tops of the bottles. By changing the amounts of water in each bottle, see if you can make seven different sounds. If you can, try to play a simple tune using the bottles of water.

Percussion instruments

You have learned that music can be made by wind and stringed instruments. Another group of instruments which can make music is the group called *percussion* [pur-KUHSH-uhn] *instruments.*

Percussion instruments are hit by a hand, a stick, or a covered hammer. Some percussion instruments, such as the drum, are made from a flexible material which is

Artstreet

Figure 21–12. Marching bands rely on percussion instruments to keep time while marching and also for making certain effects of sound while the band is playing. What percussion instruments do you see in this picture?

stretched over a frame of some kind. When the material is hit, it vibrates and starts the air vibrating.

ACOUSTICS

How can reverberation and interference cause problems with sound?
What is soundproofing?
When is sound reflected?

Problems with sound

Acoustics [uh-KOO-stihks] is the science of sounds. It deals with the making of sound waves, the way sound waves move, and the way sound affects matter. Acoustics also deals with problems caused by noise in buildings.

Two problems with sound in buildings are those caused by *reverberation* [rih-VUR-buh-RAY-shuhn] and *interference* [IHNT-uh(r)-FIHR-uhn(t)s] of sound waves. In designing and constructing buildings, engineers and architects work on these problems. They must be careful when designing and building auditoriums or broadcast studios because the quality of sound is important in such buildings.

Reverberation is the repeated reflection of sound waves from smooth surfaces in an inside place. It is like a series of echoes. If you have ever talked loudly in a large, empty room, you know what reverberation is.

Suppose you are listening to a band concert at school. The sound waves coming from the band go to all parts of the room. If the sound waves are stopped by materials in the room, you enjoy good listening. But what if the sound waves are reflected, rather than stopped? Sounds would be coming at you from all directions. Each new sound wave would be added to the waves made before. You might hear all the sound waves at the same time. Do you think the combination of sounds would be pleasant?

Interference happens when two or more series of sound waves come together. These sound waves either strengthen

Figure 21–13. A concert hall is shaped so that sound coming from the stage can be heard by each person in the hall. What problems with sound are not found in a well-planned concert hall?

Hedrich-Blessing

418

each other or wipe out each other. When two sound waves happen at the same time and their compressions and rarefactions come together in the right way, the waves strengthen each other. The sound is louder. But when the rarefactions of one wave series come together with the compressions of another wave series, the rarefactions and compressions wipe out each other and there is silence.

★ **Suppose sound waves coming from the stage in a theater wiped out each other at a certain place in the theater. Would you like to have a seat at that place to watch a play? Explain.**

Soundproofing

Today, sound engineers try to stop sound waves that are not wanted. This is done by a process called *soundproofing* [SOWN(D)-PROOF-ihng].

One way of destroying sounds that are not wanted is to cover the walls with soundproofing materials. Such materials have many tiny holes in them. Drapes, asbestos sheets, and tiles are used for soundproofing. Sound waves hitting these materials become trapped in the little holes.

Places such as movie theaters, concert halls, and auditoriums also use padded seats and rugs as soundproofing materials. They help stop reverberation.

★ **If you were interested in soundproofing a room, what are some materials you would not wish to use?**

Reflection of sound

One thing engineers study about sound is its reflection. Reflection often happens when sound waves hit a flat surface. As sound waves hit the flat surface they bounce off of it, becoming a new series of waves. How, do you think, is this like light being reflected from a mirror?

Reflected sound waves may cause problems in a theater or auditorium. For example, reflections in some parts of an auditorium may cause sound waves coming from the stage to become very concentrated. This causes loud sounds.

For You to Think About

What is the quietest time you can remember? Was it completely silent? How long did the quiet time last? Do you think you would like to live in a completely quiet world? Explain.

In other parts of an auditorium, reflections may cause sounds to wipe out each other. This causes "dead spots." Dead spots are places where people do not hear some sounds coming from the stage that people in the rest of the auditorium can hear.

Have you ever made sounds in a place such as a deep canyon? If so, you may have heard *echoes* [EHK-ohz]. An echo is a reflection of sound. In fact, each echo is very much like the original sound wave.

Have you ever tried to bounce a ball in loose sand? You know that a ball does not bounce off loose sand in the same way it bounces off pavement. Sound waves are reflected in much the same way. Sound waves bounce off hard, smooth surfaces. But soft, rough surfaces stop them.

Sound waves often travel in all directions from where the sound begins. But reflection can be used to make sound go in only one direction. For example, a cheerleader will use a cone-shaped megaphone to direct the sound of his or her voice. Much the same principle is used in the construction of a band shell. The shell directs the music toward the audience so the music can be heard clearly.

★ **A person shouts across a canyon and hears an echo 6 seconds later. If the speed of sound is 343 metres a second, how wide is the canyon?**

DO IT YOURSELF

Study echoes

Find some place where you can hear an echo. What is there about this place that causes an echo? Make a diagram of the place. Do you have to stand at a certain place to hear an echo?

Find other places in your community that cause echoes. Compare the characteristics of all these places. In what ways are they alike? In what ways are they different? What is the condition in each place that causes an echo? Which place causes the strongest echo?

Controlling Sound

Have you ever heard of environmental control? If you have, you know that it means controlling the environment so that people are healthier, happier, and safer. One of the things people complain about is sound. Factories, trucks, trains, motorcycles, jet planes, and other noisemakers can make a person's environment very unpleasant. In fact, noise can be worse than unpleasant. It can be harmful.

Today, many people work to help control sound. For example, engineers have figured out how to cut down on sound from cars and trucks by using mufflers. The people who install the mufflers also help in the control of unwanted sound. People called acoustical engineers are responsible for making factories and office buildings as soundproof as can be. Then people working in those places feel better and work more productively.

You can probably think of other examples of jobs that are involved with controlling unwanted sound. Maybe you can think of sounds that should be controlled but are not controlled now. Controlling these sounds may mean many new jobs in the future. Will the job you have someday have anything to do with controlling sound?

Courtesy of Bell Laboratories

The room these acoustical engineers are working in is an anechoic room—that is, a room free from echoes and reverberations. The engineer in the center of the room is carefully listening for sounds in the room. What do you suppose the other engineer is doing?

421

Reviewing and Extending

SUMMING UP

1. All sound begins when matter vibrates.
2. Sound energy travels as a series of compressions and rarefactions.
3. Frequency is the number of vibrations that a vibrating object makes in one second.
4. The frequency of a sound determines the pitch you hear.
5. People with normal hearing can usually hear sounds having frequencies from about 20 hertz to 20 000 hertz.
6. The lowest tone that can be made by a string on an instrument such as a violin is called the fundamental tone of that string.
7. The frequency of an overtone is a multiple of the frequency of the fundamental tone.

CHECKING UP

Vocabulary Write the numerals 1–10 on your paper. Each numbered phrase describes a term from the following list. On your paper, write the term next to the numeral of the phrase that describes it.

pitch　　vibrate　　loudness　　soundproofing
decibel　　quality　　acoustics　　reverberation
rhythm　　overtone　　interference　　fundamental tone

1. regular pattern of tones in a series or in groups
2. characteristic of music that is determined by the frequency of vibration
3. unit used to compare the loudness of sounds
4. moving back and forth
5. coming together of two or more series of sound waves
6. lowest tone that can be made by a vibrating object
7. one of the high-pitched tones made by a vibrating object
8. science of sounds
9. repeated reflection of sound waves from smooth surfaces in a large, empty room
10. way of destroying sounds that are not wanted

Knowledge and Understanding Write the numerals 11–15 on your paper. Beside each numeral, write the word or words that best complete the sentence having that numeral.

11. Sound reverberates in a large, empty room because of (*reflection, overtones, soundproofing*).

12. The number of times a material vibrates during each second is called its (*frequency, amplitude, loudness*).

13. When a string vibrates as a whole, the tone is called the (*fundamental tone, overtone, acoustics*) of that string.

14. Of the following materials, (*plaster, drapes, bricks*) would be the most effective to use in soundproofing an auditorium.

15. Sound waves are (*longitudinal waves, transverse waves, all the same size*).

Concepts   Beside each of the numerals *16–18* on your paper, write the word or words that best complete the sentence having that numeral.

16. When you hear a musical tone, the pitch of the tone depends primarily upon the (*amplitude, overtones, frequency*) of the sound waves that reach your ear.

17. One explanation of how sound moves through air is that the vibrating object disturbs the (*reverberation, transverse waves, molecules of gases*) in the air around the object by causing a series of compressions and rarefactions.

18. When the temperature of air goes up, the speed of sound in air (*goes up, goes down, stays the same*).

Application and Critical Thinking   Answer the following questions as briefly as you can without leaving out any important ideas.

19. How are all sound waves alike? How are some sound waves different from others?

20. How does the fundamental tone of a vibrating string differ from an overtone of that string? How are overtones made in vibrating strings? How are overtones related to the fundamental tone?

DOING MORE

1. Hit a tuning fork on the heel of your shoe and hold the stem of the fork on a wooden tabletop. Is there a difference in the loudness of sound when the stem is placed on the tabletop? Try tuning forks of different frequencies. Are the results always the same?

2. Stretch a metallic violin string or guitar string between two points. Pluck it with a pencil and listen to its pitch. Then heat the string and pluck it with a pencil again. Has the higher temperature changed the pitch? Why or why not?

3. Conduct an experiment to determine the speed of sound. What factors do you have to control? Report your findings to the class.

CHAPTER 22

Light and Color

Imagine you are in a cave far below the surface of the earth. You have never been in the cave before. There is no light at all. You are in total darkness. In this place, sounds seem louder than usual. In fact, if you think about the sounds, they become louder and louder. You are afraid because there is no light, and you don't know what is in the darkness around you.

Then a person carrying a lantern suddenly appears. Right away you feel better. The light from the lantern lets you see objects in the cave. When you are able to see everything around you, the cave is less frightening. You now know that light is very important in your life.

How is the sun important to the living things on the earth? Do you think there would be living things on the earth without the light from the sun?

Light is one of the forms of *radiant* [RAYD-ee-uhnt] *energy.* What is radiant energy? What are some other forms of radiant energy? How do the forms of radiant energy move? How does light help us see objects? What makes objects have color? These are some of the questions to which you will find answers in this chapter.

RADIANT ENERGY

What is radiation and what is radiant energy?
What are some forms of radiant energy?
How fast does radiant energy travel?
What does radiant energy do to objects it hits?

Giving off energy

Have you ever noticed that when an object is warmer than the air around it, the object will cool off? Somehow, the object loses heat energy.

The heat energy is lost by *radiation* [RAYD-ee-AY-shuhn]. Radiation is the moving outward of energy from an object in the form of rays or waves. When heat moves by radiation, it travels outward in the form of waves you cannot see. For example, when you put your hand near a hot iron, you can feel the heat, but you cannot see it.

L. H. Sharp

Figure 22–1. Is this candle giving off any radiation? How can you tell?

Forms of radiant energy

Energy given off by radiation is called radiant energy. An electric iron, a light bulb, the sun, and a radio transmitter each give off some forms of radiant energy.

Each of these forms of energy may be thought of as a kind of wave. All the waves of radiant energy are called *electromagnetic* [ih-LEHK-troh-mag-NEHT-ihk] *waves*. Some kinds of electromagnetic waves are listed below.

visible [VIHZ-uh-buhl] *light*
X rays
radio waves
microwaves [MY-kruh-WAYVZ]
ultraviolet [UHL-truh-VY-uh-luht] *rays*
infrared [IHN-fruh-REHD] *rays*
gamma [GAM-uh] *rays*
cosmic [KAHZ-mihk] *rays*

All the different kinds of electromagnetic waves, taken together, form what is called the *electromagnetic spectrum* [SPEHK-truhm]. See Figure 22–2. Notice that the electromagnetic spectrum covers a broad range of wave lengths. Notice, too, that each form of energy in the electromagnetic spectrum has its own range of wave lengths. For example, radio waves have a range of wave lengths from 0.000 1 metres to 0.000 000 01 metres.

Near the center of the spectrum is found the range of wave lengths called visible light. This is radiation you can see with your eyes. Other forms of radiant energy cannot be seen. But the forms that cannot be seen can be detected in other ways.

(*Text continues on page 428.*)

Figure 22–2. What kind of electromagnetic radiation has the longest wave length? The shortest wave length?

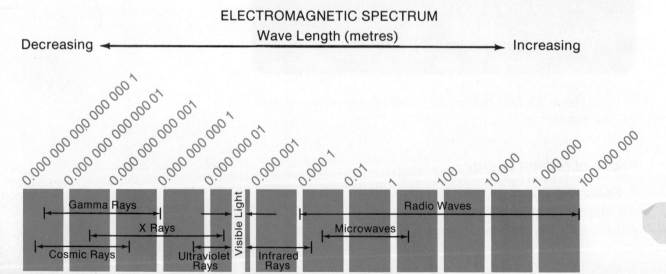

ELECTROMAGNETIC SPECTRUM
Wave Length (metres)

Decreasing ⟵⟶ Increasing

Investigate

How is a radiometer affected by radiant energy?

You Will Need

radiometer, 100-watt light bulb and lamp, hot and cold running water

Background

A *radiometer* [RAYD-ee-AHM-uht-ur] is a device that is affected by some forms of radiant energy. It was invented by Sir William Crookes. The radiometer has two pairs of very lightweight metal vanes mounted so they can turn around easily. One side of each vane is polished metal. The other side of each vane is black. The vanes are inside a glass bulb from which some of the air has been removed. When some forms of radiation come through the glass bulb and reach the vanes, they turn around and around.

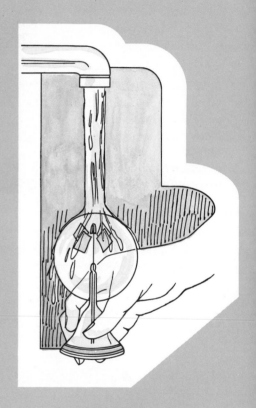

What to Do

Place the radiometer close to the lighted bulb for about thirty seconds. Observe and record what happens.

Wait about a minute with the bulb off. Then place the radiometer close to the lighted bulb again for about thirty seconds. Observe and record what happens.

Place the radiometer upright under hot running water for thirty seconds. Observe and record what happens.

Wait about a minute. Then place the radiometer upright under cold running water for thirty seconds. Observe and record what happens.

Now That You Have Done the Investigation

—What happened when you placed the radiometer close to the 100-watt bulb? What happened when the bulb was turned off?

—Did the radiometer behave in the same way when it was placed close to the light bulb again? Explain.

—What happened when you placed the radiometer under hot running water?

—What happened when you placed the radiometer under cold running water?

—What kind of energy was detected in the running water? Why do you think so?

Artstreet Artstreet

Figure 22–3. This "black-light" poster looks different when ordinary light shines on it than it does when black light, or ultraviolet rays, shines on it. How are ultraviolet rays different from ordinary light?

You cannot see the infrared rays from a hot iron. But you can feel them as heat. Ultraviolet rays are another form of radiant energy you cannot see. But if you have ever gotten a sunburn, you have seen and felt the effects of ultraviolet rays.

In some cases, you cannot detect either the radiation or its effects with your senses alone. The radiation must be detected by instruments. Your favorite radio station, for example, sends out radio waves in all directions. You cannot see, hear, or feel these waves. You cannot know they are around you unless you have a radio that receives the waves and changes them into sound waves which you can hear.

Radiant energy moves fast!

The different forms of energy in the electromagnetic spectrum have different wave lengths. However, all of them travel through space at the same speed. This speed is about 300 000 kilometres a second, or about 186,000 miles a second.

428

Figure 22–4. Light is able to pass through certain kinds of matter, but not through other kinds. What matter is light passing through in this picture?

Radiant energy does not travel only through space. It can also travel through matter. You know, for example, that visible light and other forms of radiant energy travel through air. Visible light also travels through glass, water, clear plastic, and some other forms of matter.

When light goes through matter, its speed is different than when it is going through space. Matter slows the speed of light. Different kinds of matter slow the speed of light by different amounts. For example, visible light travels through clear water at a speed of about 224 000 kilometres a second, or 139,000 miles a second. But in glass, it travels about 200 000 kilometres a second, or 124,000 miles a second.

★ **Would you expect the speed of visible light to be greater in air or in water? Why?**

What radiant energy does to materials

When radiant energy hits an object, is the energy changed? Is the object changed? In other words, do the energy and the object affect each other, or interact? The answers to these questions depend on the form of radiant energy and on what the object is like.

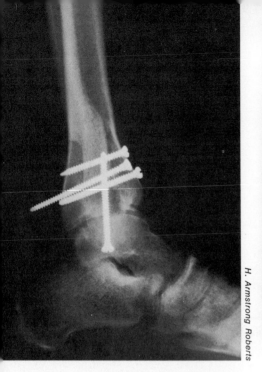

H. Armstrong Roberts

Photo Research International

Figure 22–5. Which are more transparent to X rays, bones or metal screws? How can you tell? In the picture on the right, what things are transparent to visible light? What things are opaque to visible light? How can you tell?

For example, what happens when visible light interacts with a clear glass windowpane? Most of the light passes through the glass. The light is not changed very much and neither is the glass. Since the light passes through the glass, the glass is said to be *transparent* [tran(t)s-PAR-uhnt] to visible light.

Is glass transparent to all forms of radiant energy? No, it is not. For example, most ultraviolet rays will not pass through glass. Anything through which a form of radiant energy will not pass is said to be *opaque* [oh-PAYK] to that energy. So, glass is opaque to most ultraviolet rays.

To be correct, you should not just say that something is transparent or opaque. You should also say what kind of radiant energy will or will not pass through it. Your hand, for example, is opaque to visible light, but transparent to X rays. A brick wall is opaque to visible light, but transparent to radio waves.

Something that is transparent to radiant energy is usually not changed very much by the radiant energy. But what about opaque materials? Are they changed? They usually are changed somewhat.

For example, suppose an object is opaque to a certain kind of radiant energy. The object will either reflect or stop that energy. If the energy is mostly reflected, the temperature of the object will not be changed very much. However, if the energy is stopped by the object, the object will be warmed. As the radiant energy is stopped, it is changed to heat energy. The temperature of the object goes up.

★ **Ultraviolet rays cause suntan. Can you become tanned by sunlight shining through glass? Why or why not?**

For You to Think About

Have you ever placed your hand on a black vinyl roof of a car on a sunny day? Or have you ever placed your hand on any black surface that was in the sunlight? If so, what did you find? How would you explain this?

DO IT YOURSELF

Measure warmth

Place a piece of white cloth or white construction paper on a windowsill in direct sunlight. Place a piece of dark colored cloth or construction paper alongside the white material. After leaving them in the sunlight for several minutes, place a thermometer under each one for several minutes. Which material is warmer? Why is it warmer?

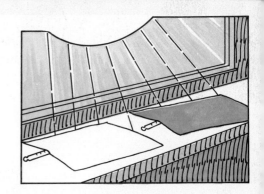

WHAT HAPPENS TO LIGHT?

What is the difference between natural light and artificial light?

How does light travel outward from a luminous object?

How is reflection from a smooth surface different from reflection from a rough surface?

Why is sunlight refracted more at sunrise and sunset than at other times?

What are luminous objects?

The rest of this chapter is about visible light. Usually the word "visible" will be left out, and visible light will be called light. You know light is given off by the sun, the stars, light bulbs, and other things that are not living. But did you know that light is made by some living

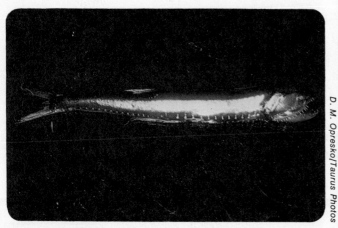

D. M. Opresko/Taurus Photos

G. R. Roberts

Figure 22–6. The fish and insects in these pictures give off light. They are said to be bioluminescent. What do you think this term means?

things? For example, fireflies can make their own light. So can some kinds of worms, some kinds of plants, and some deep-sea fish.

A thing which gives off its own light is called a *luminous* [LOO-muh-nuhs] *object.* A thing which does not give off its own light is called a *nonluminous* [NAHN-LOO-muh-nuhs] *object.*

Some objects are naturally luminous. They give off light without anything being done to them. Light from such objects is called *natural light.* But some nonluminous objects can be made to give off light. Light made in this way is called *artificial* [AHRT-uh-FIHSH-uhl] *light.* Light bulbs, flashlights, flashbulbs, and fluorescent lamps can be made to give off artificial light.

★ **How has the use of artificial light made your life different from what it would be if you had to depend on natural light?**

Whether the light is natural or artificial, it travels outward in all directions from a luminous object. As light travels outward, it travels in straight lines unless matter interferes with it in some way.

You already know that the speed of light is different in different kinds of matter. But did you know that matter

For You to Think About

The sun is responsible for almost all the natural light used on the earth. The sun also makes possible almost all the artificial light people use. How would you explain these statements?

can change the direction of light? The direction of light is changed by matter in two ways—reflection and refraction.

Reflection

The reflection, or bouncing back, of light is something you have seen many times. The surfaces of all objects—whether the objects are transparent or opaque—reflect some of the light hitting them. If the surface of an object did not reflect any light, you would not be able to see that object. But some surfaces reflect light differently than others.

In one way, the reflection of light is like the bouncing of a ball. When a ball bounces off a smooth floor, the angle at which the ball bounces is the same as the angle at which it hits the floor (if the ball is not spinning). But if the surface is rough, the way in which the ball bounces will depend on where it hits the surface. See Figure 22–7.

When light is reflected, it behaves like the bouncing ball. That is, the light is reflected so that the reflected light leaves the surface at the same angle at which it hits the surface. If light is reflected from a smooth, polished surface, all the reflected light leaves in the same direction. Look at A of Figure 22–8. If the surface is rough, however, the reflected light leaves in many different directions. Look at B of Figure 22–8.

★ **What are some examples of reflection from a smooth surface? From a rough surface?**

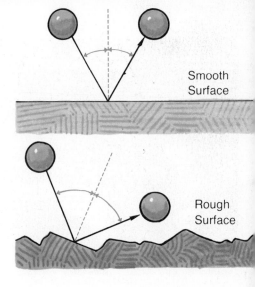

Figure 22–7. *Do you think it is easier to predict the way a ball will bounce on a smooth surface or on a rough surface?*

Figure 22–8. *Why is the reflection of the steep hills around the lake very clear in picture A and not clear in picture B?*

A

George Porter

B

George Porter

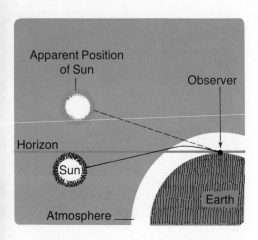

Figure 22–9. *At sunrise and sunset, an observer sees the sun, even though it is slightly below the horizon. Why does the atmosphere bend sunlight more at sunrise and sunset than when the sun is overhead?*

Refraction

Transparent objects change light in another way. As light enters and then leaves the object, its direction is changed. In other words, the light is bent. The bending of light as it goes from one material to another is called refraction. Refraction of the light entering a transparent object is caused by the slowing down of the light rays as they enter the transparent object at an angle.

Refraction takes place in air, too. When light from the sun enters the air around the earth, the sunlight is refracted. At sunset, for example, the sun appears higher in the sky than it really is because of refraction. See Figure 22–9.

The greatest amount of refraction of sunlight by the air is at sunrise and sunset. The amount of refraction partly depends on the position of the sun in the sky. At sunrise and sunset, for example, the sun is near the horizon. The sunlight hits the air at an angle and is refracted. When the sun is directly overhead the sunlight is not refracted.

Refraction also takes place in liquids. As light rays hit the surface of a liquid, they are bent. You can prove this to yourself. Think about the lines at the bottom of a swimming pool. You can see the lines while looking down into the water at an angle. But the lines are not really

(*Text continues on page 436.*)

Photo Research International

Figure 22–10. *In what ways does this picture show that the refraction of light takes place in liquids?*

Investigate

How does water refract light?

You Will Need

penny, cup, container of water

Background

Light is refracted, or bent, when it passes from water into air, or from air into water. In this investigation you will be able to "see light bend" a little bit because of refraction.

What to Do

Put the penny in the center of the bottom of the cup. Look at the penny from an angle at the side of the cup. Adjust your angle of vision so that you cannot see the penny because the rim of the cup is in the way. Then, while keeping your head in the same position, pour water into the cup without moving the penny. Record what you see.

While keeping your head in the same position, move the surface of the water with your finger. Record what you see.

Repeat the investigation using some other clear liquids, such as white vinegar and salad oil. Record your results.

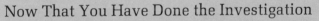

Now That You Have Done the Investigation

—What appeared to happen to the penny when you placed the water inside the cup? Explain.

—What appeared to happen to the penny when you moved the surface of the water? Explain.

—Were the results the same with other liquids as they were with water?

where they appear to be. Also, the lines seem to move when the surface of the water is moved.

★ **What are some ways in which refraction is useful to people?**

COLOR

What happens when white light passes through a prism?
What happens to white light when it passes through a piece of red glass?
What are the primary colors of light?
What are complementary colors of light?
What does reflection have to do with the color of an object that you see?

The visible spectrum

One person who studied light long ago was Isaac Newton. In 1666 he made an important discovery. Sunlight that appeared to be white could be separated into the colors of the rainbow. The colors were separated by allowing the white sunlight to pass through a prism. See Figure 22–11.

This experiment showed that white light is made up of light of many different colors. Together these colors are called the *visible spectrum*. Figure 22–11 shows the visible spectrum that is made by sunlight. Notice that

Figure 22–11. When sunlight passes through a prism, the light is separated into a spectrum of colors. What are the colors of the visible spectrum? What does the second prism do to the spectrum?

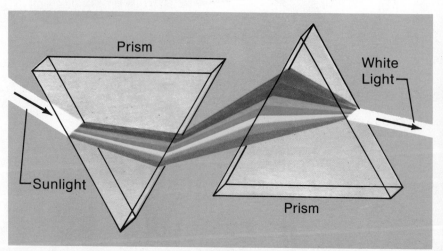
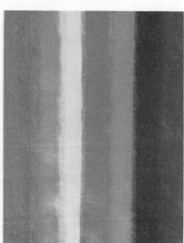

the colors of visible light range from red to violet. Orange, yellow, green, and blue are in between.

Spectrum is not a new word to you. It was used earlier in naming the whole range of radiant energy—the electromagnetic spectrum. In this part of the chapter, however, the word "spectrum" will refer only to the range of colors of visible light.

DO IT YOURSELF

Separate light into colors

Get a prism and a piece of white cardboard. Allow sunlight to pass through the prism in order to make a spectrum on the cardboard. You may have to turn the prism in different ways to get the best spectrum. Look at the position of the prism and where the spectrum is seen in relation to the position of the prism. Which color is refracted the most? Which is refracted the least? What is the order of the colors in between?

Light moving through colored objects

Light can pass through transparent objects which have color. You may have looked through transparent objects which were colored red, green, or some other color. Did you see through them as clearly as you would see through clear, transparent objects?

Why is it harder to see through transparent objects which are colored? Take a piece of red transparent glass and look through it at a white object such as a piece of white chalk. Does the chalk appear red? Hold the chalk near a lighted lamp and look at it through the red glass. No matter how bright the light is, the chalk appears to be red. Why does the white chalk seem to be red?

When a white object appears red through red glass, the glass is allowing only the red color of light through it. Other colors are said to be *filtered* [FIHL-turd] *out*, or stopped, by the red glass.

If you look at the white chalk through green glass, the chalk appears green. The green glass allows only green light to pass through. Other colors are filtered out.

★ **What would you see if you looked at the white chalk through blue glass? Why do you think so?**

DO IT YOURSELF

Look at an object through colored glass or plastic

Try looking at a piece of chalk or some other white object through different kinds of colored glass or transparent plastic. Use colors such as red, blue, yellow, and green. Try looking through each kind of colored glass or plastic. Then try looking through combinations of the kinds of colored glass or plastic. Are the results what you would expect? Why or why not?

Wave lengths of colors

WAVE LENGTHS OF VISIBLE LIGHT	
Color	Range
Red	More than 6 100 A
Orange	5 900–6 100 A
Yellow	5 700–5 900 A
Green	5 000–5 700 A
Blue	4 500–5 000 A
Violet	Less than 4 500 A

Figure 22–12. Which color has the shortest wave length? The longest wave length?

When you studied the electromagnetic spectrum, you discovered that each form of radiant energy has a range of wave lengths. The same is true for each color of visible light. Each color has its own range of wave lengths.

Red light has the longest wave length. Violet light has the shortest wave length. The other colors of light have wave lengths between red and violet.

The table in Figure 22–12 gives the range of wave lengths for each of the colors of the spectrum. The unit of length used is the *angstrom* [ANG-struhm]. This length is only used for very short distances. An angstrom is one ten-millionth (0.000 000 1) of a millimetre.

Sunlight is a well-balanced mixture of the colors of the spectrum. It has the wave lengths of all the colors. However, light from an ordinary light bulb usually has more red light in it than it has blue light. Light from a fluorescent lamp has more blue and yellow light in it than it has red or violet light.

438

Investigate

What happens when primary colors of light are mixed?

You Will Need

white screen, two pieces each of red, blue, and green cellophane, three flashlights, three rubber bands

Background

The primary colors of light are red, green, and blue. Any two of these colors of light can be mixed to make another color. In this investigation you will find out what colors of light can be made with the three primary colors of light.

What to Do

Cover the head of one flashlight with two layers of red cellophane and fasten with a rubber band. Cover the second flashlight with two layers of blue cellophane and the third with two layers of green cellophane.

Darken the room. Shine the flashlight with the red cellophane on the white screen. Record what you see. Shine each of the other flashlights on the screen one at a time. Record what you see each time.

Shine the red and green flashlights to form one spot on the screen. Record the color of the spot.

Shine the red and blue flashlights to form one spot on the screen. Record the color of the spot.

Shine the green and blue flashlights to form one spot on the screen. Record the color of the spot.

Shine all three flashlights on the screen to form one spot on the screen. Record the color of the spot.

Now That You Have Done the Investigation

—Did each of the colored flashlights make a spot of the same color as the cellophane covering the flashlight? Why or why not?

—How would you explain the color of the spot made by the red and green flashlights?

—How would you explain the color of the spot made by the red and blue flashlights?

—How would you explain the color of the spot made by the green and blue flashlights?

—How would you explain the color of the spot made by all three flashlights?

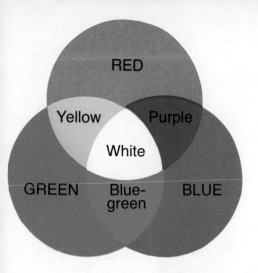

Figure 22–13. The diagram shows the colors that appear when light beams of the three primary colors overlap. Which colors of light combine to form yellow? Blue-green? Purple? White?

For You to Think About

White light from different sources appears pretty much the same to the unaided eye. In what way could you use a prism to find out if white light from different sources has different mixtures of colors in it?

Primary and complementary colors

Three colors of light—red, green, and blue—are called *primary* [PRY-mehr-ee] *colors*. Different colors of light can be made by mixing these three primary colors.

Certain pairs of colors are sometimes called *complementary* [kahm-pluh-MEHNT-uh-ree] *colors*. When two complementary colors of light are mixed in equal amounts, white light is made. For mixing light, the complementary colors are green and purple, yellow and blue, and blue-green and red. See Figure 22–13.

Seeing color

You may have wondered why opaque materials appear to have different colors. For example, why do many leaves appear green? Why does one car appear red, and another, blue? The reason is that the white light that hits these objects has light of all colors in it. When white light hits an opaque object, some colors are stopped. Other colors are reflected. The color you see is the color of the reflected light. The leaves appear green because they stop all the light that hits them except green light. The green light is reflected. A blue car appears blue because the car stops all the light that hits it except blue light. The blue light is reflected.

What color would an object be if it reflected the whole spectrum of colors? If white light hits the object and all the colors are reflected, the object would appear to be white. But if the object stopped all the colors, it would appear to be black.

Suppose an object reflects only red light. What color would it appear to be if only blue light hits it? It would appear to be black. Why? The object reflects only red light. The blue light has no red light. So, when blue light hits the object, no light is reflected. The object appears to be black.

★ **Red light is used in a photographic darkroom. If you placed a green plant in the room, what color would it appear to be?**

De Wys, Inc.

Besides a camera and film, what does every photographer need in order to take pictures?

Photography and Light

Have you ever used a camera? If so, you know that light is important to anyone who takes pictures. To professional photographers—people who make a living by using cameras—knowledge of light is especially important. They must know how much light is needed to take the kind of picture they want. They also must know what kind of light should be used.

The amount of light is important because a photographer must use light in just the right way to get the kind of picture needed. For example, an insurance company may want pictures of an automobile accident to use as evidence in a court. This kind of picture must be clear and well-lighted so that details are easily seen. But sometimes the photographers for certain advertisements use dim lighting to make a dark, spooky-looking picture. Sometimes they use bright lighting to make an open, cheerful-looking picture.

The kind of light is important, too. Photographers use different kinds of light filters to get different effects. For example, a slightly yellow filter causes clouds to show up more in a picture. Another kind of filter is called a haze filter. It helps get rid of the haze that is sometimes present in pictures taken of long-distance scenes.

If you like to work with light, you might like to work as a photographer someday. Or you might like to work at another job in which light and the control of light are important. There are many such jobs. Which ones can you think of?

Reviewing and Extending

SUMMING UP

1. Visible light is only one form of radiant energy. Some of the other forms are X rays, ultraviolet rays, radio waves, and infrared rays.
2. All forms of radiant energy travel at the same speed through space. This speed is 300 000 kilometres a second, or 186,000 miles a second.
3. Materials through which light will pass are said to be transparent to light. Materials through which light will not pass are said to be opaque.
4. Light travels outward in all directions from luminous objects. As light travels, it travels in straight lines. But its direction can be changed by reflection and refraction.
5. White light is made up of all the colors in the visible spectrum.
6. Transparent objects which have color allow only the color that they have to pass through them. All other colors of light are filtered out.
7. Each color in the visible spectrum has its own range of wave lengths.
8. When white light hits opaque objects, some colors are stopped and some are reflected.

CHECKING UP

Vocabulary Write the numerals *1–10* on your paper. Each numbered phrase describes a term from the following list. On your paper, write the term next to the numeral of the phrase that describes it.

radiation	opaque	complementary colors
ultraviolet rays	nonluminous	luminous
infrared rays	visible spectrum	transparent
electromagnetic spectrum	primary colors	

1. does not give off its own light
2. moving outward of energy in the form of rays or waves
3. all the colors which make up white light
4. rays of heat
5. rays which cause sunburn
6. range of wave lengths which includes all the forms of radiant energy
7. red, green, and blue
8. pairs of colors which will make white light when mixed in equal amounts
9. will not allow a given kind of energy to pass through
10. will allow a given kind of energy to pass through

Knowledge and Understanding   Write the numerals *11–14* on your paper. Beside each numeral, write the word or words that best complete the sentence having that numeral.

11. The bending of a light ray as it passes from one material into another is known as (*reflection, refraction, radiation*).
12. Fireflies and other living things that can make their own light are (*luminous, nonluminous, transparent*) objects.
13. The bouncing of a light ray after it hits a material is called (*reflection, refraction, radiation*).
14. Light bulbs, flashlights, and fluorescent lamps are some of the objects that give off (*artificial, natural, nonluminous*) light.

Concepts   Beside each of the numerals *15–17* on your paper, write the word or words that best complete the sentence having that numeral.

15. Whenever light travels through matter, its speed is (*greater than, less than, the same as*) that of light traveling through space.
16. An opaque object appears to be red. The red color you see is due to the color of the light (*hitting, being filtered out of, being reflected by*) the object.
17. When two complementary colors of light are mixed in equal amounts, (*white light is made, both colors are refracted, a primary color of light is made*).

Application and Critical Thinking   Answer the following questions as briefly as you can without leaving out any important ideas.

18. What is the difference between reflection from a smooth object and reflection from a rough object?
19. What color would a green object appear to be if you looked at it in red light? Why?

DOING MORE

1. Place a thermometer about thirty centimetres from a light bulb. Record the temperature after fifteen minutes. Without moving the bulb or the thermometer, place a piece of clear glass between the bulb and the thermometer. Record the temperature every minute for five minutes. What happens to the temperature? Why?
2. When you can see the edge of the sun at sunset, the sun is really below the horizon. Use references to find out more about this. Make diagrams to help you explain your findings to the class.

443

CHAPTER 23

Mirrors and Lenses

You can easily draw a "smiling face" like the one on this page. It is just a circle, with two big dots for eyes and a curved line for the mouth. But try to draw one while using a mirror to look at the face you are drawing, rather than looking at the paper. Until you get used to using the mirror in this way, drawing the "smiling face" won't be very easy.

Mirrors change the way light comes to you. So do lenses, like the ones in eyeglasses, telescopes, and binoculars. As you study this chapter, you can learn some of the ways lenses and mirrors change the way light comes to your eyes.

Try to draw the "smiling face" while using a mirror to look at the face you are drawing. Can you draw it?

Photo Research International

MIRRORS

How does the angle of incidence compare with
the angle of reflection in mirrors?
What are the differences in shape among a plane
mirror, a concave mirror, and a convex mirror?
What are real images and virtual images?

Reflecting surfaces

You have used mirrors many times. But what is a mirror? It is a smooth, shiny surface that reflects the light that hits it. Whenever light is reflected, the angle at which light rays hit a surface is equal to the angle at which reflected rays leave the surface. The angle at which light rays hit the surface is called the *angle of incidence* [IHN(T)-suhd-uhn(t)s]. The angle at which light rays leave the surface is called the *angle of reflection*. In describing reflection, scientists say the angle of incidence equals the angle of reflection.

Parallel light rays all hit the surface of a mirror at the same angle. Because the mirror is smooth, the reflected rays all leave at the same angle. If a surface is rough, parallel rays do not all hit the surface at the same angle. They reflect off in many different directions. See Figure 23–1.

Figure 23–1. The diagrams below show reflection of light from a smooth
surface and from a rough surface. Which surface would appear shiny? Why?

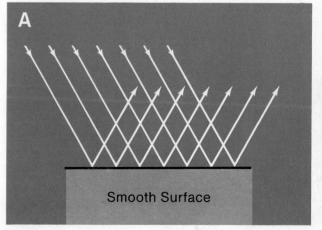

Smooth Surface

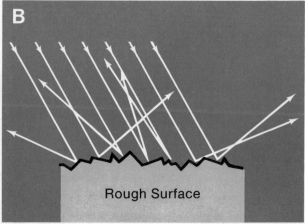

Rough Surface

Investigate

Is the angle of incidence equal to the angle of reflection?

You Will Need

ruler, flat mirror, protractor

Background

Flat mirrors are called plane mirrors. With this kind of mirror, it is easy to measure the angles of incidence (incoming light rays) and reflection (outgoing light rays). If the investigation is done properly, the angles should be exactly equal. Keep in mind as you do this activity that the reflecting surface of an ordinary mirror is on the back side of the mirror. The point at which two lines meet in the mirror is actually at the back of the mirror.

What to Do

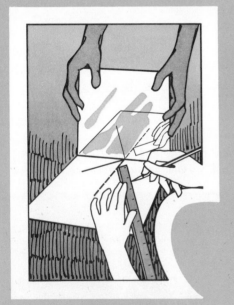

Using the ruler and a pencil, draw a dashed line down the center of a piece of notebook paper. Then draw a solid line at an angle to the dashed line. The two lines should look like those shown.

Have a classmate hold the mirror upright on the paper at the point where the two lines meet. Place the mirror on the paper so that the dashed line and the dashed line you see in the mirror appear to be a continuous straight line.

Place the ruler in front of the mirror. Position the ruler so that the edge of the ruler is in line with the solid black line in the mirror. Then draw a line on the paper so that the line you draw and the solid line you see in the mirror appear to be a continuous straight line. The line you draw forms a second angle with the dashed line.

Measure each of the angles formed by the dashed line and the solid lines with a protractor. Record the measure of each angle.

Repeat the activity by using angles of different sizes.

Now That You Have Done the Investigation

—Which angle was the angle of incidence? Which angle was the angle of reflection?

—Do you think the angle of incidence is always equal to the angle of reflection in this kind of mirror? Explain.

Plane mirrors

The kind of mirror you see most often is called a *plane mirror*. This is the kind of mirror found on medicine cabinets and on certain kinds of furniture. It is called a plane mirror because the reflecting surface is flat. That is, the reflecting surface is a plane.

When you look in a plane mirror, you see an *image* [IHM-ihj] of yourself. The image is not bigger, smaller, fatter, or thinner than you really are. So, a plane mirror reflects light rays without changing them very much. It reflects the rays in a regular pattern.

When you look at yourself in a mirror, your image appears to be behind the mirror. The image is a *virtual* [VURCH-(uh-)wuhl] *image*. The word "virtual" means that the image only appears to be behind the mirror. It is not really behind the mirror at all.

★ **Is the image you see in a plane mirror exactly like you, or is the image reversed? Explain.**

Concave mirrors

If parallel rays of light fall on a plane mirror, the reflected rays are parallel. The parallel rays of incoming light cannot be *focused* [FOH-kuhst], or made to pass through one point. See A of Figure 23–2.

By the use of several small plane mirrors, parallel rays of incoming light can be focused to pass through one point. The mirrors would have to be arranged in a curve as in B of Figure 23–2.

(*Text continues on page 449.*)

Figure 23–2. What happens to parallel rays in A when they fall on a plane mirror? What happens to the rays in B? Why?

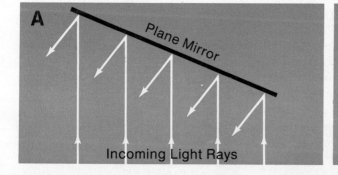

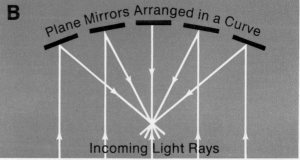

Investigate

In a plane mirror, where does the image appear to be formed?

You Will Need

plane mirror, ruler, clay, 2 pencils of the same kind

Background

Whenever two things are in the same place, they always appear to be in the same place, no matter how you look at them. But sometimes two things appear to be in the same place even though one is farther away than the other. If you look at them from a different direction, you can see that they are not in the same place. This effect is called *parallax* [PAR-uh-LAKS]. You can use parallax to find out how far behind a mirror a virtual image appears to be.

What to Do

Place the mirror upright near the edge of a tabletop. Prop it up in some way so that it is upright. Place one pencil with the point directly up a short distance in front of the mirror. Place clay around the eraser end of the pencil so that it stays upright.

Look at the image of the pencil in the mirror. Then hold the other pencil upright behind the mirror so that you can see part of the pencil above the mirror. Move the pencil upright behind the mirror so that the part you can see above the mirror is lined up with the image you see in the mirror. Then move your head from side to side. If the pencil behind the mirror does not stay lined up with the image in the mirror, you should move the pencil behind the mirror backward or forward until it does stay lined up.

Have a classmate measure the distance to the mirror of each of the pencils. Record each distance. Remember that the reflecting surface is on the back of the mirror.

Now That You Have Done the Investigation

—Do you think that the second pencil was in the same position as the virtual image? Explain.

—How far from the mirror did you place the first pencil? How far from the mirror did you place the second pencil?

—How did the distance from the mirror to the object compare with the apparent distance from the mirror to the image?

Instead of using many small plane mirrors arranged in a curve, suppose you use one curved mirror. In order to focus the light to a single point—called the *focal* [FOH-kuhl] *point*—the mirror is dish-shaped. See Figure 23–3. It curves inward, or away from you, at its center. Because it curves inward, the mirror is said to be a *concave* [kahn-KAYV] *mirror*.

What happens when you look into a concave mirror? What you see depends on how far you are from the mirror. Sometimes you see a virtual image that seems to be behind the mirror. Sometimes you see no image, only a blur. Sometimes you see an upside-down image that appears to be in front of the mirror. This kind of image is called a *real image,* because the image is where you see it. If you put a piece of paper at that place, the image would be projected onto the paper. Only real images can be projected onto another surface. Virtual images cannot.

Convex mirrors

Have you ever seen an image of yourself on the back of a shiny spoon? If you have, you looked at an image in a *convex* [kahn-VEHKS] *mirror.* How is a convex mirror different from a concave mirror? A concave mirror is a mirror which is curved inward at its center. A convex mirror is curved outward at its center.

Figure 23–3. In the diagram above, parallel light rays fall on a concave mirror. What happens to the reflected light rays?

DO IT YOURSELF

Look at images in a concave mirror

Get a concave shaving mirror or dressing-room mirror. Hold the mirror close to your face and look at yourself. Then put the mirror down and prop it up in some way. Move back from the mirror until your image is a blur. Then move back until your image is upside down. Is the upside-down image a real image or a virtual image? Could the image be projected on a screen? Try it with a flashlight in a darkened room and see.

All images seen in a convex mirror are smaller than the objects themselves. In a convex mirror, however, objects over a wide area may be seen. You may have seen a convex mirror placed so the cashier in a store can see it. This mirror lets the cashier see a wide area of the store without leaving the cash register. The image is *distorted* [dihs-TAW(UH)R-tuhd], or a little out of shape. But objects can be recognized in a convex mirror.

★ **Which kind of mirror—concave or convex—do you think is most used? Why?**

Figure 23–4. In the picture a convex mirror is shown mounted near the ceiling of a drugstore. What can a person behind the counter see by looking in the convex mirror? What is the purpose of having such a mirror?

LENSES

How would you describe a lens?
Why is a convex lens called a converging lens?
Why is a concave lens called a diverging lens?

Refracting light

A *lens* is like a mirror in one way. Both change light rays. But a lens does not reflect light as a mirror does. A lens lets light pass through it. As the light rays go through the lens, they are refracted, or bent.

A lens is made from glass or from some other transparent material. When you look at a lens from the front or back, it is often circular in shape. When you look at a lens from the side, you can see that the lens is thicker in some places than in others. Sometimes only the front or only the back of the lens is curved. Sometimes both the front and the back are curved.

The shape of a lens (as seen from the side) makes a difference in how the light rays will be bent. Light rays are always bent toward the thickest part of the lens. Light rays may be focused to a point. Or, light rays may be spread out.

Convex lenses

There are two chief kinds of lenses. One kind is thinner at its edges than it is in the middle. Lenses shaped like this are called *convex lenses*. Look at the convex

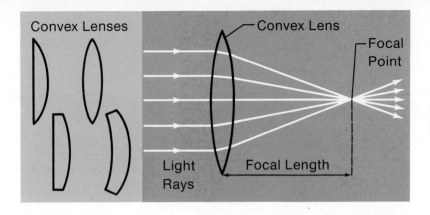

lenses in Figure 23–5. You may have seen convex lenses in cameras, telescopes, and magnifying glasses.

Convex lenses cause light rays to come together, or *converge* [kuhn-VURJ]. Such lenses are often called converging lenses because of the way they affect light rays, as in Figure 23–5. The point at which the rays meet is the *focal point*. The distance to the focal point from the lens is called the *focal length*.

★ **A converging lens is sometimes called a burning glass. How would you explain this?**

What do you see when you look through a convex, or converging, lens at some object? Just as when you use a concave mirror, what you see depends on how far the object is behind the lens. Sometimes you see a large, virtual image that seems to be behind the lens. Sometimes you see no image, only a blur. Sometimes an

(*Text continues on page 453.*)

A. Devaney, Inc.

Figure 23–6. In this photograph, a convex lens is being held over a dictionary. Why is such a lens often called a magnifying glass?

Investigate

What kinds of images are formed by convex lenses?

You Will Need

> convex (converging) lens, lens holder, candle, candleholder, cardboard screen, screen holder, metre stick and supports

Background

The focal point of a convex (converging) lens is the point at which light from a faraway source, such as the sun, is focused. The focal length of the lens is the distance from the center of the lens to its focal point—about the same as the distance from the lens to the image of a faraway object.

What to Do

Place the lens at the center of the metre stick. Place a cardboard screen at the end of the metre stick. Focus sunlight on the screen by moving the screen along the metre stick until a bright spot is formed on the screen. Quickly remove the screen from the holder so the sun does not burn it. Then record the focal length of the lens, or the distance between the lens and the place where the screen was.

Place the screen at the end of the metre stick again. Then place a candle on the metre stick and at the opposite side of the lens from the screen. Light the candle and move it so that it is slightly more than two focal lengths away from the lens. Adjust the screen so that a clear image of the candle is on the screen. Describe the image.

Move the candle closer to the lens. Move the screen to keep the image sharp. Describe any changes in the image.

Now place the candle less than one focal length from the lens. Try to form an image on the screen. Then look through the lens at the candle. Describe what you see.

Now That You Have Done the Investigation

—What did you find the focal length of your lens to be?
—Was the image of the candle always upside down? Was it always the same size? Explain.
—Could you get an image on the screen when the candle was inside the focal length?
—What did you see when you looked through the lens at the candle?

upside-down image appears in front of the lens. The upside-down image is a real image and can be projected on a screen. So, the image formed by a convex lens can be either virtual or real.

Concave lenses

A convex (converging) lens is thinner at its edges than it is in the middle. But another kind of lens is thinner in the middle than at its edges. Lenses shaped like this are called *concave lenses*. See Figure 23–7.

What happens to parallel light rays that pass through a concave lens? Look again at the figure. Notice that the rays spread apart, or *diverge* [duh-VURJ]. For this reason concave lenses are called diverging lenses. They are used in eyeglasses for nearsighted people.

All images made by diverging lenses are virtual images. They cannot be projected onto a screen. They can only be seen by looking through the lens. The images are always upright and smaller than the object.

★ **What differences do you see between the lenses in Figure 23–5 and those in Figure 23–7?**

Figure 23–7. Some concave lenses are shown in the diagram. What happens to parallel rays of light passing through a concave lens?

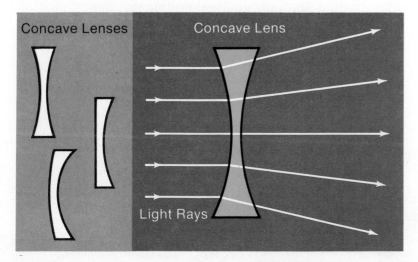

DO IT YOURSELF

Look through a concave (diverging) lens

Get a concave (diverging) lens or some eyeglasses that are for a nearsighted person. Look through the lens at an object. How would you describe the image? Place the object at different distances from the lens. Do differences in distance cause differences in the image you see? In what ways is the image made by the concave (diverging) lens different from the image made by the convex (converging) lens?

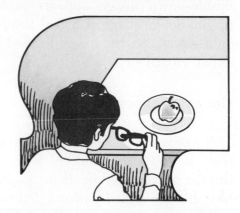

THE EYE

What part of the eye focuses light?
On what part of the eye is an image formed?
What kind of lens is used in eyeglasses to help a nearsighted person? A farsighted person?

Parts of the eye

You can see the words on this page because light is reflected from the page. Then the reflected light comes into your eyes. Light enters each eye through an opening called the *pupil*. The light then passes through a liquid and enters the *lens*. The lens refracts the light so that, after passing through another liquid, the light forms an image on the *retina* [REHT-uhn-uh]. The retina is the surface at the back of the eye. Look at Figure 23–8.

Figure 23–8. Examine the diagrams of the eye shown here. What parts of your eyes can you see when you look in a mirror?

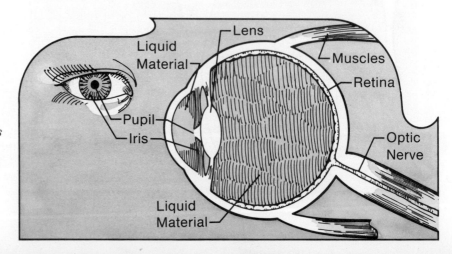

Comparing eyes to cameras

In some ways your eyes are like cameras. The amount of light coming into a camera can be changed by a device called a *diaphragm* [DY-uh-FRAM]. Each eye also has something like a diaphragm. It is called the *iris* [EYE-ruhs]. Muscles in the iris adjust the size of the pupil, so that the right amount of light enters the eye.

A camera has a lens to focus the light. The light then forms an image on film. Each eye also has a lens to focus the incoming light and form images. Muscles can change the shape of the lens. So, in a normal eye, the image is properly focused no matter how far away the object is.

The retina is like the film in a camera. It receives the images. The retina is made up of millions of living cells. As light hits each of these cells, electric *nerve impulses* [IHM-PUHL-suhz] move to the brain through a large nerve. Bright spots on the image send many nerve impulses to the brain. Dark spots send fewer. The brain "sorts out" the pattern of impulses.

Your eyes, then, are your "cameras." They collect and focus light. They send impulses to the brain. These impulses are like a coded message. The brain figures out what the message is. Without your brain, your eyes would be like cameras taking pictures that are never developed.

For You to Think About

A human eye is sometimes compared to a television camera. What are some ways they are alike? What are some ways they are different? Are the images you see similar to color TV or black-and-white TV? Why can't you get "instant replays" or "stop action" with your eyes?

DO IT YOURSELF

Look closely at a camera

Get a camera in which you can adjust the amount of light that enters. Make sure the camera does not have film in it. Open the back of the camera. Hold the camera near one eye. Look at your finger through the lens of the camera. What do you note about the image? Adjust the diaphragm of the camera to change the amount of light. Is the image changed? Explain.

Figure 23–9. When a nearsighted person looks at a distant object, the light coming into the eye is focused in front of the retina. What kind of lens corrects this condition? When a farsighted person looks at a nearby object, the light is focused behind the retina. What kind of lens corrects this condition?

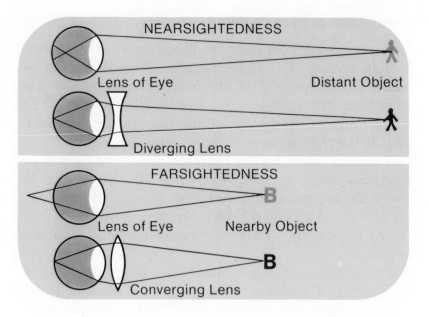

You might say the brain "develops" the pictures your eyes take.

Nearsighted and farsighted

What does it mean to be nearsighted or farsighted? People who are farsighted can see things at a distance well. However, they cannot see nearby things well. People who are nearsighted can see nearby things well. But they cannot see faraway things well. In either case, images are not being properly focused on the retina.

Eyeglasses can help images to be properly focused on the retina. See Figure 23–9. When a nearsighted person is looking at something far away, the image is formed in front of the retina. The lens of the eye is bending the light too much. A concave (diverging) lens in front of the eye can help a nearsighted person.

When a farsighted person is looking at something nearby, the image is focused behind the retina. The lens is not bending the light enough. A convex (converging) lens in front of the eye can help a farsighted person.

★ **In order to read the newspaper, some people hold it at arm's length. Would you say these people are farsighted or nearsighted? Explain.**

456

Lens Makers

Do you know how a lens is made? Many people do not. For one thing, lenses may be made from different materials. Some lenses are plastic, for example. But most lenses are made of glass.

If a lens is made of glass, the glass must be ground down. That is, the surface of the glass must be shaped by rubbing it with rough materials. This shaping is usually done by machine, but sometimes it is done by hand. To make a large lens, a great deal of grinding must be done. A lot of grinding is needed because glass is a very hard material.

There are several separate processes in making a lens. Each process must be carefully done to make a good lens of the right shape and size. The first process is cutting a block of glass with a diamond saw. The other processes involve more cutting, much grinding, and much smoothing and polishing. In a small shop, the same person may do all the processes. In a large shop, different people may take care of each process. But doing each process requires some skill.

Lenses are used in a wide variety of things. For example, they are used in eyeglasses, binoculars, microscopes, telescopes, and many other things. As you can see, the lens maker has an important job. Do you think you might like to make lenses for a living?

Courtesy of Carl Zeiss

Making lenses is a process that involves many steps. This lens maker is inspecting a lens that is almost finished.

Reviewing and Extending

SUMMING UP

1. A mirror is a surface that reflects light in a certain way.
2. The angle at which light hits a mirror is equal to the angle at which it leaves the mirror.
3. The images in a plane mirror are virtual images.
4. When you are close to a concave mirror, you see a virtual image of yourself. As you move farther away from the mirror, you see only a blur. Still farther away you see a real, upside-down image of yourself.
5. All images in a convex mirror are smaller than the objects reflected in it, but many objects over a wide area may be seen in it.
6. A lens refracts, or bends, light which passes through it.
7. When you look through a convex (converging) lens, sometimes you see a virtual image of the object. Sometimes an upside-down, real image appears in front of the lens.
8. Images made by concave (diverging) lenses are virtual images.
9. The shape of the lens of the eye can be changed by certain muscles, so that light waves are focused on the retina.
10. Eyeglasses can be used to help focus light on the retina of the eye.

CHECKING UP

Vocabulary   Write the numerals *1–10* on your paper. Each numbered phrase describes a term from the following list. On your paper, write the term next to the numeral of the phrase that describes it.

iris	convex lens	convex mirror
retina	concave lens	concave mirror
diverging	real image	angle of incidence
converging	virtual image	angle of reflection

1. spreading apart of light rays
2. surface at the back of the eye
3. angle at which light comes in to a reflecting surface
4. coming together of light rays at a point
5. image that can be projected onto another surface
6. mirror which curves inward, or away from you, at its center
7. shape of a lens which causes light to converge
8. shape of a lens which causes light to diverge
9. mirror which curves outward, or toward you, at its center
10. part of the eye which controls the size of the pupil and allows the right amount of light to enter the eye

Knowledge and Understanding Write the numerals *11–14* on your paper. Beside each numeral, write the word or words that best complete the sentence having that numeral.

11. Specially shaped pieces of transparent material that can be used to focus light are called (*lenses, mirrors, retinas*).
12. The kind of lens a nearsighted person would use in front of the eye is a (*concave, convex, converging*) lens.
13. The diaphragm of a camera is used to change the amount of light coming into the camera. The diaphragm may be compared to the (*lens, pupil, iris*) of the eye.
14. The images made when light waves pass through a concave (diverging) lens are (*real, virtual, upside down*).

Concepts Beside each of the numerals *15–16* on your paper, write the word or words that best complete the sentence having that numeral.

15. A concave mirror may be used to (*spread out light in all directions, focus light to a point, make several rays of light*).
16. Many more nerve impulses will be sent to the brain when there (*are many dark spots in the image, are many bright spots in the image, is a strong lens in the eye*).

Application and Critical Thinking Answer the following questions as briefly as you can without leaving out any important ideas.

17. When you go to a movie theater and see images on the screen, are the images real images or virtual images? How do you know?
18. What is the difference in the way light is reflected from a convex mirror and the way it is reflected from a concave mirror if a light bulb is at the focal point of each of the mirrors?
19. Why are the lenses in the eyeglasses of nearsighted people made to be thinner in the middle than at the edges?

DOING MORE

1. Make a pinhole camera. In a darkened room, show your class that the camera makes an image that is upside down on the back of the camera. Try to explain how an image is formed even though no lens is present.
2. Figure out how to make a device that will allow you to see around corners without being seen. Explain to your classmates how the device works, and make a list of its possible uses.

CHAPTER 24

The Electromagnetic Spectrum

Waves of invisible energy are all around you at this very moment. These waves are part of the electromagnetic spectrum. Your eyes are able to see only the part of the spectrum called visible light.

Even though you cannot see the invisible waves of the electromagnetic spectrum, these waves play a very important part in your life. They hit your body all the time. They may sometimes burn your skin. Some of these waves pass right through your body. Some of them can warm you. Others are used for communication. Still others are used for finding out where objects are.

What are some kinds of waves in the electromagnetic spectrum? Where do they come from? How are the different kinds of waves in the electromagnetic spectrum alike? How are they different? How can these waves be used? You will explore these and other questions as you study this chapter.

In what ways, do you think, do the pictures show how waves of the electromagnetic spectrum are used for communication?

Photos from Artstreet

INFRARED RAYS AND ULTRAVIOLET RAYS

How are other forms of energy in the electro-
magnetic spectrum different from visible light?
How were infrared rays discovered, and how are
they used today?
How were ultraviolet rays discovered, and how
are they used today?
In what ways can ultraviolet rays harm people?

What is the electromagnetic spectrum?

Different kinds of waves make up the electromagnetic spectrum. Visible light is the part that can be seen. But visible light is only a small part of the spectrum.

How does visible light compare with other kinds of radiant energy in the electromagnetic spectrum? Look at Figure 24–1. Notice that some kinds of radiation are called rays, and some are called waves. Even though the different kinds of radiant energy have different names, each is a part of the electromagnetic spectrum.

The range of wave lengths in the electromagnetic spectrum is very great. The longest waves are *radio waves.*

Figure 24–1. There are many kinds of radiation in the electromagnetic spectrum. By looking at the figure, find out the range of wave lengths for each kind of radiation. How do the frequencies change as the wave lengths increase? How do the frequencies change as the wave lengths decrease?

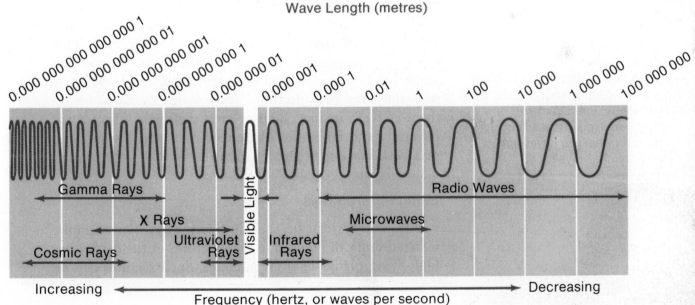

ELECTROMAGNETIC SPECTRUM
Wave Length (metres)

0.000 000 000 000 000 1
0.000 000 000 000 01
0.000 000 000 001
0.000 000 000 1
0.000 000 01
0.000 001
0.000 1
0.01
1
100
10 000
1 000 000
100 000 000

Gamma Rays

X Rays

Cosmic Rays

Ultraviolet Rays

Visible Light

Infrared Rays

Microwaves

Radio Waves

Increasing ⟷ Decreasing

Frequency (hertz, or waves per second)

They can be about 100 000 kilometres (about sixty thousand miles) long. The shortest waves are cosmic rays. They are very short—only about 0.000 000 000 000 000 1 metre long. Visible light is between these wave lengths. The wave lengths of visible light are from about 0.000 000 4 metre to about 0.000 000 7 metre.

Infrared rays, microwaves, and radio waves have longer wave lengths than visible light. Ultraviolet rays, X rays, gamma rays, and cosmic rays have shorter wave lengths than visible light. But all kinds of electromagnetic waves travel through space at the same speed. They travel 300 000 kilometres (186,000 miles) in one second.

How infrared rays were discovered

As long ago as 1672, scientists knew that sunlight is made of light of several colors. In 1800, one scientist wondered which color gave off the most heat. So he used a prism to make a spectrum of all the colors of light. He then placed a thermometer in each of the different colors. The temperature was higher in some colors than in others. In which color do you think the temperature was highest?

He also placed the thermometer where no visible light was falling. The temperature just outside the red color of the spectrum was high. It seemed that some kind of invisible waves were causing heat. This important discovery was made by Sir William Herschel.

The invisible waves that were causing the heat are called *infrared rays*. "Infrared" means "below red." This experiment shows that when infrared rays are stopped by matter, they cause the matter to warm up. Black materials stop the rays best. Light-colored materials do not stop them as well. In fact, light-colored materials reflect some infrared rays. Since the black materials stop the infrared rays best, black materials warm up more than light-colored materials do.

Using infrared rays

Infrared rays can be used in many ways. For example, infrared film can be used to take pictures of the earth from high-flying planes or from satellites. Such pictures can be

(*Text continues on page 464.*)

For You to Think About

Perhaps you have noticed that most people wear light-colored clothing on hot summer days and that black cars are hotter when you touch them than light-colored cars are. How would you explain these things, based on what you have learned about infrared rays?

Investigate

What happens when a thermometer is placed just outside the visible spectrum?

You Will Need

large prism, piece of white cardboard, 4 thermometers

Background

Visible light is just one kind of electromagnetic energy that is present in the electromagnetic spectrum. As you know, there are other forms of electromagnetic energy in the electromagnetic spectrum. But these forms of energy are invisible. Only visible light can be detected with your eyes. To find out more about the invisible kinds of energy in the electromagnetic spectrum, you must use some way of detecting them other than seeing them.

What to Do

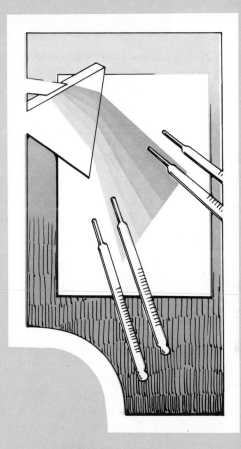

Using the prism in sunlight, project a visible-light spectrum on the floor. Then place the piece of white cardboard on the floor so that the spectrum is on the cardboard. Make sure the sunlight is not falling directly on the cardboard. Place the bulb of one thermometer in the violet light of the visible spectrum. Place the bulb of the second thermometer in the red light of the visible spectrum. Place the bulb of the third thermometer just outside the red light of the spectrum. Place the bulb of the fourth thermometer just outside the violet light. Observe and record the temperature of each thermometer every minute for five minutes.

Now That You Have Done the Investigation

—What were the differences among the temperatures of the thermometers after five minutes?

—What was the difference between the temperature in violet light and the temperature just outside violet light?

—What was the difference between the temperature in red light and the temperature just outside red light?

—Do you think that there is another form of energy just outside the red light of the visible spectrum? Why or why not?

Figure 24–2. These pictures of trees were taken with infrared film. Diseased and insect-damaged trees appear darker than healthy trees.

used to find diseased trees in a forest. On the pictures the infrared radiation from diseased trees does not look the same as the radiation from healthy trees.

Infrared rays can also be used for heating and cooking. The coils in electric heaters and electric ovens give off great amounts of infrared rays.

★ **What kind of electromagnetic waves are given off by heat lamps? Why do you think so?**

How ultraviolet rays were discovered

One year after infrared rays were discovered, another kind of invisible energy was discovered. Remember, infrared rays were discovered just outside the red end of the visible spectrum. Does it seem likely that there are also invisible rays just outside the violet end of the visible spectrum?

Invisible rays *were* discovered just outside the violet end of the visible spectrum. The discovery was made by Johann Ritter, a German scientist. A beam of sunlight was allowed to pass through a prism. The prism divided the beam into the colors of the visible spectrum. Then a chemical called *silver chloride* [KLOH(UH)R-EYED] was placed in each color of light to see what would happen. Red light caused little change in the silver chloride. But violet light made the silver chloride become darker.

Then, silver chloride was placed just outside the violet end of the visible spectrum. The silver chloride became very dark. It would not have become dark unless there were invisible rays just outside the violet end of the visible spectrum.

These rays were named ultraviolet rays. Ultraviolet means "just beyond the violet." These rays travel at the same speed as visible light. But these rays have shorter wave lengths than visible light.

Using ultraviolet rays

Ultraviolet rays are used in identifying certain costly stones, certain metals, and certain important papers. Dentists can use ultraviolet rays to find out if a person's tooth is living or dead. A live tooth glows under ultraviolet light. A dead tooth does not. Ultraviolet rays also help your body make vitamin D. This vitamin makes healthy teeth and bones in the body.

Ultraviolet rays kill germs too. The rays have a high frequency and will often destroy germs hit by the rays. Ultraviolet rays can also be used to treat skin diseases.

★ **Ultraviolet rays can cause sunburn if people are exposed to them for too long a time. If this is true, why do you think such rays are sometimes used to treat skin diseases?**

RADIO, TELEVISION, AND RADAR

What are the frequencies and wave lengths of radio waves?
How are radio waves used?
How are TV waves different from radio waves?
What are some uses for TV?
What are some uses for radar?

Radio wave lengths and frequencies

Did you know that radio waves cannot be heard or seen? It's true. You cannot hear radio waves, but a radio set can detect the waves and change them into sound.

465

The wave lengths of radio waves are from 0.000 1 metre (those near infrared rays) to over 100 000 000 metres. See Figure 24–1 on page 461 again.

Radio waves are usually described by their frequencies instead of by their wave lengths. Radio frequencies are given in *kilohertz* [KIHL-uh-HURTS] or *megahertz* [MEHG-uh-HURTS]. One kilohertz is one thousand waves a second. One megahertz is one million waves a second. Maybe you have heard a radio announcer say something like, "This is WDHF, broadcasting at 95.5 megahertz."

The full range of radio frequencies is from about three hertz to about three billion megahertz. However, the frequencies most used are from three kilohertz to thirty thousand megahertz. See Figure 24–3.

AM radio stations use frequencies from 535 kilohertz to 1 605 kilohertz. The wave lengths of these frequencies are from about 200 metres to about 600 metres. FM stations use frequencies from 88.1 megahertz to 107.9 megahertz. These frequencies cover wave lengths from about three metres to about three and one-half metres.

When you turn the tuning knob on a radio set, you are adjusting the set so it will receive certain wave lengths. Suppose two radio stations decided to use the same frequency for broadcasting. Then you would hear both stations at the same setting on your radio. In fact, you would not be able to separate their messages. For this reason each station has a certain frequency. No other station is allowed to use that frequency.

Figure 24–3. This diagram shows the relationship between the wave length and the frequency of radio waves. Starting at the left, notice that radio waves are short in length and high in frequency. Moving to the right, the wave lengths increase. What happens to the frequency?

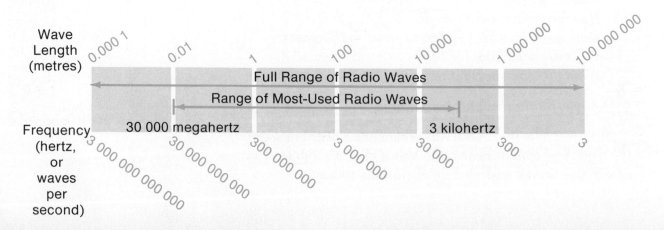

THE RANGE OF RADIO WAVES

Investigate

How can you cause static in a pocket radio?

You Will Need

pocket radio, 1.5-volt dry cell, insulated copper wire

Background

The static you hear in a radio is due to unwanted radio waves coming to the radio. For example, whenever electric sparks are created, radio waves are also created. These waves often cause static. The static could be due to something natural, such as lightning. It could also be due to some electric appliance that is making sparks and radio waves as it operates. Usually the unwanted radio waves made by an appliance are very weak and do not affect a radio unless the radio and the appliance are close to each other.

What to Do

Turn the radio on and tune it so that no station is being received. Then turn the volume up to full.

Remove about two centimetres of insulation from a piece of insulated copper wire. Connect one end of the wire to a dry-cell terminal.

Place the dry cell about thirty centimetres (about one foot) from the radio. Take the loose end of the wire and scrape it against the other terminal of the dry cell. Listen for sounds from the radio as you scrape the terminal.

Now place the dry cell farther from the radio. Scrape the terminal again and listen for sounds from the radio.

Move the dry cell still farther from the radio and scrape the terminal. Listen for sounds from the radio as you do so.

Now That You Have Done the Investigation

—Did you hear a sound coming from the radio when the terminal was scraped? If so, did you hear it at each distance from the radio?

—What, do you think, caused the sound in the radio?

—Did the distance between the dry cell and the radio make a difference in the amount of sound made in the radio?

—Do you think it would make a difference in the amount of sound you hear coming from the radio if you used a weak, or old, dry cell? Why or why not?

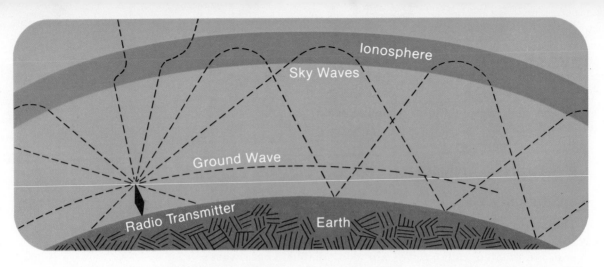

Figure 24–4. Radio signals travel in all directions. The ground wave follows the curved surface of the earth. Sky waves travel around the curve of the earth by reflecting off the ionosphere.

How radio waves travel

Radio waves often travel long distances. The waves are sent out in all directions from a device called a *radio transmitter* [tran(t)s-MIHT-ur]. Waves that go upward from the transmitter are called *sky waves*. Those waves that follow the surface of the earth are called *ground waves*. See Figure 24–4.

Ground waves can travel from 80 to 160 kilometres (50 to 100 miles) over the earth's surface. High things in their way will block them easily. But these waves can travel long distances over water.

★ **Why, do you think, can ground waves travel long distances over water?**

Some radio waves are reflected back to earth by a layer of air called the *ionosphere* [eye-AHN-uh-sFIH(UH)R].This layer ranges from about 50 kilometres to 500 kilometres (about 30 miles to 300 miles) above the surface of the earth.

The ionosphere reflects radio waves, sending them back to earth. Sometimes there are several reflections between the ionosphere and the earth. The reflections make it possible to receive broadcasts far from where they were sent. See Figure 24–4 again.

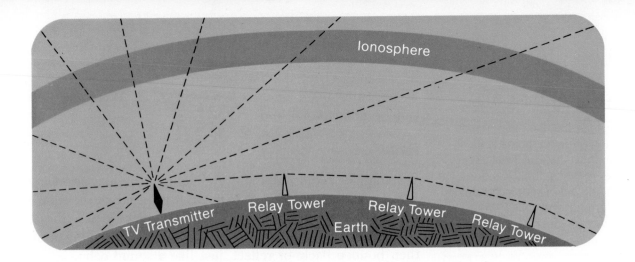

Ionosphere

Relay Tower Relay Tower Relay Tower

TV Transmitter Earth

Television

Did you know that TV is another example of using electromagnetic waves? The waves used in TV are a kind of radio wave. However, the radio waves used for TV broadcasting are shorter than those used for radio broadcasting. The shorter wave lengths used for TV cannot be sent over great distances like the longer radio waves can.

Waves used for radio broadcasting travel great distances by reflecting back and forth between the ionosphere and the earth's surface. But waves used for TV are not reflected. They travel only in straight lines. They pass through the ionosphere. For these waves, the TV transmitter and the TV set must be in a "direct line of sight." So, TV shows are sent by a series of towers. The first tower receives the waves from the transmitter. The waves are made stronger and sent on to the next tower. This process is repeated from tower to tower so that the waves can be sent great distances. See Figure 24–5.

TV has many uses. Some are listed below.

—Students and doctors can watch an operation taking place without bothering the doctors who are working.
—Workers can see and control dangerous jobs from a safe distance.
—Scientists can look at the deep parts of the ocean and the surfaces of other planets.
—Passengers at large airports can see the times when planes will arrive and leave.

Figure 24–5. The wave length of television signals is short. They are not reflected by the ionosphere. So, relay towers must be used to transmit these signals. Relay towers can transmit many different programs at the same time. Have you ever seen a relay tower? If so, where was it?

For You to Think About

For most people, the main reason for having TV in the home is its entertainment value. But TV is useful for other reasons, too. How does TV in the home aid in keeping people well informed and safe? What are some ways in which TV in the home is educational?

But the chief uses of TV today are in the home. Most homes in the United States have TV sets. People watch TV to be entertained and to keep informed. Watching TV can be educational, too.

Radar

Radar, or *radio detecting and ranging*, is like an echo. But it is not a sound echo. Instead, it is based on the sending and receiving of certain radio waves. When these radio waves are sent out, the waves hit something and then bounce back, or reflect, just like a sound echo.

Radar is used very much in aviation. Some airplanes have a device called a radio altimeter. This device uses radar to let the pilot know how far above ground the plane is flying. By using the radio altimeter, the pilot can also detect mountains or hills in the path of the plane.

Radar is used to control air traffic near large airports. It is also used to help the landing of planes whenever the pilot cannot see the ground very well.

Besides its use in aviation, radar is used in sailing. It is used to guide ships through fog. Things hidden by the fog can be "seen" and avoided by using radar.

Figure 24-6. The radar dish-antennas on the ship are used to track satellites. The man is looking at a radar screen that shows the positions of airplanes flying near an airport.

Photos from Photo Research International

Radar is used in predicting weather. It is also used by police to check the speed of a car. Radar has even been used to measure the distance from the earth to the moon.

★ **Could sound waves be used to find the distance from the earth to the moon? Explain.**

X RAYS

Who discovered X rays? When were they discovered?

How are X rays and visible light alike? How are they different?

What are some ways in which X rays are used?

The discovery of X rays

One important discovery having to do with the electromagnetic spectrum dates back to 1895. That was the year William Roentgen discovered X rays. Although he learned how to make X rays, he did not find out what X rays were. Because no one knew what these rays were, the rays were called X rays. Later, scientists discovered that X rays are a part of the electromagnetic spectrum.

Comparing X rays and visible light

For you to better understand X rays, it may help to compare them to visible light. In some ways, X rays and visible light are alike. Both move through space at about 300 000 kilometres (186,000 miles) a second. Both can cause photographic film to darken.

Then how are X rays different from visible light? Of course, visible light can be seen. X rays cannot. There are other differences, too. For example, visible light will not go through paper, cardboard, and skin. But X rays will easily go through these materials.

X rays are different from visible light in another way. Large amounts of X rays can damage living things. Of course, visible light does *not* damage living things. Instead, it helps some of them grow.

Find Out More

From different kinds of reference books, find out about the use of radar by the Federal Aviation Agency. Who are the Air Traffic Controllers? How do they use radar to control or assist every flight throughout the United States? How is radar used to identify commercial and military aircraft?

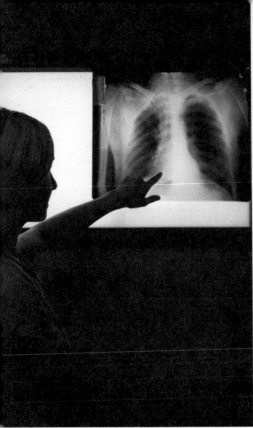

Barbara Van Cleve/Van Cleve Photography

Courtesy of United Air Lines

Figure 24–7. What is the relationship between a chest X ray and the way people and baggage are checked at airports?

But what is the difference between the waves that make up X rays and visible light? The difference is wave length. X rays have shorter wave lengths than visible light.

★ **How do the wave lengths of infrared rays compare with those of X rays?**

How are X rays used?

Have you ever had an X-ray photograph taken? If so, you know X rays may be directed through objects, such as bones or teeth, and onto photographic film. Such X-ray photographs are useful to doctors and dentists. For example, such photographs are useful in setting bones. They are also useful in examining lungs for diseases and in finding cavities in teeth.

In some cases, diseases are treated through the use of X rays. That is, the rays are used to stop or slow down the spread of a disease. For example, X rays can be used to destroy cancer cells.

In industry, X rays are used to inspect the insides of packages. X rays are used to find cracks and breaks in metal. Artwork, such as paintings and sculpture, can be identified and studied through the use of X rays. A list of all uses of X rays would be very long.

For You to Think About

When you have an X-ray photograph taken, say, of your teeth or a broken bone, the person who takes the picture is very careful to be shielded from the rays. Why? Are the rays harmful to that person? If so, why are they not harmful to you? Why might they be harmful to one person, but not to another?

472

The Radiologist

Do you know what a *radiologist* [RAYD -ee-AHL-uh-juhst] is? According to one dictionary, a radiologist is a person skilled in "the science of dealing with X rays or the rays from radioactive substances, especially for medical diagnosis and treatment." In other words, a radiologist uses X rays to examine, photograph, or treat bones, organs, and other parts of the body.

You probably have had X-ray photographs taken to find tooth cavities or to see the break in a bone. But did you know that X rays are also used to find and treat cancer? Finding and treating cancer requires a skilled radiologist.

First, the cancer must be found. It is often found through the use of X-ray photographs. Then, the X rays from an X-ray machine are directed to the place where the cancer cells are known to be growing in the person's body. The rays kill the cancer cells. Unfortunately, the rays may kill other cells too. The radiologist must know how to direct the rays so that the fewest number of healthy cells are killed. The radiologist must give many treatments to kill the cancer cells. If the cancer is detected in time, the radiologist may be able to kill all the cancer cells. Then the person who had the cancer may be free of the disease.

You probably agree that a radiologist has a very important job. Do you think you might like to be a radiologist someday? If so, you must get a lot of training. A radiologist is a highly trained specialist.

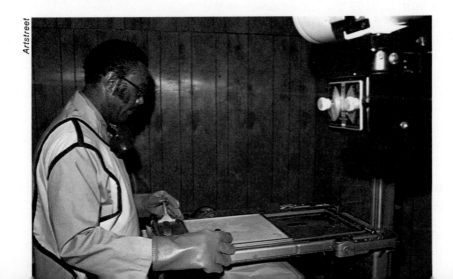

Artstreet

The radiologist in the picture is shown giving treatment to a patient. Why is the radiologist wearing gloves and protective clothing?

Reviewing and Extending

SUMMING UP

1. All electromagnetic waves travel through space at the same speed—300 000 kilometres (186,000 miles) a second. Each kind of wave has a different wave length.
2. Infrared rays, microwaves, and radio waves have longer wave lengths than visible light. Ultraviolet rays, X rays, gamma rays, and cosmic rays have shorter wave lengths.
3. Some uses of infrared rays are in photography, to find diseased trees, to provide heat, and to cook food.
4. Some uses of ultraviolet rays are to identify things, to kill germs, and to treat skin diseases.
5. Some uses of radio waves are radio broadcasting, TV broadcasting, and radar. Radio, TV, and radar each have many uses.
6. Some uses of X rays are to take X-ray photographs of parts of the body, to treat certain diseases, and to inspect the insides of packages.

CHECKING UP

Vocabulary   Write the numerals *1–8* on your paper. Each numbered phrase describes a term from the following list. On your paper, write the term next to the numeral of the phrase that describes it.

ultraviolet rays	radio waves	megahertz
visible light	ionosphere	X rays
infrared rays	kilohertz	radar

1. rays just outside the red color of the visible spectrum
2. rays that easily go through paper, cardboard, and skin and may be used to make photographs of bones and teeth
3. rays just outside the violet color of the visible spectrum
4. radio detecting and ranging
5. rays used for radio, television, and radar
6. one thousand waves a second
7. one million waves a second
8. layer of air that causes radio waves to be reflected

Knowledge and Understanding   Write the numerals *9–13* on your paper. Beside each numeral, write the word or words that best complete the sentence having that numeral.

9. Electromagnetic waves that can cause sunburn are called (*infrared rays, X rays, ultraviolet rays*).

474

10. The rays that were discovered by William Roentgen are (*infrared rays, X rays, ultraviolet rays*).
11. A scientist by the name of (*Ritter, Roentgen, Herschel*) found invisible electromagnetic waves just outside the violet end of the visible spectrum.
12. A scientist named (*Ritter, Roentgen, Herschel*) experimented with a spectrum and thermometers and discovered infrared rays.
13. Some radio waves are reflected in the air by (*sky waves, the ionosphere, ultraviolet rays*).

Concepts   Beside each of the numerals *14–17* on your paper, write the word or words that best complete the sentence having that numeral.

14. Electromagnetic waves that have very long wave lengths are (*radio waves, ultraviolet rays, infrared rays*).
15. (*Dark-colored materials, Light-colored materials, Green-colored materials*) stop infrared rays best.
16. Radio communication across the ocean is possible because (*nothing gets in the way of the ground waves, the ionosphere stops the sky waves, the ionosphere reflects the sky waves*).
17. When silver chloride is placed just outside (*the red end, the violet end, both ends*) of a visible spectrum, the silver chloride becomes very dark.

Application and Critical Thinking   Answer the following questions as briefly as you can without leaving out any important ideas.

18. Infrared and ultraviolet rays are invisible. How were scientists able to find out that these rays exist?
19. How are the radio waves used for radar different from the radio waves used in radio broadcasting?
20. What is one way in which X rays differ from visible light?

DOING MORE

1. Write or call a local radio station or television station. Ask if you can visit the studio and transmitting station. Find out all you can about the station.
2. Take a picture of some familiar part of the sky at night with infrared film. Also take pictures of certain warm or hot objects at night. What are the differences between the pictures of both the sky and the objects taken with infrared film and the way they really looked? Explain.

Pros and Cons

People who sunbathe at a beach can get a tan. But they may absorb too much ultraviolet radiation if they are not careful. Then what might happen to their skin?

Radiation—Is It Helpful or Harmful?

You have read about the forms of radiant energy, or radiation, in the electromagnetic spectrum. You may remember that if your skin is exposed to ultraviolet rays for too long a time, you may become sunburned. But ultraviolet rays hitting your skin may cause your body to make a vitamin it needs. So there are reasons why exposing the skin to ultraviolet rays is good. There are also reasons why it is bad. In other words, there are pros and cons concerning ultraviolet rays.

You may know, too, that infrared rays may be used to cook your food or heat your home. But such rays may also cause food to burn up or people to become overheated. So infrared rays may be helpful or harmful to people.

X rays may be used to find and treat diseases, such as cancer. But if people who do not have cancer are exposed to X rays for too long a time, the X rays may cause cancer cells to grow in their body. In fact, Marie Curie, the discoverer of radium, died of leukemia. Leukemia is a kind of cancer. Many people believe that she became ill as a result of working with radium. Radium gives off X rays, as well as other kinds of radiation. So X rays may be helpful or harmful to people.

One kind of radio waves, called microwaves, are used for television, radar, and microwave ovens. These things are usually thought to be helpful to people. But TV sets that are not working properly may give off dangerous rays. Radar and microwave ovens may be harmful to people if they are not used properly.

What about visible light? Can it also be harmful to people or other living things? Yes, it can. Visible light may be so bright that it can cause a person to be blinded temporarily. Of course, because the person is not able to see, many things may happen to that person that would not usually happen. The person may trip or fall easily, for example.

The most harmful radiation has yet to be mentioned. This radiation is the kind that comes from nuclear reactions. It is harmful to all living things. Radiation from nuclear reactions is harmful because such great amounts of radiation come from the reactions and because the radiation is very strong.

But radiation from nuclear reactions can be useful too. This radiation can be used to make materials radioactive. Then the radioactive materials can be used to treat diseases. Some radiation from nuclear reactions is in the form of heat. This heat can be used to generate electricity at nuclear power plants.

You have learned some of the pros and cons concerning different forms of radiation. You can see that many questions may come up when you think about radiation. Do the helpful things about radiation far outweigh the harmful ones? Or, do the harmful things outweigh the helpful ones? Should people try to avoid any form of radiation that is not found in nature? Would people be better off if radiation were not used at all? Can only the

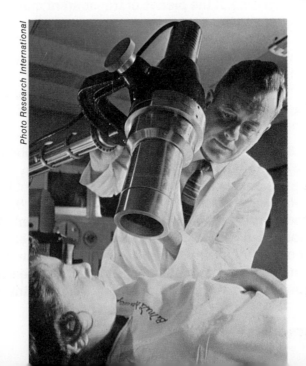

A person is being treated with radiation in the picture at the left. Is the radiation helpful or harmful in this case? Explain. Plants that have been exposed to radiation are being examined in the picture above. Is radiation helpful or harmful in this case? Explain.

helpful forms of radiation be used, and all the harmful ones be avoided? If so, how? You might want to discuss these questions with your classmates. Find out what they think.

Investigate On Your Own

1. Get a tuning fork. Also get a block of metal, a piece of wood, a cork, a felt pad, and a sponge-rubber pad, all about one centimetre in thickness. Hit the tuning fork and touch its base to the panel of a door. Note how loud the sound is. Now place each of the materials, one at a time, between the door panel and the base of the tuning fork. Hit the tuning fork each time you change the material. Note how loud the sound is in each case. Which materials seem to move the sound very well? Which materials would be good to use in soundproofing a room?

2. Get two prisms and several pieces of transparent materials, such as glass or cellophane, of different colors. Let sunlight or light from a light bulb pass through a narrow slit in a piece of cardboard and then through one of the prisms. Then let the spectrum of colors pass through one of the pieces of transparent material. What happens to the light that passes through the transparent material? Allow the light that has passed through the material to pass through the second prism. What happens to the light when this is done? Try each of the other pieces of material in the same way. What happens to the light each time a different piece of material is used? How would you explain what happens?

3. Do an experiment to see how a bean plant is affected by different kinds of electromagnetic energy. Place six bean plants in a dark room. Get an ultraviolet lamp, or "black light." Also get an infrared lamp, or "heat lamp," and an ordinary lamp. Expose two bean plants to ultraviolet rays for one hour each day for two weeks. Expose two bean plants to infrared rays for the same amount of time. Expose two plants to visible light in the same way. Be sure to keep the lamps far enough away so that all the

478

leaves will receive the same amount of radiation. Take care of all the plants in the same way except for the kind of radiation they get. Keep a record of what you do and what you see happening. In which kind of radiation did the plants grow best? Explain.

Read On Your Own

Bamberger, Richard, *Physics Through Experiment.* New York: Sterling Publishing Co., Inc., 1969.

Experiments on noise and music and on heat are included in this book. Simple materials are used in all the experiments.

Hellman, Hal, *Communications in the World of the Future.* (World of the Future Series, Number 2) New York: M. Evans & Co., Inc., 1969.

This book deals with many kinds of communications, including picturephones, computers, and even machines "talking" to machines.

Hoskin, Michael, *The Mind of the Scientist: Imaginary Conversations with Galileo, Newton, Herschel, Darwin, and Pasteur.* New York: Taplinger Publishing Co., 1972.

You will find out what these scientists did and what their personality was like from this book.

Moellring, F. K., *Beginning with the Microscope.* New York: Sterling Publishing Co., Inc., 1972.

The parts of a microscope are discussed, as well as just what each lens in the microscope is designed to do. The book has many photographs and diagrams.

Taylor, Rupert, *Noise.* Baltimore, Maryland: Pelican Books, 1971.

This interesting book is about noise pollution. It has many diagrams. It also has many definitions of terms used in the study of acoustics.

UNIT **6**

TECHNOLOGY

Using Science

This unit is about some ways science is used. The ways described are certainly not the only ways science is used. They are not necessarily the most important either. But the uses of science that you can study in this unit do show that changes in our life occur when science is put to use. By studying this unit, you might also get some ideas about what might happen in the future as new principles of science are discovered and used.

Chapters

CHAPTER 25

Technology and Engineering

In the past month, have you heard or read about some new space flight? About a new building, bridge, or highway being built? About some new product for the home? About a new design in automobiles or airplanes? If so, you have heard or read about things that have something to do with *technology* [tehk-NAHL-uh-jee] and *engineering* [EHN-juh-NIH(UH)R-ihng].

The terms "technology" and "engineering" may not be new to you. You may even know some people whose jobs are in technology and engineering. But do you have a good understanding of the meanings of the terms? Do you know how they are related to science? What does the future hold for persons interested in technology and engineering?

As you study Chapter 25, some of these questions will be answered. Hopefully, you will learn more than just answers to these questions. Perhaps you will also see how technology and engineering will continue to cause changes in our lives. Maybe you will decide to be an engineer or technician and help make these changes happen.

Daniel Brody

Courtesy of Pratt & Whitney Aircraft

Technology and engineering are involved in testing materials (above) and building a jet engine (right).

TECHNOLOGY

What are the characteristics of technology?
How are science and technology related?
*In what ways is technology good? In what ways
is technology bad?*
How will technology change in the years ahead?

What is technology?

People use technology in meeting their daily needs
and desires. In order for you to understand this, you need
to have a clear understanding of what technology is.

Technology has three important characteristics. (1) It
is based on discoveries in science. (2) It has to do with
the use of tools and machines. (3) It depends on energy
and power.

Science and technology are closely related, but they
are not the same. Scientists are making new discoveries
about matter and energy all the time. Technology is the
way these discoveries are put to use.

In the past, certain people helped to make great advances in technology even though they had very little
schooling. For example, Thomas Edison, who attended
school for only three months, patented 362 inventions.

Culver Pictures, Inc.

*Figure 25–1. This photograph shows Thomas
Edison holding one of his electric lamps. The
electric lamp is only one of his many inventions. What were some of his other inventions?*

483

Figure 25–2. The computer shown below could not be operated without the development of circuits such as the one being drawn at the right.

Herb Taylor/Editorial Photocolor Archives, Inc.

A. Reininger/De Wys, Inc.

Today, however, technology seems to depend more and more on well-trained scientists. Scientists were the key people in most of the recent advances in technology. The basic principles of such things as transistors, computers, and atomic reactors were developed by teams of scientists.

★ **What reasons would you give to explain why, today, technology depends more on well-trained scientists than it did 100 years ago?**

How long does it take for new scientific discoveries to become useful to people? No one can say for sure. However, it seems as though the time between when a discovery is made and when the discovery is used is becoming less and less.

Why is this time becoming less and less? One reason is that today's scientists are working on certain problems, not just trying to discover something new.

Often when a new need arises, scientists are called in right away. For example, the nose cones of missiles and space vehicles have to withstand very high temperatures. Most materials melt at such high temperatures. Scientists were called in to find a new material that could be used. They were able to use what they knew about matter to find a material for the nose cones that could withstand high temperatures.

Find Out More

Pick a famous inventor and, using library materials, make a report to the class on what this person invented. Thomas Edison, Norbert Rillieux, and James Watt are examples of such people. In your report, try to answer such questions as these. Was this person a scientist? How much education did the person have? How did the inventions improve American technology?

The good and bad sides of technology

Not everyone has the same ideas about the overall value of technology. Some people point out that technology has made possible many comforts and conveniences. On the other hand, many people believe technology has caused many of the problems in the world today.

These different views about technology point out the need for everyone to know more about technology. Everyone should know how technology can be helpful. Everyone should also know how it can be harmful. Some examples from everyday life can be used to show the good and bad sides of technology.

Have you ever been without electricity for several days? If so, you know that living without electricity can be very hard. So using electricity is helpful in many ways.

You might be wondering how using electricity can be harmful. For one thing, most generating plants burn coal to generate electricity. The burning of coal in large amounts causes air *pollution* [puh-LOO-shuhn]. As you know, air pollution may cause certain health problems.

For You to Think About

What are some of the things that electricity is used for in the home? Which of these things could you learn to do without in your own home?

Figure 25–3. The burning of coal causes the air pollution seen in the picture. Which smokestack do you think is releasing materials that are the most harmful?

Daniel Brody

Figure 25–4. Technology is sometimes blamed for the pollution of rivers. Technology is sometimes blamed for automobile accidents, too. Can you explain these statements?

Another example of the good and bad sides of technology is the automobile. Automobiles are widely used for business and pleasure. They provide an easy and comfortable way to get from one place to another.

But the fact that automobiles are so widely used has caused some major problems. Air pollution is reaching dangerous levels, especially in cities. The exhaust from automobiles is a major cause of this pollution. Automobiles, trucks, and buses also add to the high level of noise in many places. But perhaps the worst thing about automobiles is the great number of injuries and deaths each year from automobile accidents.

Technology is also blamed for much of the pollution of streams, rivers, ponds, lakes, and even oceans. Where does this pollution come from? Part of it comes from factories and farms. Some factories dump waste materials that are not treated into rivers and lakes. Some chemical fertilizers and insecticides, such as DDT, are washed from farmers' fields into streams, rivers, ponds, and lakes.

DO IT YOURSELF

Look for evidence of pollution

Visit one or more streams, rivers, ponds, or lakes in your community. Look for evidence of pollution in the water or at the edges of the water. What evidence of pollution do you find? Do you think this pollution is the result of technology? Explain.

But technology itself can be used to solve many of the problems blamed on technology. For example, devices to cut down on the pollution caused by automobile exhausts have been made. Air and water pollution from factories can be cut down by having factories use newly developed devices and follow certain practices. In fact, pollution of all kinds could be cut down if technology were used as much as possible.

★ **How would you explain the following statement? Technology is neither good nor bad; it is what we make of it.**

Technology in the future

Many of the things people have and do today are clearly the result of advanced technology. Advanced technology has made possible automobiles, airplanes, television, atomic energy, permanent-press fabrics, and detergents that are all very much a part of our daily life. Because of advanced technology, people have been able to live underwater for months and have been able to go to the moon and back.

What will happen in the future? Can anyone predict how technology will change in the years ahead? Some scientists have made the following predictions.

—Robots will do much of the housework in the homes.
—On major highways drivers will be able to put their cars on "automatic pilot."

For You to Think About

Think about the great changes in transportation in the last 75 years. Then think about how these changes have made your life different from that of your grandparents. How are the differences the result of changes in transportation? Do you eat different foods than they did? Are your vacations different than theirs were? Have jobs been affected by these changes? What changes in transportation do you think might occur in the next 75 years?

—Doctors will help people to live much longer than they live now.

—Minerals will be "mined" from the ocean.

—Great amounts of food will be obtained from the ocean.

—People will travel to other planets in our solar system.

> ★ **What do you think about these predictions? Do you think these things will happen in the next fifty years? Why or why not?**

ENGINEERING

What is meant by the term "engineering"?
What did scientists have to do with Mariner 10?
What did engineers have to do with Mariner 10?
Why is engineering so important today?

What is engineering?

Engineering is the changing of scientific discoveries into technology. Or, to state it another way, it is putting science to use in making new things or providing new services. A person who puts science to use in this way is called an *engineer*.

Many people do not know the difference between scientists and engineers. Perhaps an example of what some scientists have done and what some engineers have done will help make the difference clear.

The flight of Mariner 10

On November 3, 1973, powerful rockets launched the spacecraft *Mariner 10* up and away from the earth. The rockets soon made its speed reach thousands of kilometres an hour. As *Mariner 10* moved from the earth, radar was used to track it. In the days and months following its launch, *Mariner 10* was guided so that it came close to the planet Venus on February 5, 1974. On that day two television cameras sent pictures back to the earth.

After bending somewhat around Venus, *Mariner 10* moved on to the planet Mercury. On March 29, 1974, the

Courtesy of NASA

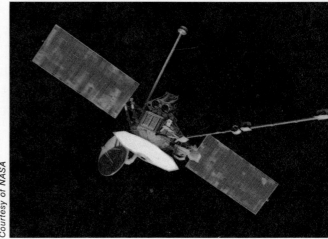

Courtesy of NASA

Figure 25–5. The spacecraft Mariner 10 *took this picture of the planet Mercury. What other heavenly body has a surface that looks like this?*

spacecraft came very close to Mercury. On that day the cameras again took pictures and sent them to the earth. Before this, the only pictures of Mercury were from telescopes either on the earth or close to the earth.

The flight of *Mariner 10* was a "first" in many ways. For example, *Mariner 10* was the first spacecraft to have the gravity of one planet (Venus) bend its course toward another planet (Mercury). Television cameras allowed scientists to get the first close look at Mercury. It was the first time that pictures had been sent such long distances. Because of these "firsts" and many others, the flight of *Mariner 10* was a great success.

★ **Why would scientists want to get a close look at the planet Mercury?**

What made Mariner 10 *possible?*

Mariner 10 was a success for many reasons. Perhaps the major reason it was a success was that so many talented scientists and engineers had worked to make the flight possible. Many things had to work, and work correctly. They did. But there were some problems too.

For example, the cameras on *Mariner 10* were equipped with heaters. The heaters had to work in order to get

---

Find Out More

Using references such as science magazines, find out what things scientists discovered about Mercury and Venus from the flight of *Mariner 10*. What things could not be discovered from the pictures? What things were known about Mercury before the flight of *Mariner 10* took place?

pictures of Venus and Mercury. But at first the heaters didn't work when they were turned on from the earth. By signaling the heaters over and over, engineers were finally able to get the heaters working.

Knowing what is wrong with a spacecraft that is thousands of kilometres away and traveling thousands of kilometres an hour is itself a great achievement. But getting that faraway spacecraft to work properly is an even greater accomplishment.

Many different scientists and engineers worked together on *Mariner 10*. The flight could not have taken place without a knowledge of the basic laws that had been learned by scientists over the years. Forces and speeds needed for space travel were figured out by scientists. Using different ideas about matter, scientists were able to make powerful rocket fuels. They discovered the principles of radar and television. They even discovered how to use sunlight to make electricity that a spacecraft could use.

The major part of the work on *Mariner 10*, however, was done by engineers. Engineers had to plan ways to put the scientific principles to work. They had to build the powerful rockets. They had to plan and build the spacecraft so that it would send out information. They also had to plan and build the stations that would receive the information from the spacecraft. Everything having to do with *Mariner 10* had to be tested again and again. Nothing could be left to chance. All this and much more was the work of engineers.

★ **Was "Mariner 10" the job of scientists alone? Was it the job of engineers alone? What do your answers indicate about how science and engineering are related?**

Today's engineer

The engineer of today is a person who looks to science for information and ideas. Then the engineer works with other people and with machines to find the best way to do a certain job. The job may be making a great bridge or skyscraper. It may be finding a better way to make nylon. It may be improving color television. Or, it may be designing a new kind of automobile.

Some people have the idea that the relationship of science and engineering is a sort of parent-child relationship. They see science as the parent and engineering as a very young child, just following along. But the truth is that engineering does not just follow along behind science, using scientific discoveries to make new things. In all the work between engineers and scientists today, engineering is more a partner of science than a child of science.

DO IT YOURSELF

Look for projects that have been done by engineers

Look around in the area in which you live. What projects do you think have been planned and built by engineers? Make a list of these and try to find out what other projects are planned for your part of the country in the future. If these projects are carried out, how will they affect your part of the state?

SOME BRANCHES OF ENGINEERING

What were some of the engineering wonders of ancient times?
What kinds of jobs are done by civil engineers? Mechanical engineers? Chemical engineers? Electrical engineers?

Early engineering wonders

In ancient times there were no schools for engineering. It would be a mistake, however, to think that there were no engineers long ago. The great pyramids in Egypt were well made. The temples in Babylon and Sumeria, the wonderful buildings of Greece, the Roman roads and aqueducts, the Great Wall of China, the Mayan temples in

491

Central America, and the cathedrals in Europe were well made too. Some of them are still standing today. There had to be engineers to plan such great structures.

★ **How, do you suppose, did the engineers of ancient times learn to build such great structures?**

Civil engineering

Until about 250 years ago, engineering was concerned chiefly with two kinds of projects. One kind was building military structures and making machines of war. The other was building structures to honor gods or rulers. Gradually, however, engineers began to do other kinds of engineering projects.

The first branch of engineering to be named was *civil* [SIHV-uhl] *engineering.* The term "civil engineer" was used to indicate that this kind of engineer had nothing to do with the building of military structures. Today, civil engineering is related to such things as the construction of highways, bridges, buildings, dams, and waterways.

Much of a civil engineer's work involves building. This engineer must know how strong different materials are. The civil engineer must also understand how construction equipment is used. You may be surprised to know that the civil engineer must know something about the different kinds of soil and rock too.

★ **How would you explain why civil engineers should know something about the different kinds of soil and rock?**

Figure 25–6. In the picture a dam is being constructed. What kind of engineers do you think designed this dam? Why do you think so?

Investigate

Which balsa-wood bridge is the strongest?

You Will Need

balsa wood, knife, glue, weights

Background

This activity is not an investigation in the true sense of the word. It is more like a contest to see who can build a strong balsa-wood bridge that is also pleasing to look at. In building the bridge, each person must follow certain agreed-upon rules. Doing this activity will help you to understand some of the things that civil engineers have to think about.

What to Do

Divide your class into several groups. Each group should have the same amount of balsa wood, the same kind of knife, and the same amount of glue. The same kind of glue should be used by each group.

Each group should build a bridge to span a 30-centimetre (about 1-foot) distance. No material other than balsa wood and glue should be used. The knife should only be used for cutting the balsa wood. The design of the bridge and the method of building it should be worked out by each group. There should be a deadline for finishing the bridge. You may decide that certain other rules must be followed. Make sure everyone knows the rules before building the bridges.

After the bridges have been built, select judges to decide which bridge looks the best. Then find out which bridge is the strongest. To find out which bridge is the strongest, carefully place weights on the center of each bridge until the bridge falls. The weights should be added in the same order to each bridge. The bridge which held the most weight before breaking would be the strongest.

Now That You Have Done the Investigation

—Which group had the best-looking bridge?

—Which group had the strongest bridge?

—What do you think made the strongest bridge the strongest? Why do you think so?

Figure 25–7. Testing an automobile roof and constructing an airplane engine are two kinds of work that mechanical engineers do. What other kinds of work do you know of that mechanical engineers do?

Photo Research International

Courtesy of Pratt & Whitney Aircraft

Mechanical engineering

Another branch of engineering is called *mechanical* [mih-KAN-ih-kuhl] *engineering*. The work of mechanical engineers has to do with making and using mechanical energy. That is, mechanical engineers plan, operate, and test all kinds of machines. Nearly all industries need these engineers. As you might expect, many mechanical engineers work in the automobile industry and in the airplane industry.

Many other industries also depend on mechanical engineers. Nearly all manufacturing companies use machines planned by mechanical engineers. The generating of electric power involves mechanical engineering. Trains, trucks, and ships all move as a result of mechanical engineering. In short, mechanical engineers plan and build engines that do work. This work is done by using the energy from such things as moving water, steam, gasoline, and nuclear reactions.

For You to Think About

What machines can you name that are run by moving water? Steam? Gasoline? Nuclear reactions? Which of these machines have you seen?

Chemical engineering

Chemical [KEHM-ih-kuhl] *engineering* involves taking chemists' discoveries and using them in a practical way. The chemical engineer, then, plans and directs the way in which chemists' discoveries are made into useful products.

Suppose a chemist discovers a way to make a better paint. The paint, however, has been made only in small amounts. A chemical engineer would be given the job of finding a way to make the paint cheaply and in large amounts.

After working out how to make the paint, the chemical engineer has other jobs. The chemical engineer must help in planning the paint factory and in planning the equipment needed to make the paint.

Many industries depend on chemical engineers. Some of these industries are the ones involved in the making of plastics, rubber, explosives, paper, rocket fuels, and chemicals. However, more chemical engineers are involved in the oil industry than in any other industry.

Find Out More

Using references, find out about the things that chemical engineers do in the oil industry. For example, find out what fertilizers and plastics have to do with the oil industry and chemical engineers.

Figure 25–8. Do you think you would like to work in a laboratory like these chemical engineers are?

A. Devaney, Inc.

Courtesy of Dow Chemical Company

Electrical engineering

Electrical [ih-LEHK-trih-kuhl] *engineering* is another branch of engineering. The first electrical engineers had jobs having to do with telegraphs, lighting, and the making and sending of electricity. But today devices such as radio, radar, television, and computers use electricity. These devices are called *electronic* [ih-LEHK-TRAHN-ihk] *devices*. In fact, electronic engineering has almost become a separate branch of engineering. Some engineering schools have two courses of study that are called electrical engineering. One course deals chiefly with electric power. The other deals chiefly with electronics.

If you stop to think about all the ways that electricity is used, you will realize one thing about electrical engineers. Electrical engineers do many different kinds of work.

Electrical engineers plan the huge generators that are used in hydroelectric power plants (plants that use falling water to make electricity). They plan all the other kinds of electric-generating plants too. Electrical engineers must also plan the system for moving the electricity from where it is generated to the many places where it will be used. Electrical engineers plan all the devices that use electricity and electronics in homes and factories too.

★ **What do you think high-voltage power lines are used for?**

DO IT YOURSELF

Write to a college for information on engineering

Some colleges offer courses in many different branches of engineering. Some colleges offer courses only in certain branches of engineering. If you want to find out what branches of engineering are offered by colleges and what courses engineers have to study, write to colleges which offer courses in engineering. If you are interested in engineering as a career, you might ask what kinds of courses you should take in high school.

Courtesy of Department of the Army,
Seattle District, Corps of Engineers

The mechanical engineer in the picture is carefully planning the thing he wants to build. Why do you think planning is important?

A Day in the Life of a Mechanical Engineer

Bill Snyder arrived at the Harris Equipment Company on time. He went right to his desk in the Engineering Section and began looking at the plans he had been working on for a new machine. An idea had come to him for improving the machine. He would use the principle of the sewing machine bobbin.

Bill's wife, Joanne, had mentioned something about the bobbin on her sewing machine not working properly. Bill knew how the sewing machine worked. He had fixed it some time ago. He knew that a bobbin was a device on a sewing machine on which thread was wound. He also knew that thread from the bobbin is released at the same time that thread from the spool of thread on top of the machine is released. While he was thinking about how the bobbin released its thread, the idea for improving the plans for the new machine had come to him.

Bill worked hard all day on the plans for the new machine. When it came time to go home, Bill felt he had done a good day's work. If his ideas were approved by the company, he would be very happy. It might even mean a raise in salary. On the way home he thought about how simple a device a bobbin was. He wondered if the person who first thought of a bobbin would have any understanding at all of how he was planning to use the principle of the bobbin. That's progress, Bill thought. Then he wondered if he would be able to fix Joanne's sewing machine again.

Do you think you might like to do the things Bill does? If so, you must get a lot of training in mechanical engineering. Four or five years of college are needed before starting work as a mechanical engineer.

497

Reviewing and Extending

SUMMING UP

1. People use technology in meeting their daily needs and desires.
2. Science and technology are closely related. Scientists are making new discoveries about matter and energy all the time. Technology is the way these discoveries are put to use.
3. The time between when a scientific discovery is made and when the discovery is used is becoming less and less.
4. Technology will probably change a great deal in the years ahead.
5. Engineering is the changing of scientific discoveries into technology.
6. Science and engineering are partners in using scientific discoveries to make new things or in finding out how something can be done in a better way.
7. Some branches of engineering are civil engineering, mechanical engineering, chemical engineering, and electrical engineering.

CHECKING UP

Vocabulary   Write the numerals *1–6* on your paper. Each numbered phrase describes a term from the following list. On your paper, write the term next to the numeral of the phrase that describes it.

technology   civil engineering   chemical engineering
engineer   mechanical engineering   electrical engineering
scientist   electronic engineering

1. branch of engineering in which engineers plan, operate, and test all kinds of machines
2. branch of engineering which is related to the construction of highways, bridges, buildings, dams, and waterways
3. way scientific discoveries are put to use
4. branch of engineering in which engineers direct the ways in which chemists' discoveries are made into useful products
5. branch of engineering which deals with electronic devices
6. person who puts science to use in making new things or providing new services

Knowledge and Understanding   Write the numerals *7–11* on your paper. Beside each of the numerals, write the word or words that best complete the sentence having that numeral.

7. Today, structures such as the pyramids in Egypt would be planned and built by (*mechanical, civil, chemical*) engineers.

8. Finding a way to make a new paint cheaply and in large amounts is the job of a (*civil, mechanical, chemical*) engineer.
9. Designing a new kind of automobile would be the job of a (*civil, mechanical, chemical*) engineer.
10. The major part of the work on *Mariner 10* was done by (*astronauts, scientists, engineers*).
11. The time between when a scientific discovery is made and when the discovery is used is (*becoming less and less, becoming longer and longer, not changing very much*).

Concepts Beside each of the numerals *12–13* on your paper, write the word or words that best complete the sentence having that numeral.

12. Technology is (*the making of new discoveries about matter and energy, closely related to science, not closely related to science*).
13. The job of an engineer is (*to change principles of science into technology, to change engineering principles into science, the same as that of a scientist*).

Application and Critical Thinking Answer the following questions as briefly as you can without leaving out any important ideas.

14. Thomas Edison patented many inventions, and yet he had very little schooling. Why is it less likely that a person with little schooling could do the same thing today?
15. How can technology do good things for people and yet cause problems for people at the same time?
16. What are some ways technology might change in the years ahead?

DOING MORE

1. Make a list of famous structures in your city or state that were planned by engineers. Include buildings, dams, bridges, monuments, highways, and canals in your list. Try to find information on these structures concerning materials, costs, and how they were constructed. Visit these structures if possible. Prepare a report on what you find out.
2. Talk or write to people who work in different branches of engineering. Find out what they do. Also find out how the jobs of people in different branches of engineering are alike and how they are different. Report your findings to the class.

CHAPTER 26

Flight

People's desire to fly goes back through the ages. People first used balloons and gliders for flight more than 200 years ago. But the first successful powered flight was not achieved until the twentieth century. Although many changes have taken place since the first powered flight, people are still trying to fly farther, faster, and more safely.

Today, large airplanes can carry hundreds of passengers. Rocket planes can fly thousands of kilometres an hour. People have even flown to the moon and back. How have people learned to do these things? How did people first learn to fly? What was needed before a working airplane could be built? How were people able to get to the moon and back? These and other questions about flight will be explored in this chapter.

Jets like the one in the picture are very large and fly very fast. Do you think bigger, faster, safer planes will someday be built? Why or why not?

Courtesy of The Boeing Co.

Cal Harbert/Alpha

Peter Fronk/Van Cleve Photography

HISTORY OF FLIGHT

When were balloons first used for flying?
What was the first heavier-than-air aircraft?
When did the first engine-powered airplane flight take place?
What kinds of engines are being used in airplanes today?

Balloons

It was not until the 1750's that flight really began. The earliest flights were in large balloons filled with hot air. But why was hot air used in balloons? As you may know, hot air rises. It rises because it is lighter in weight, or less dense, than cold air. If enough hot air is trapped in a large balloon, the balloon will be pushed up by the cooler air around it.

At first, hot-air balloons carried animals into the air. But later flights carried people. In fact, some long trips were made using hot-air balloons. Hot-air ballooning became a popular sport that is still enjoyed today.

Balloons were used during the Civil War. These balloons were fastened to the ground by long ropes. Each balloon carried one or two soldiers high into the air to watch enemy soldiers and to direct artillery fire.

For You to Think About

What do you suppose happens to a hot-air balloon when the hot air becomes cool? What would be a way of keeping the air hot?

The balloons used in the Civil War were not filled with hot air. They were filled with *hydrogen* [HY-druh-juhn]. Hydrogen is a very lightweight gas that rises easily in air. Because hydrogen rises so easily in air, balloons filled with hydrogen also rise easily. However, using hydrogen can be dangerous because it burns very easily.

★ **What might cause hydrogen in a balloon to burn?**

Airships

Airships were another kind of flying machine that used lightweight gases. Airships were built in Germany, England, and the United States during the 1920's and the 1930's. Each airship had a rigid but lightweight frame. Inside the frame were several large gas bags. The outside of the frame was covered by a fabric skin. Outside the framework was a cabin in which people could ride. Engines were mounted on the frame, too.

Because they had engines, airships could fly against the wind. Some of them carried passengers across the Atlantic regularly. The use of airships was not very safe. A number of airships were destroyed by fire. Others were lost in storms. So the use of airships was soon stopped.

Brown Brothers

Figure 26–2. Thirty-six people died in this fire in 1937. Hydrogen from the airship Hindenburg *somehow caught fire as the airship was landing. People knew that hydrogen burned very easily and yet they used it in airships. How would you explain this?*

Figure 26–3. Otto Lilienthal, a pioneer in glider flight, was flying gliders like the one at the left in 1891. The glider above is a modern glider. What differences can you see between these gliders?

Gliders

Balloons and airships are called lighter-than-air aircraft because they are filled with very lightweight gases. The first flights in heavier-than-air aircraft were made in *gliders* [GLYD-urz]. Gliders look like airplanes, but they do not have engines.

A glider is built of very lightweight materials. It has long wings so that it will stay in the air as long as possible. It stays in the air by moving into upward-moving currents of air called *updrafts* [UHP-DRAFTS]. There are many updrafts on very warm and sunny days.

Glider pilots search for updrafts to help keep the glider in the air. Hawks, vultures, and eagles also search for up-

503

drafts. Glider pilots may sometimes find updrafts by looking for these birds circling in the sky.

★ **Why do you think certain kinds of birds search for updrafts?**

DO IT YOURSELF

Look at small updrafts and downdrafts

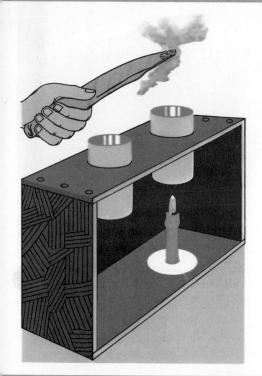

Make a convection box like the one in the diagram. Use two small juice cans with the ends cut out, a candle, and a cardboard or wooden box. (Hint: You will be able to see the smoke better if you paint the inside of the box black.) Smoke can be made by first rubbing petroleum jelly onto a cloth. Then wrap the cloth around a stick, and light the cloth with a match. *CAUTION: Be careful with matches. Also, be sure to do this activity in a room that is well ventilated.* When the cloth is smoking, light the candle in the convection box. Hold the smoking cloth above each can. Look at the currents of air (updrafts and downdrafts).

Think of the two cans as chimneys. If you were a glider pilot and needed to go up higher, over which chimney would you be able to do it? What would happen to a glider if it flew over one chimney and then the other? From this activity, can you figure out where updrafts might be found in nature?

The first airplane flight

Many inventors built and tried to fly engine-powered airplanes at the beginning of this century. But Wilbur and Orville Wright were the first to really fly in an engine-powered airplane. Their first flight was made on December 17, 1903, at Kitty Hawk, North Carolina. The airplane was in the air for only twelve seconds, but with that flight the air age had begun.

A large number of different airplanes were built in the ten years following the first powered airplane flight. People in the United States, Russia, France, England, Canada, and Italy began making airplanes and flying them.

A Russian named Sikorsky planned and built a six-engine airplane that, in 1913, carried the largest load of its time. Later, Sikorsky came to the United States and built the first working helicopter.

Airplane engines

The time was right in 1903 for the first powered flight in a heavier-than-air aircraft. Some principles of flight had been discovered through the use of gliders. The idea of a propeller for moving the plane had been worked out. A lightweight, yet powerful, engine was needed to turn the propeller. The gasoline engine was being developed about this time. The Wright brothers thought that this kind of engine would be just what they needed. They planned and built the engine used in the first airplane flight.

As time passed, more powerful airplane engines were made. Bigger planes that flew faster were built. By 1945, planes were flying about as fast as they could with propellers. A new way of moving a plane faster—one that did not use propellers—was needed.

One way of moving a plane without a propeller is called *jet propulsion* [pruh-PUHL-shuhn]. Engines called jet engines are used. The principle of jet engines is simple. Air is taken in at the front of the engine and then compressed, or squeezed together. The compressed air is mixed with a spray of fuel. The mixture is burned. The burning causes the gases to expand or spread out. The expanding gases rush out the rear of the engine. As the gases rush out, the plane moves forward. See Figure 26–4.

Find Out More

If you do not know about Newton's laws of motion, find out what they are. Which of the laws can be used to explain jet propulsion?

Figure 26–4. The principle of action and reaction is shown here. How would you explain how this principle works?

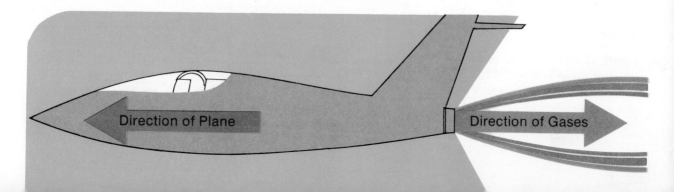

Direction of Plane

Direction of Gases

Today both propeller-driven planes and jet-propelled planes are used. Small planes that fly less than 500 kilo-metres (about 300 miles) an hour are often propeller driven. Very large, very fast planes are, in general, jet propelled.

★ **Which kind of engine would be better to have on a plane which crosses the ocean? Why? Which kind of engine would be better to have on a plane which has to fly at slow speeds? Why?**

THE SCIENCE OF AIRPLANE FLIGHT

What are the four forces needed to explain how airplanes fly?
How does Bernoulli's principle help to explain flight?
How is an airplane controlled?
What is needed to provide thrust for an airplane?

Forces involved in flight

What is needed to cause an aircraft which is heavier than air to stay in the air and to move through the air? The answer to this question has to do with *forces* [FOH(UH)R-suhz], or pushes and pulls.

Suppose an airplane weighing 100 000 newtons (about 22,400 pounds) is flying at a certain height above the ground. A force of 100 000 newtons is pushing upward on the plane. The upward force, called *lift,* is balancing the downward pull of gravity, or *weight,* which is also 100 000

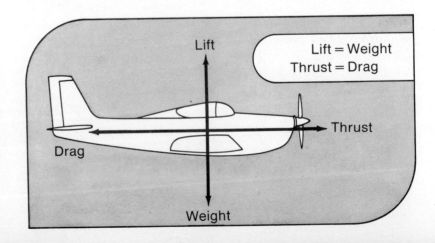

Figure 26–5. Four main forces act on an airplane in flight. When a plane flies at a constant speed and at a constant height, the forces are balanced.

newtons. The lift must balance the weight of the plane in order to keep the plane at a certain height.

Airplanes not only stay in the air; they also move forward. The force which moves an airplane forward is called *thrust*. Thrust is needed to move an airplane through the air because the resistance of the air tends to slow the plane down. The force of air resistance is given a special name. It is called *drag*. Drag becomes greater as an airplane moves faster. That is, the resistance of air increases as the speed of the airplane increases.

When an airplane is flying at a certain height and a certain speed, all the forces acting on the airplane are balanced. That is, the thrust is equal to the drag, and the lift is equal to the weight of the airplane.

DO IT YOURSELF

Observe thrust

Securely fasten a small electric fan to a roller skate, or to some other object that rolls easily. Make sure the fan is attached to the skate as in the illustration. An extension cord may be needed if the cord on the fan is short. Turn the fan on, and observe what happens. Do the turning blades of the fan produce a thrust? If so, which way does the skate move? How is the fan like a propeller?

Producing lift

Two things are needed to produce lift. First, air has to flow over the surface of the wing. The easiest way to get air flowing over the wing is to move the airplane through the air. Thrust (provided by propellers or by jet engines) keeps the airplane moving forward. So thrust helps provide the lift for an airplane.

The second thing that produces lift is the special shape of the wing. But what is special about the shape of an airplane's wings? If you were to look at several wings from a side view, you would see that almost all of them are made

---

For You to Think About

You know that an airplane propeller turns rapidly. But how does a rapidly turning propeller provide thrust and lift for an airplane?

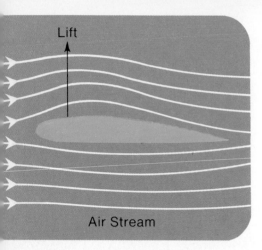

Lift

Air Stream

Figure 26–6. The lines on the diagram show the paths of air as it flows over and under an airfoil, or airplane wing. Which paths are longer—the ones over the airfoil or the ones under it?

so that the upper surfaces of the wings are curved more than the bottom surfaces. This shape is called an *airfoil* [A(UH)R-FOYL]. It is this shape which causes an upward force as air flows past the wing. See Figure 26–6.

Bernoulli's principle

But how does an airfoil cause an upward force? To answer this question, you should know something about how fluids behave. Both water and air are fluids. One person who studied how moving fluids behave was Daniel Bernoulli. Bernoulli found that if a fluid is moving along a surface, the fluid will cause a force on that surface. This force will be perpendicular to the surface. If the fluid moves faster, it will cause less force on the surface. This effect has been called *Bernoulli's principle*.

Think about a fluid flowing through a pipe like the one in Figure 26–7. The fluid flows faster through the part of the pipe having a smaller diameter. According to Bernoulli's principle, the pressure is less in the smaller part of the pipe where the fluid flows faster. If pressure gauges are attached to the small and wide parts of the pipe, the pressure gauge on the small part will have a lower reading than the other gauges.

★ **Why does the fluid flow faster in the small part of the pipe than in the wide part of the pipe?**

Figure 26–7. The diagram illustrates Bernoulli's principle. Where is the fluid flowing fastest? Where is the pressure the greatest?

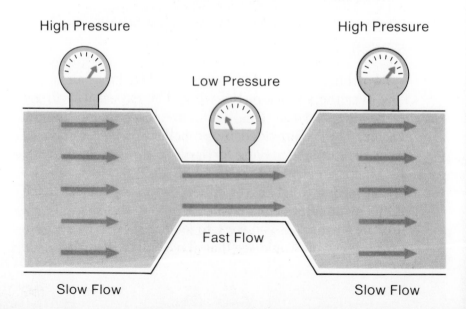

High Pressure

High Pressure

Low Pressure

Fast Flow

Slow Flow

Slow Flow

DO IT YOURSELF

Demonstrate Bernoulli's principle

Hold a piece of notebook paper on the two corners of one of its sides. Hold the paper near your mouth so that the side you are holding is parallel to the top of your desk or table. Blow air over the top of the paper. What happens? How does what you have learned about Bernoulli's principle help to explain what happens?

Another way to demonstrate Bernoulli's principle is to tape string to two objects, such as two table-tennis balls, and let the objects hang next to each other. Be sure to leave space (two to five centimetres) between the objects. Blow air between the objects. What happens? Use Bernoulli's principle to explain what you observe.

Movement of air over the airfoil

As an airplane is in flight, air hitting the front of the wing separates. Some air flows over the wing and some flows under the wing. The air meets again at the back of the wing. The air flowing over the top has a longer distance to travel in the same amount of time. Because of the curvature of the wing, then, the air flowing over the top of the wing flows faster than the air that flows under the wing. Due to Bernoulli's principle, the downward force of the faster-moving air on the top of the wing is not as great as the upward force of the slower-moving air under the wing. So there is a net upward force on the wing— a lift.

Lift can be increased in several ways. One way is to increase the size of the wing. Larger planes need a greater lift. So larger planes often have larger wings. Another way to increase lift is to increase the *angle of attack*. The angle of attack is the angle at which the flow of air hits the airfoil. See Figure 26–8. If the front, or leading, edge of the wing is tipped up, the air going over the wing has farther to go, and so it moves much faster. Moving faster, it causes less downward force, and increases the lift.

Figure 26–8. When the leading edge of an airfoil is tipped up, the angle of attack is increased. How is the path of air over the airfoil changed when the angle of attack is increased? How does this change affect lift?

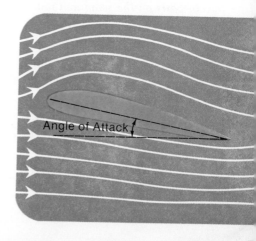

Angle of Attack

509

If the angle of attack becomes too great, however, the air moving over the wing does not flow smoothly. When the air does not flow smoothly, there is less lift. When lift becomes less than weight, an airplane cannot stay in the air.

A way to increase the lift of the wings at low speeds is to use the *wing flaps*. Wing flaps are movable parts on the rear of the wings. They can be let out and down. See Figure 26–9.

When the wing flaps are down, the wing has both a greater area and a greater curvature. So the plane has a greater lift in the air. Wing flaps are most often used when an airplane is taking off or landing. They provide the extra lift needed at low speeds.

Control of an airplane

Three kinds of moving parts are used to control an airplane. They are the *ailerons* [AY-luh-ʀᴀʜɴᴢ], the *elevator* [EHL-uh-ᴠᴀʏᴛ-ur], and the *rudder* [RUHD-ur]. The ailerons are on the back edge of the wings, near the tips. The elevator and the rudder are on the tail of the airplane. See Figure 26–9.

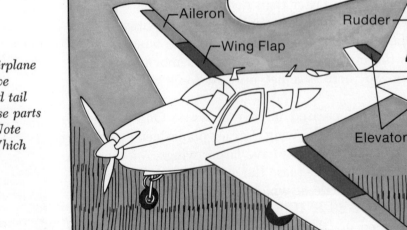

Figure 26–9. To control an airplane in flight, the pilot has to move certain parts on the wing and tail surfaces of the airplane. These parts are labeled in the diagram. Note the position of each part. Which parts occur in pairs?

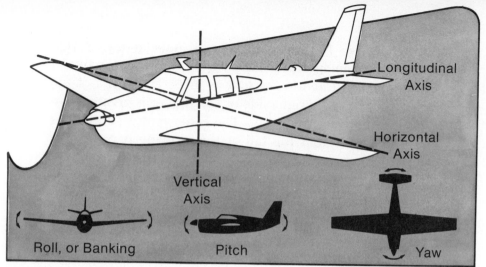

Figure 26–10. These diagrams show the three different axes of an airplane and show how the airplane moves about each of these axes. What axis is involved in roll? In pitch? In yaw?

Controlling the airplane involves motion about three different axes. See Figure 26–10. One axis, called the *longitudinal* [LAHN-juh-T(Y)OOD-nuhl] *axis,* is through the length of the airplane. Motion about this axis is called *roll,* or banking. Roll is controlled by the ailerons.

Another axis, the *horizontal* [HAWR-uh-ZAHNT-uhl] *axis,* is in the direction of the wings of the airplane. Motion about this axis is called *pitch.* The elevator controls this kind of motion. Motion about the *vertical* [VURT-ih-kuhl] *axis* is called *yaw.* Yaw is controlled by the rudder.

Look at a rudder as it would look from above in Figure 26–11. In *A* the rudder is in its normal position. That is, the forces acting on the rudder are balanced. In *B* and *C* the rudder is being used to turn the airplane. The forces acting on the rudder are now unbalanced.

Figure 26–11. In these diagrams, the position of the rudder is shown for straight flight (*A*), turning to the left (*B*), and turning to the right (*C*).

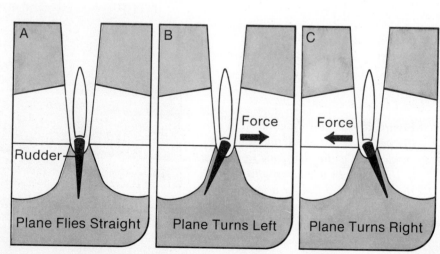

What causes the forces to become unbalanced? Again, Bernoulli's principle plays a part. Suppose, for example, the rudder is turned to the left, as in *B*. The speed of the air flowing past the right side of the rudder is greater than the speed flowing on the left. The faster-moving air causes less pressure so that the tail of the airplane is pushed to the right. If the tail is pushed to the right, the direction of flight of the whole airplane is changed to the left.

If the rudder is moved to the right, as in *C*, the forces acting on the rudder are unbalanced toward the left so that the plane turns to the right.

In order to turn the plane smoothly and quickly, the pilot must use both the rudder and the ailerons. The ailerons cause the plane to turn on its longitudinal axis. That is, one wing tip goes up, and the other goes down. This is called banking, and it causes the airplane to turn more smoothly than if only the rudder was used. See Figure 26–12.

If the pilot wants to turn the airplane toward the left quickly, the aileron on the left is raised, and the aileron on the right is lowered. If he wants to turn the airplane toward the right quickly, the aileron on the right is raised, and the aileron on the left is lowered. The rudder must also be moved in the direction in which the turn is to be made.

★ **Suppose a pilot wants to make an airplane go higher. According to Bernoulli's principle, should the elevator be raised or lowered? Why?**

Figure 26–12. This diagram shows the positions of the ailerons and the rudder that cause the plane to turn to the right. In what positions would the ailerons and rudder be to make a turn to the left?

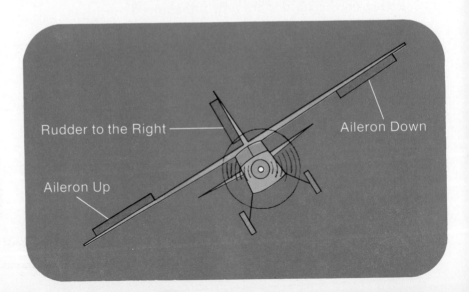

Rudder to the Right —

Aileron Down

Aileron Up

Figure 26–13. In the picture, a SYNCOM satellite is shown in orbit about the earth. How do you suppose the satellite was put into orbit?

FLIGHT IN SPACE

What are satellites?
What shapes can orbits have?
How are satellites controlled?
What does the term "weightlessness" mean?

Satellites

Do you know what *satellites* [SAT-uhl-yts] are? Satellites are objects that travel all the way around another object. For example, the moon is a natural satellite of the earth. It takes about a month for the moon to travel around the earth. Not all satellites are natural satellites. Some artificial satellites—satellites made by people—are also traveling around the earth.

The path a satellite follows as it travels is called its *orbit* [AWR-buht]. Depending on the characteristics of its orbit, an artificial satellite will remain in its orbit for a certain amount of time. If the orbit of a satellite is high enough above the earth and its speed is great enough, the satellite may stay in its orbit for hundreds of years.

Find Out More

Using references, find out what satellites are being used for. Also find out if all the satellites that have been put in orbit are still in working order.

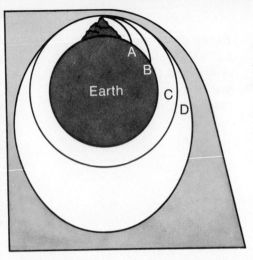

Figure 26-14. About 300 years ago, Sir Isaac Newton used a drawing similar to this to explain his ideas about orbits. Are you surprised that orbits were thought of that long ago?

Shapes of orbits

Imagine a very, very tall mountain on the earth. Also imagine that objects can be shot horizontally from the top of the mountain. If the objects are shot at different speeds, each will have a different path. See Figure 26-14.

Objects in paths A and B do not have enough speed to become satellites. These objects fall to the earth. The speed of the object in path C is very great. The speed is so great that, as the object falls, its path just matches the curvature of the earth. The object falls, but it does not hit the earth. So this object becomes a satellite with a round orbit. The object in path D has an even greater speed than the one in path C. The result is a satellite with an oval-shaped orbit.

Think again about the satellite in path C. It is falling toward the earth all the time, but it never reaches the earth. To see how this can happen, look at Figure 26-15.

As the satellite moves from *Position A* to *Position B*, it falls a distance of 150 kilometres (about 90 miles). But because of the way the surface of the earth is curved, the satellite is still 150 kilometres above the surface. If the speed of the object is not changed, the object will stay in an orbit 150 kilometres above the earth.

★ **Suppose that satellites are given speeds even greater than that of the satellite in path "D." What would the orbits of these satellites be like?**

Figure 26-15. An orbiting satellite is constantly falling toward the earth. But it stays in orbit. How would you use this diagram to explain why the satellite stays in orbit?

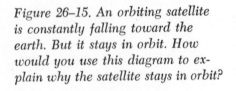

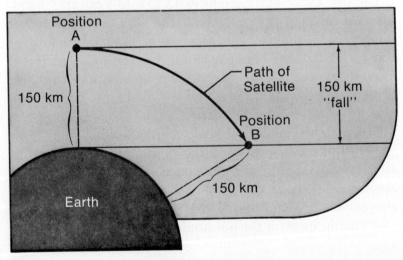

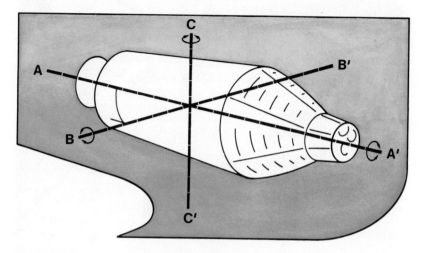

Figure 26–16. Roll, pitch, and yaw may be used to describe the motions of a satellite about certain axes, just as these terms are used for airplanes. What axis do you think the letters "AA'" represent? The letters "BB'"? The letters "CC'"?

Controlling a satellite in orbit

In addition to its forward motion, a satellite can move in other ways. It can roll, pitch, or yaw just as an airplane, a boat, or a car can. Figure 26–16 shows the different motions of a satellite.

Roll, pitch, and yaw are not wanted. Control jets are used to control these movements and keep the spacecraft in its proper position. In one way, control jets are like small jet engines. Gases are forced out of a nozzle, causing a force that can be used to push the spacecraft in a certain direction. However, control jets do not burn fuel as jet engines do. The gases forced out of control jets are simply compressed gases that have been stored in a tank.

DO IT YOURSELF

Demonstrate pitch, roll, and yaw

Obtain models of a spacecraft, an airplane, a boat, and a car. Use each model to demonstrate pitch, roll, and yaw in each of the different vehicles. Give examples of the different motions in everyday experiences. For example, how would you describe the motion of a car going over a rough railroad crossing? Of a car skidding on ice?

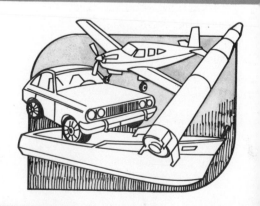

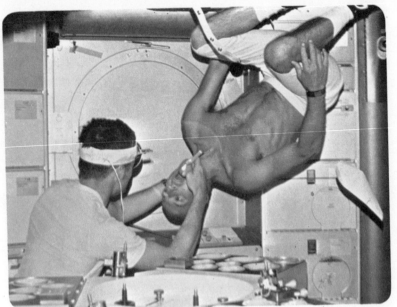

Figure 26–17. In the photograph, an astronaut's teeth are being examined. What makes it possible for the two men to be in the positions shown?

A. Devaney, Inc.

Weightlessness

Have you ever heard of *weightlessness* [WAYT-luhs-nuhs]? The term "weightlessness" is used to describe a condition in which an object seems to have no weight. You may remember that the weight of an object is the force exerted by gravity on that object. Sometimes people say that objects in space are weightless. This is not true. For example, at a height of 250 kilometres (about 150 miles) above the earth, the force of gravity on an object would be almost the same as it is at the earth's surface. Why, then, do objects in orbit at this height appear to be weightless? Why do astronauts "float" in their spacecraft?

One way to explain this weightlessness is to remember that the orbiting astronaut is really falling toward the earth. But the spacecraft is falling also. If the astronaut were outside the spacecraft, he would simply appear to be falling. But inside the spacecraft, he appears to be floating because the spacecraft and the things in it have the same motion.

★ **What would happen to an astronaut floating weightlessly in a spacecraft if one of the control jets were fired to change the motion of the spacecraft?**

516

Become a Pilot

You have read about airplane flight in this chapter. Would you like to fly a plane someday? In order to be a pilot you have to have a license. You cannot get a pilot's license unless you have certain training and pass certain tests. Some kinds of pilot licenses include private pilot, commercial pilot, and airline transport pilot.

A private pilot's license allows you to fly small planes. To get the license, you must pass a physical exam, have at least twenty hours of flying instruction, and fly "solo," or alone, for at least twenty hours. Such a license does not permit you to carry cargo or passengers for pay.

Commercial pilots are licensed to carry cargo and passengers for pay. To become a commercial pilot, you must pass harder written and physical tests than those for a private pilot. Most commercial pilots work for business companies or operate their own companies for carrying cargo or passengers.

Airline transport pilots must attend a school for pilots or be trained by an airline. Most airlines require a person who is going to be trained as an airline pilot to have a commercial pilot's license. Airline pilots often start as flight engineers. Then they become copilots and, finally, pilots.

Does being a pilot sound interesting? Piloting a plane can be fun. It can also be a highly paid career.

Courtesy of United Air Lines

Why do experienced pilots have to attend classes? Why do pilots want to check over a long list of items before taking off?

Walt Oleksy/Van Cleve Photography

Reviewing and Extending

SUMMING UP

1. The first successful flights were in balloons. Later on, people flew in airships, gliders, and airplanes.
2. Four forces that act on an airplane in flight are thrust, drag, lift, and weight.
3. Thrust in an airplane is provided by a rapidly turning propeller or by jet propulsion.
4. The wings of an airplane produce lift because of their special shape and because air moves over them at a high speed.
5. Bernoulli's principle is important in keeping an airplane in flight. This principle helps explain how lift and thrust are produced and how the airplane is controlled.
6. A satellite in orbit is falling toward the earth all the time.
7. Weightlessness is a condition in which an object seems to have no weight.

CHECKING UP

Vocabulary   Write the numerals *1–9* on your paper. Each numbered phrase describes a term from the following list. On your paper, write the term next to the numeral of the phrase that describes it.

weight	jet engine	thrust	ailerons	roll
glider	elevator	drag	rudder	yaw
pitch	satellite	orbit	airfoil	lift

1. force needed to move an airplane forward
2. part of the airplane which controls yaw
3. path of travel of an object all the way around another object
4. motion of an airplane which is controlled by the ailerons
5. heavier-than-air aircraft that does not have engines
6. object which orbits another object
7. motion of an airplane which is controlled by the elevator
8. special shape of an airplane's wings
9. force due to the downward pull of gravity

Knowledge and Understanding   Write the numerals *10–14* on your paper. Beside each numeral, write the word or words that best complete the sentence having that numeral.

10. On an airplane in level flight, the force that balances weight is (*drag, thrust, lift*).
11. On an airplane flying at a steady speed, the force that balances drag is (*weight, thrust, lift*).

12. The first flights were in (*gliders, balloons, airships*).
13. Rocket planes and satellites in orbit are controlled by (*ailerons, propellers, control jets*).
14. Airplane wings produce lift because of their (*shape, yaw, drag*).

Concepts   Beside each of the numerals *15–18* on your paper, write the word or words that best complete the sentence having that numeral.

15. Hydrogen inside a balloon lifts the balloon upward because it is (*heavier, lighter, stronger*) than air.
16. The lift caused by air flowing over the wings of an airplane is an example of (*pitch, air resistance, Bernoulli's principle*).
17. An object in orbit about the earth is said to be (*falling toward the earth, falling away from the earth, not moving with respect to the earth*).
18. In talking about the flight of an airplane, the angle of attack is (*the angle at which the wings are swept back, the angle between the propeller blades, the angle at which the flow of air hits an airfoil*).

Application and Critical Thinking   Answer the following questions as briefly as you can without leaving out any important ideas.

19. Describe how the ailerons and rudder are positioned in order to cause an airplane to make a sharp left turn.
20. Can the earth be considered a satellite? Explain.
21. Why are some orbits oval and some circular?

DOING MORE

1. Stick a straight pin through the center of a 3 x 5 card. Then hold the card beneath a large spool with the pin extending up into the hole in the spool. Keep the hole in the spool upright. Hold the spool to your lips and blow through the spool. While blowing through the spool, release the card. Can you blow the card off the spool? What happens if you blow very hard? What happens if you stop blowing? Use Bernoulli's principle to explain what happens.
2. Find out what a sonic boom is. Write a report explaining why high-speed aircraft produce a sonic boom. Can a sonic boom be harmful? Is there any known way for aircraft flying faster than sound to avoid producing a sonic boom?

CHAPTER 27

Environmental Pollution

Do you think there is anyone in your neighborhood who has not heard of pollution? If you listen to the radio, watch TV, or read the newspapers, you know that many people are talking about the environment. They are saying that many things are being put into the environment that should not be there. Because of this, our environment is not as safe as it used to be. That is, our environment is being *polluted* [puh-LOOT-uhd].

Pollution, the fouling of the environment, is not something new. People and other living things have always polluted the environment. But in the past, pollution was not as great a problem as it is now.

What are some kinds of pollution? Why is pollution a greater problem today than it was many years ago? Has technology caused some pollution? What can be done about pollution? These are only a few of the questions about pollution that are answered in this chapter.

Grant Heilman

Air, water, and land are being polluted, or have been polluted, in the area pictured here. What are the things that cause this pollution?

Figure 27-1. One cause of air pollution is automobile exhaust. If the exhaust is blue in color, it means that a great deal of hydrocarbons are being put into the air. What do you think can be done about such pollution?

AIR POLLUTION

What are some causes of air pollution?
What is an inversion?
What are some ways in which technology may be used to control air pollution?

Must we have dirty air?

The air is a very important part of our environment. In fact, our life depends on air. When we breathe, we take air into our body to get the oxygen we need. When we look at the things around us, we are looking through air. As we move about, we are moving through air. Having clean air is good for everyone.

But the air is not always clean. People often make the air dirty, or polluted. For example, you have seen smoke coming from a chimney. You have seen smoke coming from an automobile tail pipe. You have probably smelled these things too. The smoke you have seen and smelled is something that does not belong there. The smoke is called a *pollutant* [puh-LOOT-uhnt].

521

Without the smoke from burning fuels, the air would be cleaner. But if fuels were not burned, we might not have warm homes in the winter. We might not have electricity to light our homes, offices, schools, and factories. We would not be able to use automobiles, buses, trains, and planes for going places.

Can we have clean air and still do everything we want to? That's a good question. Many people think we can. Scientists are working on ways to have clean air without giving up the way of life we are used to. Everyone can benefit by knowing more about air pollution and ways of controlling it.

★ **What are some air pollutants you can see? What are some you can smell?**

Some causes of air pollution

Most air pollution results from burning. You can probably think of many examples of burning. Fuels are burned in automobiles, buses, trucks, trains, planes, and boats. Much of the electricity we use is generated by burning coal or oil. Many homes have furnaces that burn fuel oil or natural gas.

Whenever a fuel is burned, some kind of pollutant is formed. Too often the pollutants are released into the air. The pollutants can be in many different forms. Some are invisible gases. Others, such as black smoke, are easily seen. Some are *particulates* [pur-TIHK-yuh-luhts], or tiny particles of solid or liquid matter.

Burning fuels to heat homes, offices, and factories produces two chief pollutants. One is sulfur dioxide. The other is nitrogen dioxide. Both are gases. Both can harm living things. See Figure 27–2.

Burning fuels in automobiles, buses, trucks, trains, planes, and boats can also cause pollution. The chief pollutants from this kind of burning are hydrocarbons, nitrogen dioxide, and carbon monoxide. The diagram in Figure 27–2 shows what some of these pollutants can do.

Another kind of burning also puts pollutants into the air. The burning of garbage and trash puts particulates

(*Text continues on page 524.*)

For You to Think About

Automobile engines that are not adjusted properly do not burn fuels as completely as these engines would if they were properly adjusted. As a result, such engines cause a lot of air pollution. But all automobile engines get out of adjustment when parts become worn. How, do you think, can we make sure that people have their engines properly adjusted?

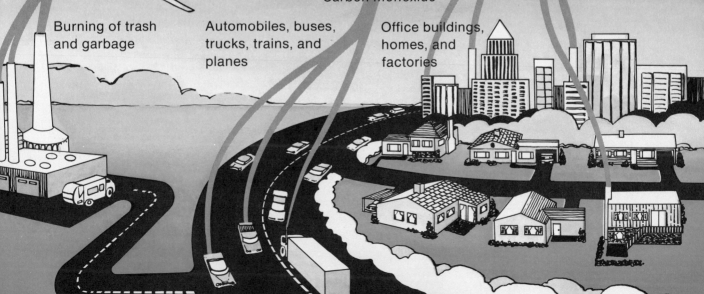

Figure 27–2. Which of these pollutants have you seen being put into the air?

In sunlight, nitrogen dioxide combines with hydrocarbons to form smog. Smog irritates the eyes and harms the lungs. It also harms plants.

Sulfur dioxide combines with oxygen and water vapor to form sulfuric acid which harms the lungs and corrodes metal.

Hydrocarbons harm plants.

Particulates harm the lungs, make it difficult to see clearly, and affect the weather.

Sulfur dioxide harms the lungs.

Nitrogen dioxide harms the lungs of animals. It also harms plants.

Carbon monoxide gets into the blood through the lungs. It causes headaches and dizziness.

Mercury harms the brain and nerves.

Particulates
Mercury

Hydrocarbons
Nitrogen dioxide
Carbon monoxide

Sulfur dioxide
Nitrogen dioxide

Burning of trash and garbage

Automobiles, buses, trucks, trains, and planes

Office buildings, homes, and factories

into the air. Small amounts of mercury are sometimes put into the air by the burning of garbage and trash too.

Not all air pollution is caused by people. Even if there were no people, the air would not be perfectly clean. Volcanoes put great amounts of gases and dust into the air. Forest fires put smoke and gases into the air. The wind can blow dust, sand, and soil particles many miles through the air.

★ **Have you ever seen dust in the air due to a windstorm? If so, where do you think the dust came from?**

Weather and air pollution

Sometimes weather conditions can help cut down on the amount of pollutants in the air. Wind can blow away polluted air. Rain and snow carry pollutants to the ground. However, we cannot depend on the weather to stop air pollution. In some places—especially cities—pollutants are put into the air faster than they are carried away, even under normal conditions.

The weather does not always help cut down on pollution. Sometimes a weather condition called an *inversion* [ihn-VUR-zhuhn] can increase the amount of pollutants in the air.

During an inversion, a layer of cool air is trapped near the surface of the earth. This happens when there is a quick drop in temperature near the surface. Then, a layer of warm air is above a layer of cool air.

(*Text continues on page 526.*)

Figure 27–3. In an inversion a boundary exists between a layer of warm air above and a layer of cool air below. Where is this boundary in the picture?

Artstreet

Investigate

What is an inversion like?

You Will Need

ice cubes, large plastic bag, large aquarium tank, food coloring or ink, pin, hot and cold water

Background

It is hard to see an inversion taking place in the air because the warm air layer looks just like the cold air layer. It would be much easier to see an inversion if the layers were different colors. You can make an inversion in water using water of different colors. Perhaps doing this will help you understand what an inversion in air is like.

What to Do

Fill the tank about three-fourths full of cold water. Add the ice cubes to the water in the tank. Allow the ice cubes to melt for several minutes, causing the water to become even colder.

Fill the plastic bag with hot water. *CAUTION: Do not use water so hot that it will burn your skin.* Place a few drops of food coloring or ink into the hot water. Carefully seal the plastic bag in some way so that very little air is left in the bag.

Take the ice cubes out of the tank. Then put the plastic bag filled with hot water into the tank. The plastic bag should be at or near the top of the cold water in the tank. Wait until the water in the tank is calm. Then stick the pin into the plastic bag in several places. Record what happens to the hot water.

Now That You Have Done the Investigation

—Did the hot water move from the top of the tank? Why or why not?

—Did the cold water move from the bottom of the tank? Why or why not?

—How would you explain what happened to the hot water and the cold water in the tank?

An inversion is not always a problem. But when pollutants are constantly being added to the air, the inversion does not allow them to escape. The air close to the surface becomes highly polluted. This polluted air can be dangerous for people and other living things. For example, in 1952 there was a serious inversion in London, England. The inversion lasted several days. Pollution became so bad that 3,500 to 4,000 people died. There have been other such incidents, too.

Controlling pollution

Most air pollution is caused by the activities of people. Most of these activities involve the use of fuel-burning engines. So, some people think that technology is the cause of air pollution. The use of engines, together with the fact that there are many more people living today than in the past, is partly the cause of air pollution. But science and technology can also help control air pollution.

The exhaust gases from older automobiles contain many harmful pollutants. But automobiles made today have many pollution-control devices. See Figure 27–4.

Burning coal to make electricity can cause air pollution in the form of smoke. Burning fuel in furnaces and burning trash can also cause pollution. This kind of pollution

Figure 27–4. Diagrams like this one, showing pollution-control devices, may be found in the Owner's Manual of a new automobile. Why are pollution-control devices needed on automobiles today?

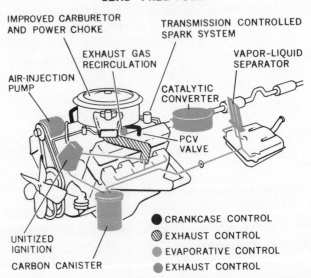

1975 EMISSION CONTROL SYSTEM
LEAD-FREE FUEL

IMPROVED CARBURETOR AND POWER CHOKE

TRANSMISSION CONTROLLED SPARK SYSTEM

EXHAUST GAS RECIRCULATION

VAPOR-LIQUID SEPARATOR

AIR-INJECTION PUMP

CATALYTIC CONVERTER

PCV VALVE

UNITIZED IGNITION

CARBON CANISTER

● CRANKCASE CONTROL
◍ EXHAUST CONTROL
● EVAPORATIVE CONTROL
● EXHAUST CONTROL

can be controlled. One way is to use a device called a *scrubber* [SKRUHB-ur]. Steam and other chemicals clean the gases as they pass through the scrubber.

Another way to clean smoke is with an *electrostatic precipitator* [ih-LEHK-truh-STAT-ihk prih-SIHP-uh-TAYT-ur]. These devices remove particulates. The tiny pieces of pollutant are attracted to a metal plate because of the electric charge on the plate.

Technology is being used to control pollution in yet another way. Scientists and engineers are trying to find new sources of energy and power. For example, solar energy and fuel cells are being studied. If they could become very efficient, the amount of fuel burned would be much smaller than it is now. Air pollution, in turn, would be much less. Several different kinds of low-pollution engines are also being tested. If these engines could be perfected, air pollution would be cut down.

The ways of controlling air pollution are often costly. One reason automobiles cost more today is that so many pollution-control devices have been added to them. Adding scrubbers and electrostatic precipitators to buildings is also costly. Using new sources of energy and power may be costly too.

★ **Do you think having cleaner air is worth these extra costs? Explain.**

Find Out More

There are other sources of energy which may help us control pollution. Using references, find out what geothermal energy is and where it is being used to generate electric power. Also find out what areas in the world may be good for the construction of power plants that can use geothermal energy. Why are some areas better than others?

WATER POLLUTION

What are some causes of water pollution?
What is eutrophication?
What are some ways in which technology may be used to control water pollution?

The goal—Clean water

Water, like air, is a very important part of the environment. All living things need water to live. Most living things—including people—need clean water to live. If you have ever looked at a map of the United States, you may have noticed that many large cities are located near a river or a lake. Cities first started in these places because the river or the lake provided transportation and was a good place to get water.

Today, many cities are faced with a special problem. Their supply of water is not clean. Their water is becoming polluted in one way or another. The pollutants come from many different places. The pollutants get into the water in many different ways. It seems as if water pollution becomes worse whenever many people live close together.

Since more and more people are living in cities, finding ways to cut down on water pollution is very important. But before water pollution can be cut down, water pollution must be understood. What are some pollutants in the water? Where do they come from? How can they be controlled? If answers to all these questions can be found, everyone will benefit by having cleaner water.

★ **Do you think everyone is concerned about having clean water? Why or why not?**

A. Devaney, Inc.

Figure 27–5. Small streams often become polluted when people dump garbage and junk into them. What has caused the water in the picture to become polluted?

Some causes of water pollution

Many kinds of water pollution come from the activities of people. That is why the water near cities, in general, is more polluted than the water in places where fewer people live.

One kind of pollution is *sewage* [SOO-ihj]. Sewage is the waste material carried away by sewers. This includes body wastes, garbage that has been ground up by garbage disposals, and detergents from washing.

Body wastes and garbage are sometimes called *organic* [awr-GAN-ihk] *pollutants*. The term "organic" is used to mean matter that is living or comes from living things. A body of water such as a river or a lake can take in some organic matter without becoming polluted. That is, the water seems to clean itself.

The cleaning takes place in several different ways. Oxygen in the water combines with the organic matter, causing the matter to change into other substances. In addition, certain bacteria in the water feed on the organic matter and remove it in that way. Some heavy particles settle to the bottom and stay there.

The important thing to remember is that the water can rid itself of only a certain amount of organic matter. But what happens if there is too much sewage? The water changes. The amount of oxygen in the water becomes much less. Without plenty of oxygen, many fish and other animals in the water will die. Tiny plants called *algae* [AL-jee] grow in great numbers. This kind of change in the water is called *eutrophication* [yu-TROH-fuh-KAY-shuhn].

Detergents in sewage also speed up eutrophication. So do fertilizers that wash into water from fields and lawns. Detergents and fertilizers speed up eutrophication because they have chemicals called *phosphates* [FAHS-FAYTS] in them. It is the phosphates that help algae grow.

★ **Have you seen bodies of water which you think are polluted? If so, why do you think they are polluted?**

For You to Think About

What are some natural forms of water pollution—that is, water pollutants that are not caused by people? What do you think happens to these pollutants? Why?

Figure 27–6. What evidence is there that eutrophication has changed the water shown here? What kinds of pollutants cause eutrophication?

Artstreet

Investigate

How do detergents and fertilizers affect how fast algae will grow?

You Will Need

3 gallon jars, distilled water, laundry detergent, lawn fertilizer, teaspoon, pond water, graduated cylinder, marking pencil

Background

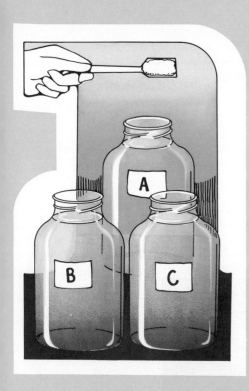

Distilled water is about as pure as water can be. Very few algae would grow in distilled water because of the lack of nutrients. On the other hand, pond water usually contains organic matter in the form of decaying leaves, twigs, and other plant materials. As you may know, pond water often looks very clear. But even though pond water looks clear, it usually contains organic matter. Because pond water contains organic matter, many algae will grow in pond water.

What to Do

Label one jar A, another B, and another C. Fill each jar to within two centimetres of the top with distilled water. Then add a teaspoon of detergent to jar A. Add a teaspoon of fertilizer to jar B. Leave jar C as it is.

Next, measure about ten millilitres of pond water in the graduated cylinder, and add this amount to jar A. Add the same amount to each of the other jars. Leave the jars uncovered, and set them in a well-lighted place for two weeks. At the end of that time, compare the three jars. Record your observations.

Now That You Have Done the Investigation

—Did more algae grow in some jars than in others? If so, which jars?

—What might cause more algae to grow in some jars than in others?

—Based on what you have learned, what might happen to a body of water if larger amounts of detergents and fertilizers were added to it? Explain.

Sewage treatment

Because it causes water pollution, untreated sewage should not be put into streams, rivers, and lakes. But what should be done with sewage? Most cities and towns change sewage so that it is less likely to cause pollution. The changing of sewage into less harmful kinds of matter is called *sewage treatment* [TREET-muhnt].

There are three steps in treating sewage. The first step is *primary* [PRY-MEHR-ee] *treatment.* In this step, the sewage passes through a coarse screen. The screen removes large objects. Then the sewage goes into a large tank where sand, soil, and other small particles are allowed to settle out. Primary treatment removes only solid organic matter. In places where the number of people is small, primary treatment may be good enough. But further steps are usually needed.

The second step in treating sewage is called *secondary* [SEHK-uhn-DEHR-ee] *treatment.* During this step, bacteria eat up to ninety percent of the organic matter in the sewage. After bacteria work on the sewage for several hours, the solid matter is allowed to settle out. This solid matter is called *sludge* [SLUHJ].

In some places secondary treatment is enough to avoid water pollution. The water that is left after the sludge settles out is treated to kill bacteria. Then the water is put into a stream, a river, a lake, or an ocean.

In some places secondary treatment is not enough. Many kinds of harmful chemicals are not removed by secondary treatment. A third step is needed to remove these pollutants from sewage. The third step is called *tertiary* [TUR-shee-EHR-ee] *treatment.* After secondary treatment, the amount of pollutants left in the water is small. You might think that removing this small amount would not be very costly. This is not true. The cost of tertiary treatment is greater than the total cost of primary and secondary treatment.

Tertiary treatment removes almost all the pollutants. After tertiary treatment, the water that once had sewage in it is sometimes clean enough to drink.

Find Out More

To find out about an excellent facility for sewage treatment, write to the South Lake Tahoe Chamber of Commerce, Inc., P.O. Box 3418, South Lake Tahoe, California 95705. Ask them to send you information about wastewater purification at Lake Tahoe.

A. Courtesy of Sewerage Commission of the City of Milwaukee, Milorganite Division
B & C. Daniel Brody

D & E. Photo Research International

Figure 27–7. Some stages in sewage treatment are pictured. Sewage passes through a screen (A). Small particles are allowed to settle out (B). The sewage is aerated by spraying it into the air (C). After bacteria have worked on the aerated sewage, sludge is allowed to settle out (D). Treated water is stored in a holding pond (E) before being put into a stream or lake.

DO IT YOURSELF

Visit a sewage-treatment plant

Get permission to visit a sewage-treatment plant in your area. Find out what steps in sewage treatment are taken in the plant. Also try to find out what happens to the extra sewage if the amount of sewage is greater than what the treatment plant can handle. Try to follow what happens to the sewage during each step or have someone at the plant explain what happens during each step. How pure is the water that is released from the plant?

LAND POLLUTION

What is the cause of land pollution?
How are things recycled in nature?
How can people help in the recycling of used materials?

What is land pollution?

Have you ever seen a junkyard? Have you ever seen a garbage dump? Have you ever seen a street littered with paper? If you have seen any of these things, you have seen land pollution.

Land pollution is often caused by things that people throw away. As you know, people throw away things made of paper, wood, glass, plastic, or metal. They also throw away food wastes.

Land pollution, like other kinds of pollution, seems to be a bigger problem today than it was many years ago. You can probably think of some reasons why. One reason is that there are more people today. The greater the number of people, the greater the number of things that are thrown away.

Another reason has to do with the kinds of things that people throw away. People have always thrown things away, but the kinds of things they throw away today are

533

Daniel Brody

Figure 27–8. This is a picture of a biodegradable milk carton. Why, do you suppose, is the milk carton called biodegradable?

different. Today, for example, we throw away many glass bottles and jars. We also throw away bottles, bags, and other containers made of plastic.

Glass and plastic are two substances that do not break down easily in nature. They tend to stay the way they are. For example, suppose you are in a park and you drop a plastic bag on the ground. If no one picked it up, the bag would just stay there for years. Imagine the mess that would result if a lot of people littered the park with plastic bags. Unless someone cleaned up the mess, the bags would clutter up the park.

Littering the park with bags made out of paper would be bad, too. But after several weeks, the paper would start to disappear. It does not really disappear, however. Instead, it becomes a part of the soil. This happens because paper is a kind of material that is said to be *biodegradable* [BY-oh-dih-GRAYD-uh-buhl]. The word "biodegradable" means that the material can be broken down easily in nature. Usually the breaking down is because of the action of bacteria or molds.

★ **What materials, other than glass and plastic, are not biodegradable?**

Natural recycling

To some extent, the land part of the environment can clean itself, just as the water part can. That is, many waste products can be *recycled* [ree-SY-kuhld] in nature. Recycling means changing some used material into a form that can again be useful.

Paper and garbage can be recycled in nature. These materials break down and become a part of the soil. After they break down, they supply some of the chemicals that green plants need to grow. But this kind of recycling takes time. In places where many people live close together—in cities, for example—more garbage is made than can be recycled in nature. In cities, then, getting rid of garbage can be a problem.

Land pollution from garbage is a very ugly kind of land pollution. Have you ever seen garbage piled up in an

Figure 27–9. Getting rid of garbage is a big job, requiring machines and land space. What happens when garbage is not picked up and disposed of properly?

De Wys, Inc.

alley? If so, you know that garbage can be ugly. It also has a bad smell. Furthermore, if garbage is not covered, it becomes a health problem. It attracts rats and insects that carry disease.

Even if garbage is hauled away, it has to be taken somewhere. In many cities garbage is taken to a place where it can be dumped on vacant land. Then it may be burned or it may just be allowed to rot. Of course, piles of garbage that are not covered provide homes for rats and insects.

A better way to get rid of garbage is in a *sanitary* [SAN-uh-TEHR-ee] *landfill*. A sanitary landfill is a place set aside for careful filling. After garbage is dumped at this place, bulldozers spread out the garbage. The garbage is covered with a layer of dirt at the end of each day.

As time passes, the garbage in the deeper layers is naturally recycled. It becomes a part of the soil.

★ **Why do you think a sanitary landfill is covered with a layer of dirt each day?**

Help in recycling

Glass and plastic break down very slowly, if at all. Other materials are also slow to break down. Old tires, aluminum cans, and worn-out cars and appliances are not recycled very fast by natural processes. What can be done with such things?

535

Unfortunately, these kinds of things are often just left in the environment. They are ugly. They make the land unfit for other uses, such as recreation or the growing of food. In other words, they pollute the land.

Even though nature does not recycle these items, people can recycle them. That is, the used materials can be put into some form that can again be useful.

Many communities have recycling centers. Maybe you have taken glass bottles and jars to such a center for recycling. Most of the glass is melted and then made into glass bottles and jars again.

As you know, paper is recycled in nature. But people use so much paper that natural recycling is not fast enough. Also, there is a shortage of paper in this country. So, paper is recycled to make new paper. You may have seen a book, newspaper, or magazine that was printed on recycled paper. Perhaps you have seen a label such as "Recycled Paper" or "This book is printed on recycled paper."

Scrap metal, such as aluminum and iron, can be recycled too. Perhaps you have taken used cans to a recycling center. Like glass, scrap metal is taken to a place where it is melted and used to make metal objects, such as cans, again.

★ **What other things can you think of that people can recycle?**

Find Out More

Using references, find out what has to be done to paper in order to recycle it. What is the cost of recycling paper compared to the cost of producing paper from trees?

DO IT YOURSELF

Visit a junkyard

Look for a junkyard near your home. You may have to go to an out-of-the-way area to find one. If you can, look through the whole junkyard. What kinds of things may be found in the junkyard? Try to find out how long some of the junk has been in the yard and what may eventually happen to it. How is a junkyard like a recycling center?

Robert Buchbinder

An air-pollution field inspector has to check out many complaints during the day. What does the inspector in this photograph seem to be doing?

Air-Pollution Field Inspector

It was a cold morning in the large city. The amount of traffic steadily increased until the morning rush hour was in full swing. In factories, office buildings, and homes, fuel was being burned to supply power and heat. The burning of fuels could cause a lot of air pollution in the form of smoke or odors.

Ralph Bowen was on the job as a field inspector for the department of environmental control. Ralph was one of several dozen inspectors, both men and women, who patrolled the city by car. It was their job to look for buildings that were violating the air-pollution laws. It was also their job to investigate any complaints about air pollution which were received on the car radio.

Any complaint about air pollution had to be investigated quickly. If Ralph found that the complaint about air pollution was true, he would write up a ticket. Then the people who caused the pollution would have to pay a fine. The fine would go up each time the same people were given a ticket. In this way the people causing the air pollution would be encouraged to stop polluting the air.

Ralph was proud of his work. He felt that he was doing something worthwhile about air pollution. He also felt that more and more people were beginning to respect him and his department for the work it was doing.

Would you like to help control air pollution, water pollution, or land pollution? There are many kinds of jobs in what is often called environmental control. To find out what these jobs are, you might want to call or write the department of environmental control in your area.

Reviewing and Extending

SUMMING UP

1. Most air pollution results from burning fuels.
2. Weather conditions affect air pollution.
3. Air pollution may be controlled by using certain pollution-control devices and by using new sources of energy and power.
4. Many kinds of water pollution come from the activities of people.
5. A body of water can take in some organic matter without becoming polluted.
6. Water pollution from sewage may be controlled by treatment plants.
7. Land pollution is often caused by things that people throw away.
8. Paper and garbage can be recycled in nature.
9. Glass, paper, and scrap iron can be recycled by people.

CHECKING UP

Vocabulary Write the numerals *1–10* on your paper. Each numbered phrase describes a term from the following list. On your paper, write the term next to the numeral of the phrase that describes it.

pollutant	particulate	sewage
inversion	electrostatic precipitator	eutrophication
algae	organic matter	biodegradable
sanitary landfill	recycling	sludge

1. anything in air, in water, or on land that causes pollution
2. name given to the waste material that is carried away by sewers
3. material that is living or comes from living things
4. place set aside for careful filling with garbage
5. broken down easily in nature
6. changing of a body of water because of organic matter
7. tiny plants that grow in great numbers in polluted water
8. device which is used to remove particulates from smoke
9. changing a used material into a form that can again be useful
10. layering of air so that pollutants are trapped near the earth

Knowledge and Understanding Write the numerals *11–14* on your paper. Beside each numeral, write the word or words that best complete the sentence having that numeral.

11. All the pollutants in sewage may be removed by (*primary, secondary, tertiary*) treatment.

538

12. Not all air pollution is caused by people. Volcanoes, wind, and (*hydrocarbons, forest fires, inversions*) also place pollutants into the air.
13. As a problem, land pollution seems to be (*bigger than, smaller than, the same as*) it was many years ago.
14. A device called (*a scrubber, a sludge, an inversion*) can be used to clean the gases that come from burning fuel in furnaces and from burning trash.

Concepts Beside each of the numerals 15–17 on your paper, write the word or words that best complete the sentence having that numeral.

15. Water cleans itself of small amounts of organic matter because (*algae, bacteria, fish*) eat most of the organic matter.
16. Glass and plastic are two widely used substances that (*break down in nature, are biodegradable, are not recycled very fast by natural processes*).
17. Air pollutants can build up to dangerous levels (*when winds blow gases and dust long distances, during an inversion, as a result of tertiary treatment*).

Application and Critical Thinking Answer the following questions as briefly as you can without leaving out any important ideas.

18. Why aren't changes made quickly once it is discovered how to control a certain kind of pollution?
19. What does the presence of a large amount of algae in water indicate about the water?

DOING MORE

1. Look around your community to see what different kinds of pollution you can find. Make a list of the kinds of pollution that you find and where you find them. For example, is garbage or litter to be found anywhere? Are any chimneys or smokestacks pouring particulates into the air? Is there junk lying around? List each thing that you find.
2. Smear petroleum jelly on several pieces of cardboard. Leave each piece of cardboard in a different place. For example, you might leave one near a chimney, one on a playground, and one near a busy street. After one hour, look at the pieces of cardboard. Where did the material on each piece of cardboard come from?

CHAPTER 28

The Technology of Computers

Scientific work that is being done today is speeded up a great deal by *computers* [kuhm-PYOOT-urz]. Computers are able to do calculations (adding, subtracting, multiplying, and dividing) very rapidly. No longer do scientists and engineers spend hours and hours on a calculation that involves many steps. Computers are able to do these calculations quickly and correctly. The scientists and engineers get the answers they need quickly. Then they are free to continue their work in other ways.

Scientific work is not the only kind of work in which computers are important. Computers are used in businesses such as banks and large stores. Schools use computers. Computers are used in making and inspecting many different products.

What are computers? How do computers work? What are some of the things computers can do? These and other questions about computers will be answered in this chapter.

Many people are needed to operate computers. The engineer below is making some adjustments in a computer. The keypunch operator is typing data cards to be put into a computer. Each person's work is important for fast, accurate results.

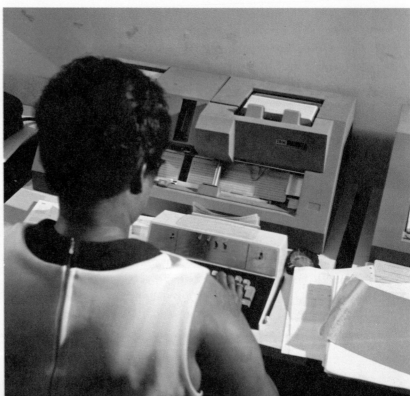

Photo Research International

De Wys, Inc.

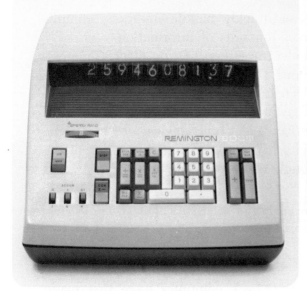

Figure 28–1. *What differences are there between a desk calculator and a computer?*

THE HISTORY OF COMPUTERS

What is a computer?
*What three inventions were important in reducing
the size of computers?*

What is a computer?

You have probably heard a great deal about computers. You may have heard that they can do many things for people. But what is a computer?

One way to answer this question is to say that a computer is an electronic device that does things people design it to do. There are two parts to this answer you should think about. First, a computer is an *electronic device,* or a piece of machinery that uses electricity in a certain way. Second, it does what *people* design it to do.

Computers can add, subtract, multiply, and divide quickly. But so can calculators. Large computers, however, are able to do more than just calculations. Computers can work with any meaningful group of numbers, words, charts, or symbols. The numbers, words, charts, or symbols that computers work with are called *data* [DAYT-uh]. The term "data processing" refers to the many different

For You to Think About

What are some reasons why computers must be able to work very quickly?

541

ways a computer can quickly handle numbers, complicated ideas, and great amounts of information.

A computer uses electric energy. So do electric motors, light bulbs, radios, and TV sets. Electric motors and light bulbs are called electric devices. The electric current in these devices always flows through a wire. Radios, TV sets, and computers are electronic devices. In electronic devices, the electricity is not always in a wire. Part of the current moves through *electron tubes* and/or *transistors* [tranz-IHS-turz].

★ **What are some characteristics of electronic devices that you can think of?**

Early calculators

The forerunners of today's computer were first made over 300 years ago. In 1642, Blaise Pascal built a device with wheels geared together. It could add and subtract. In 1694, Gottfried Wilhelm von Leibniz built a more advanced device that could also multiply and divide. These devices did not use electricity. They were operated by turning a crank or pulling a lever.

It was not until the early 1830's that the key idea which led to the development of today's computer was proposed. Charles Babbage was the person who first proposed a calculator with a memory. That is, the calculator would be able to store the information and instructions given to it.

Unfortunately, Babbage's calculator was never built. There was no way to build a calculator with a memory by using wheels and gears. The work of Charles Babbage was forgotten for many years.

Computers come of age

In the 1930's, some scientists began to explore ways to make a calculator with electric circuits rather than with wheels and gears as Babbage had tried to do. Such a calculator was the first real step in the development of today's computer, or electronic calculator with a memory.

In 1945, at the University of Pennsylvania, the first very large computer was built. This computer had 18,000 elec-

Find Out More

Using references, find out more about the history of computers. Who were some people, other than those mentioned in this chapter, who helped develop computers? What did they contribute to the development of computers?

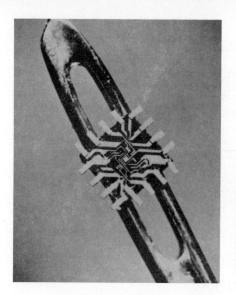
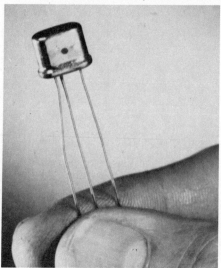
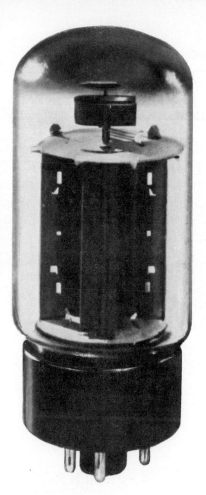

Figure 28–2. Why are transistors (center) and integrated circuits (left) often used instead of electron tubes in electronic devices?

tron tubes in it. It took up about 1 400 square metres (about 15,000 square feet) of floor space. Later, a design that allowed the computer to store more than one *program* [PROH-gram], or set of instructions, in the computer's memory was added. But the size of this computer was a disadvantage. It was almost impossible to move. Also, many buildings were not big enough to hold such a large computer.

Then two new inventions set the stage for a new size in computers. In 1947, the transistor was invented. Transistors can do the same job that electron tubes do. But transistors are very small. They use only a small amount of power.

At about this same time, the *magnetic memory core* [mag-NEHT-ihk MEHM-(uh-)ree KOH(UH)R] was developed. Like transistors, magnetic memory cores are much smaller than the memory parts of computers that used electron tubes. Later, the space taken up by many transistors was cut down by using *integrated* [IHNT-uh-GRAYT-uhd] *circuits*. These tiny circuits might be only one or two millimetres across.

★ **What do you suppose happened to the size of computers as these new developments took place?**

543

Compare an old and a new radio

Compare the size of an old vacuum-tube radio with the size of a portable transistor radio. Then take the cabinet off the old radio and open up the case of the transistor radio. Describe the inside of each radio. What is in the old radio that is not in the transistor radio? How would you explain the difference in size between the two radios?

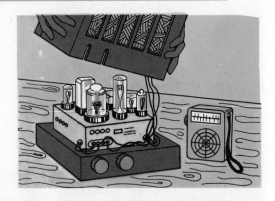

HOW COMPUTERS WORK

Why is a cash register called a computer?
What is the difference between input and output?
What is a program?
*What is the difference between direct output
   and indirect output?*

The cash register

You have seen a cash register in a supermarket. On many cash registers, the prices of the things you buy are printed on a tape. When all the things you are buying are recorded, the cashier pushes a certain key, and the prices are added up. Suppose your bill is $17.23. You give the cashier $20.00. The cashier presses the keys for $20.00 and then presses a certain key so that the cash register prints on your tape the amount of change you should receive.

The cash register prints a tape for each customer. The cash register does more, too. At the end of the day, or at any time during the day, the store manager can check the total amount of money received at the cash register.

In some large department stores, cash registers are also used for keeping track of inventories and making credit checks. As you can see, the cash register is more than an adding machine that prints out data. The cash register is also a computer. It uses data given to it by the cashier. It stores data. It prints out whatever data are called for.

The way a cash register works can be used as a model for computers in general. Not all computers do the same kinds of things a cash register does. But the many different kinds of computers are like a cash register in some general ways.

★ **How do you suppose a large computer differs from a cash register in ways other than size?**

Input

Before any computer can perform any operations, some data must be put into the computer. Such data are called *input*.

Think about a cash register again. The cashier puts the prices of the things you buy into the cash register by pushing down the proper keys. A different key also has to be pushed to tell the machine to add up the prices. All the data put into a computer are input.

Computers have many uses other than as cash registers. So there are many kinds of input other than numbers to be added. Sometimes data are typed in on a keyboard that looks like a typewriter keyboard. Another way of putting in data is by having the data on punched cards. Then the cards are passed through the computer.

There is one more thing to remember about input. No matter how the input is supplied, the computer can only act on the input it gets. If the input is wrong, the data from the computer will be wrong.

★ **Do you think more mistakes are made by computers or by people who use computers? Explain.**

Output

The kinds of data you get back from a computer are called *output*. The cash-register tape you get at a supermarket is output. But that is not the only output from the register. Some data are kept inside the register. These data become output when the store manager "asks" for them.

The output from a cash register is sometimes called *direct output*. Direct output means the output comes from

For You to Think About

Now that you know that a cash register is a computer, what other machines do you think might be called computers too? Why do you think so?

equipment connected directly to the computer which handled the input. So, direct output is controlled by the computer that handled the input.

Another kind of output is called *indirect output.* Sometimes the output of a computer is in some form that cannot be seen or read directly. For example, the output may be on a punched card. This kind of output must be put into another machine in order to be put into a readable form. You can read indirect output only after it comes from some machine other than the one that handled the input.

The program

All computers have programs. Programs are sets of instructions that go into the computer. The computer is often "programmed," or given its set of instructions for handling data, before data are put into it. In using a cash register, however, the cashier programs the cash register by pushing the proper keys. In most computers the programs are more complicated. These programs are "stored" in the computer by means of electric circuits. The programs are written by people called *computer programmers* [PROH-GRAM-urz].

To better understand what a program is, look at the diagram in Figure 28–3. This kind of diagram is called a *flowchart.* A flowchart is not a program. A flowchart is an easy way to show the series of steps the computer follows in carrying out a task.

Figure 28–3. Follow the steps in the flowchart. What happens when the computer reads an eighth-grader's card? A seventh-grader's card? The last card?

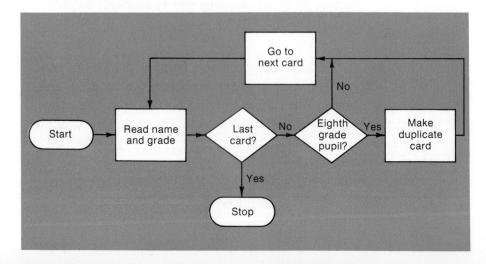

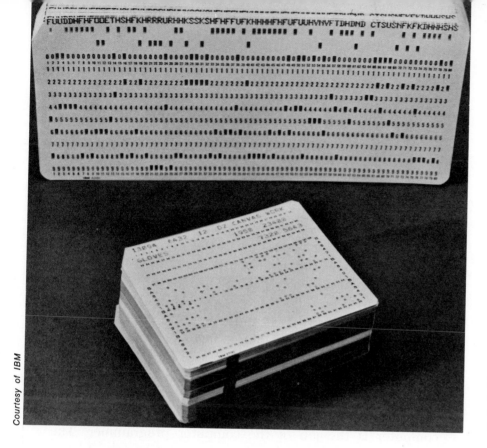

Figure 28–4. Not all computers can read the same kind of punched cards. Two different kinds are shown here. Have you ever seen cards like either of these? If so, where?

Suppose a school uses a computer for scheduling classes. The computer could be programmed to pick out the schedules of all the eighth-grade pupils in the school and print duplicates of these schedules.

The input is a deck of punched cards similar to those shown in Figure 28–4. The holes in each card contain data the computer can "read." Each card gives the name, grade, and class schedule of each pupil in the school. The last card in the deck is a "Stop" card. This card has holes punched in it in such a way that when the computer reads the card, the computer stops.

The direct output is to be a duplicate card for each eighth-grade pupil. An indirect output might be to run these cards through another machine which prints out the data from each card on a separate piece of paper. Then each pupil can have a copy of his or her schedule.

A flowchart of the program would look like the one in Figure 28–3. Notice that other than for Start and Stop, there are two kinds of boxes. The rectangles are instructions for the computer. These boxes have one input and one output. The diamonds are "Decide" instructions. They have one input and two outputs. The computer can decide whether the answer to the question in the box is Yes or No. One output is for the Yes answer. The other output is for the No answer.

The use of Decide instructions allows the computer to process a long series of inputs without having a new program for each input. The computer "loops" through the same instructions as many times as necessary to do the job.

Remember that the flowchart is not a program. A flowchart is a diagram of what the computer will be programmed to do. A flowchart does represent a program, however, if the instructions in the boxes and diamonds can be carried out by the computer. The flowchart shows that a program is a series of steps that lead to a desired result. Of course, the necessary data (input) must also be given to the computer.

Planning the program and providing the input for the computer is the job of the computer programmer. The computer programmer has a very important job.

Figure 28–5. After a program of instructions is written, the program must be put into the computer. This is usually done by typing the instructions, using a special computer language, on the special typewriter keyboard connected to the computer. This process is called "keying in" the program.

DO IT YOURSELF

Make a flowchart

Suppose that a community hospital has a computer. Suppose, too, that the hospital has a separate punched card for every person in that community. Each card has a person's name, address, and blood type on it. In an emergency, the hospital wants to get in touch with all the people having a certain blood type. Make a flowchart for finding the cards of these people and for making a duplicate card for each.

COMPUTER ARITHMETIC AND CODES

How are binary numerals written?
How does a computer add numbers?
How can letters and words be shown on a punched card?

Binary numerals

When you do arithmetic problems, you use *numerals* [N(Y)OOM-(uh-)ruhlz]. A numeral is a symbol that stands for a number. The numerals you use are made with ten digits—0, 1, 2, 3, 4, 5, 6, 7, 8, and 9. Numerals written with ten digits are called *decimal* [DEHS(-uh)-muhl] *numerals.*

Think about the numerals you usually use. If you want to represent none, you use the numeral 0. The number one is 1, two is 2, and so on to 9. But how do you write numbers from ten to nineteen? You put a 1 in the next column to the left, or the "10" column, and start using each of the ten digits again. See the decimal numerals in Figure 28–6.

Computers use numerals to do arithmetic, just as you do. But computers use numerals called *binary* [BY-nuh-ree] *numerals.* The prefix "bi–" means two. The numerals used by a computer are called binary numerals because they contain only two digits—0 and 1. Binary numerals must be used for carrying messages to a computer because a

Number	Decimal Numeral		Binary Numeral				
	10	1	16	8	4	2	1
None		0					0
One		1					1
Two		2				1	0
Three		3				1	1
Four		4			1	0	0
Five		5			1	0	1
Six		6			1	1	0
Seven		7			1	1	1
Eight		8		1	0	0	0
Nine		9		1	0	0	1
Ten	1	0		1	0	1	0
Eleven	1	1		1	0	1	1
Twelve	1	2		1	1	0	0
Thirteen	1	3		1	1	0	1
Fourteen	1	4		1	1	1	0
Fifteen	1	5		1	1	1	1
Sixteen	1	6	1	0	0	0	0

Figure 28–6. Compare the decimal numerals and binary numerals in the list above. How are two, four, eight, and sixteen written as binary numerals? How are these numerals similar? How are they different?

Binary Numerals	Decimal Numerals
1 0 . . . . . (2+0)	2
1 1 . . . . . (2+1)	3
1 0 1 . . . (4+0+1)	5

transistor in a computer has two conditions–"on" and "off." When the transistor is on, it represents 1. When the transistor is off, it represents 0.

Any numeral that can be written using ten digits can also be written using only two digits. See the binary numerals in Figure 28–6. You start with 0 for none. Then there is 1. But how do you write the numeral for two? You put a 1 in the "2" column and a 0 in the "1" column. Three is written as 1 1, meaning one "2" and one "1". But how do you write the numeral for four? You put a 1 in the "4" column and a 0 in both the "2" column and the "1" column. The binary numerals up to sixteen are in Figure 28–6.

★ **Based on the list in Figure 28–6, how would you write the binary numeral for the number seventeen? Eighteen? Nineteen?**

Except for the numeral for none (0), binary numerals always begin with the digit 1. Also, each time 1 is moved another column to the left, the 1 stands for a different number. In the "1" column, the 1 stands for one. In the "2" column, as in the binary numeral 1 0, the 1 stands for two, or 1×2. In the "4" column, as in the binary numeral 1 0 0, the 1 stands for four, or 2×2. In the "8" column, as in 1 0 0 0, the 1 stands for 8, or $2 \times 2 \times 2$, and so on.

Now you have an idea of how binary numerals are written. But how does a computer add two numbers? It adds numbers the same way you do, except it uses binary numerals. Suppose a computer adds the binary numerals 1 0 and 1 1. The problem is shown at the left.

Using binary numerals, the sum of 1 0 and 1 1 is 1 0 1. In a computer, a transistor is used for each digit of a binary numeral. A transistor that is on represents 1. A transistor that is off represents 0. If the transistor is on, that part of the numeral is counted. If it is off, it is not counted. The diagram on the next page shows which transistors would be on and which would be off in adding two and three.

Notice that when the sum in a column is two (as in the "2" column), the transistor is off, or 0, and a 1 has been put in the next column to the left (in this case, the "4" column).

"4" Column	"2" Column	"1" Column		Binary Numerals		Decimal Numerals
OFF	ON	OFF	or	1 0	or	2
OFF	ON	ON	or	1 1	or	3
ON	OFF	ON	or	1 0 1	or	5

DO IT YOURSELF

Do arithmetic problems using binary numerals

Try adding the following pairs of numbers written as binary numerals: 1 0 1 and 1 1 0; 1 0 0 and 1 1 1; and 1 0 1 1 and 1 1 0 0. How would these numbers be written as decimal numerals? Use the decimal numerals for adding the numbers. Do you get the same answer as when using binary numerals for adding?

You may want to try subtracting using pairs of binary numerals. Figure out how these numerals would be written as decimal numerals in order to check your work. You might even like to try figuring out how to multiply and divide using binary numerals.

Computer codes

Punched cards are one kind of input for computers. But how does the computer read what is on a card? The answer is that certain combinations of holes in the card stand for different letters, numbers, and symbols. You could say the data are in the form of a code.

Look at the cards in Figure 28–7 on the next page. Card *A* shows one kind of card code that is used. The digits 0 to 9, the letters of the alphabet, and some other symbols are written on the card. Each digit, letter, or other symbol is called a *character* [KAR-ihk-tur]. In the column below each character, holes can be punched to stand for that

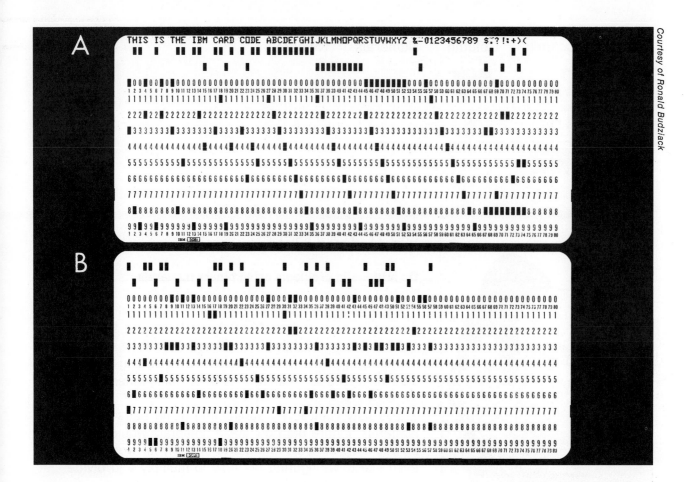

Figure 28–7. Card B is marked with a message. Use the code on card A to figure out what the message on card B is.

Find Out More

Using references, find out what is meant by the term "computer language." How is computer language related to computer codes? Are the same languages and codes used for business as well as for scientific work? Explain.

character. On card *A*, the dark spots show where holes would be punched to stand for each character. Any column can be used for any character, but only one character may be recorded in any one column.

For example, look at the first character on card *B*. Notice that there is a dark spot (representing a hole) at the very top of the card and another dark spot in row 7. If you look at the code for letters on card *A* you will see that this character is the letter G.

Keep in mind that other codes can also be used. In fact, other sizes and kinds of cards are used in some computers. Also remember that punched cards are not the only form of input. Punched paper tapes, magnetic tapes, and typewriter keyboards are other ways to feed data into a computer.

Computer Programming

Marva O'Neil frowned.

The supervisor looked at her and asked, "What's wrong?"

"The results aren't what I expected at all," said Marva.

"Why not?"

"I think something's wrong with the program I wrote."

"Check it out and let me know."

Marva looked at the program which had been given to the computer. She thought the program she had worked out was a good one. Perhaps there was only one instruction which needed to be changed so that the computer would give the right output.

After looking at the results and the program, Marva knew what part of the program was wrong. Now she had to find out which particular instruction was wrong. So, she carefully worked out that part of the program again. It took her nearly an hour to find it. She had made a mistake in the instructions.

Now Marva had to make the correction in the program that was stored in the computer's memory. Fortunately, she could make the correction using the console keyboard. She instructed the computer to print the part of the program she needed. It was easy to make the correction. "Now," she thought, "I'll run the program again and see if it gives me what I want." Sure enough, it worked beautifully.

Writing programs is a part of Marva O'Neil's job. Do you think you might like to do the things she does someday? If so, you must be trained as a computer programmer. It is an interesting and rewarding career.

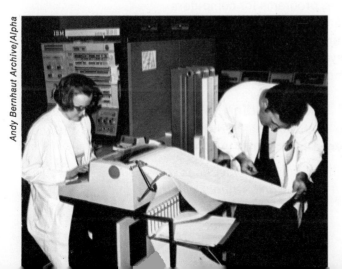

Andy Bernhaut Archive/Alpha

A computer programmer may key in a program on a console keyboard. The computer console may also be the place where the results will come from the computer. What is one advantage of such an arrangement?

553

Reviewing and Extending

SUMMING UP

1. A computer is an electronic device that does what people design it to do.
2. The development of the transistor, the magnetic memory core, and the integrated circuit helped to cut down the size of computers.
3. Many cash registers are computers because they use data given to them by the cashier, they store data, and they print out whatever data are called for.
4. Data that come into a computer are input. One way input comes in is on punched cards.
5. Data you get back from a computer are output.
6. Programs are sets of instructions that go into the computer. They are written by programmers.
7. Computers use binary numerals for arithmetic. Only the digits 0 and 1 are used.
8. The input for a computer is often in the form of a code.

CHECKING UP

Vocabulary   Write the numerals *1–9* on your paper. Each numbered phrase describes a term from the following list. On your paper, write the term next to the numeral of the phrase that describes it.

input	output	character
program	programmer	integrated circuit
transistor	binary numerals	flowchart
magnetic memory core	decimal numerals	

1. data you get back from a computer
2. instructions for a computer
3. small device that does the same job in a computer that an electron tube used to do
4. data that come into a computer
5. person who writes programs for computers
6. numerals that are written using only the digits 0 and 1
7. numerals that are written using the digits 0–9
8. digit, letter, or symbol which is to be coded
9. part of the computer used for storage of programs and data

Knowledge and Understanding   Write the numerals *10–13* on your paper. Beside each numeral, write the word or words that best complete the sentence having that numeral.

10. A large, modern computer (*only does calculations, does what people design it to do, works without electricity*).

554

11. The output from a cash register is sometimes called (*direct output*, *indirect output*, *a Decide instruction*).
12. In using a card code, any column on the card can be used to make a (*word*, *program*, *character*).
13. A diagram that shows the series of steps the computer follows in carrying out a task or solving a certain kind of problem is known as a (*card code*, *flowchart*, *binary numeral*).

Concepts   Beside each of the numerals *14–16* on your paper, write the word or words that best complete the sentence having that numeral.

14. If the input given to a computer is wrong, the data from the computer will be (*on a flowchart*, *indirect output*, *wrong*).
15. In writing binary numerals, each time the digit 1 is moved another place to the left the 1 stands for (*a different number*, *the same number*, *two*).
16. Computers can add, subtract, multiply, and divide many times as a part of (*the same job*, *each input*, *the work it can do without electricity*).

Application and Critical Thinking   Answer the following questions as briefly as you can without leaving out any important ideas.

17. Why did the development of the transistor, magnetic memory core, and integrated circuit reduce the size of computers?
18. If a computer does not give the right output even though the input data are correct and the computer is working properly, what is probably wrong?
19. What is one reason why computers are used in figuring out difficult problems instead of having people figure them out?

DOING MORE

1. Go to a large business office, such as a bank or central telephone office. Ask permission to visit their computer operations. Find out what kinds of jobs the computer is programmed to do. Ask to see some input and output materials. What kinds of input and output materials does the office use?
2. Examine the punched cards that come to your home in the mail. Try to find two cards from the same company. Look at the punched places on the cards. Try to figure out how much information may be included on a punched card. Why are cards punched in this way?

Pros and Cons

Computers are widely used in space exploration. Computers can calculate orbits, control flights, and analyze the great amounts of data that are constantly received from spacecraft in flight.

Computers—Are They Helpful or Harmful?

Computers are used in many ways today. You can see the results of the use of computers in some everyday experiences. Many bills that come to your home are on punched cards. Bank accounts, too, are handled by computers. Company payrolls, class scheduling, and the reporting of grades in schools are some other uses of computers. When given the proper data, a computer can do jobs like these quickly and accurately.

Computers are also used in ways that are not so easy to see. Without computers, for example, the exploration of space would probably not be as far advanced as it is now. The many calculations needed for designing the parts of a spacecraft and for figuring out orbits would take much longer and be much more likely to contain mistakes if done without computers.

The use of computers has been helpful to people in many ways. Few, if any, people would disagree with that. But most people would also agree that using computers has caused some problems, too.

One problem is that using computers has caused some people to lose their job. Because computers are fast and accurate, they can do much of the paperwork that people used to do. The number of people needed to program the computer and to handle input and output is much smaller than the number needed to handle the paperwork. So, some people lose their job.

There is another way in which using computers may be "not helpful" to people. Computers are impersonal. That is, a computer doesn't treat you as if you are a person. You are just a number to a computer.

A frequently heard complaint about computers concerns billing. Suppose a customer uses a credit card to purchase several things. Later, when the bill issued by a computer comes in, the customer finds charges for things that were not bought. Of course, the computer is not at fault. The computer was given incorrect data, but often the computer is blamed for the error anyway.

Upon calling the store to complain, the customer may be told to send payment for only the things purchased and to write a note explaining why the rest of the bill was not paid. This may work. Often, however, the computer is not given the new data right away. Then the customer will be billed again for things not bought.

The computer may also start adding interest on the "amount owed" for things not bought. Again, the reason is that the computer was not given the correct data. Sometimes this kind of improper billing takes months to correct. Impersonal service involving computers makes people angry and frustrated. The store probably will lose a customer. So instances like this are bad for the customer and bad for the store.

You have learned some of the pros and cons concerning the use of computers. You can see that when you think about

Do you think a situation like this could ever occur? How would you feel if someone thought a computer was more important than you?

FUNKY WINKERBEAN by Tom Batiuk,
Courtesy of Field Newspaper Syndicate.

computers, you have to think about people, too. Do you think the helpful things about computers outweigh the harmful ones? Should people try to adjust to new jobs or new ways of customer billing and think of the advantages of computers to people in general? Discuss these questions with your classmates.

Investigate On Your Own

1. Obtain some small wooden or plastic propellers of different sizes. Also obtain some wooden dowels, each fifteen centimetres long. Attach each propeller to a separate dowel so that when the dowel turns, the propeller turns with it. Twirl each dowel as fast as you can between the palms of your hands and release it. The propeller should go up. If it does not, twirl it again in the opposite direction and release it. Keep track of how far each propeller goes. Which one traveled the shortest distance? Which traveled the farthest? What does the size of a propeller have to do with how far it travels? What does Bernoulli's principle have to do with how the propellers travel?

2. By doing the following activity, you can get a better idea of how the speed of a satellite is related to the height of its orbit above the earth. Tie a small rubber stopper to the end of a piece of nylon fishing line about one metre long. Insert the other end of the line through a piece of glass tubing about fifteen centimetres long. The tubing should have fire-polished ends and be wrapped with tape for safety. Tie a larger rubber stopper on the end which was inserted through the tubing. Hold the glass tubing upright and whirl the small rubber stopper in a circle. Whirl the stopper so that it is parallel to the floor. Whirl the stopper just fast enough to keep it in a circle having a radius of about 40 cm. Next, make the stopper travel a little faster. What happens to the distance of the stopper from the tubing? Now make the stopper travel still faster. What happens to the distance of the stopper from the tubing? What is the difference between the speed of the stopper when it is moving in a small circle and when it is moving in a larger circle? How does this activity help to explain the relationship between the speed of a satellite and the size of its orbit?

Read On Your Own

Grey, Jerry, *The Facts of Flight.* Philadelphia: The Westminster Press, 1973.

> The basic ideas of how planes fly are presented. There are pictures of many different planes, including the most modern. A glossary of terms is also included.

Lodewijk, T., and others, *The Way Things Work.* New York: Simon and Schuster, 1973.

> This book is an illustrated encyclopedia of technology. Some of the things described are gasoline engines, jet engines, gliders, and rockets.

Marzani, Carl, *The Wounded Earth.* Reading, Massachusetts: Young Scott Books, 1972.

> This book is about pollution and technology. The relationship of environment, pollution, and technology is brought out very well.

Meadow, Charles T., *The Story of Computers.* New York: Harvey House, Inc., 1970.

> This book tells how computers are used and how they are programmed to solve problems. Examples of problems solved by computers, such as guiding a spacecraft and predicting weather, are presented.

Vorwald, Alan, and Clark, Frank, *Computers: From Sand Table to Electronic Brain,* third edition. New York: McGraw-Hill Book Company, 1970.

> Binary numerals, codes, and programming are just a few of the topics in this book. Instructions for building computers are also included.

GLOSSARY

When certain science words or words related to science topics are used for the first time in this book, or in some cases for the first time in a unit, they are spelled in a special way to help the reader learn how to say them. These words are also spelled in this way in this Glossary. The special spellings always appear in [ ]. When a word has two or more syllables, certain syllables are stressed more than others. In the special spelling of a word, the syllable stressed the most is spelled in large capital letters. The syllable stressed second most is spelled in small capital letters. The syllable or syllables not stressed are spelled in small letters. If there are ( ) around one or more letters within the [ ], those letters may or may not be said.

Below is a list of the letter or letters used for the special spellings. Next to each letter or letters is a description of the way the letter or letters should be said.

a . . . . . *a* in *hat* [HAT]
ah . . . . . *a* in *father* [FAHTH-ur] and *o* in *hot* [HAHT]
aw . . . . . *a* in *all* [AWL] and *o* in *order* [AWRD-ur]
ay . . . . . *a* in *face* [FAYS]
ch . . . . . *ch* in *child* [CHYLD] and in *much* [MUHCH]
ee . . . . *e* in *equal* [EE-kwuhl]

eh . . . . . *e* in *let* [LEHT]
eye . . . . the first *i* in *iris* [EYE-ruhs]
g . . . . . *g* in *go* [GOH]
ih . . . . . *i* in *hit* [HIHT]
oh . . . . . *o* in *open* [OH-puhn]
oo . . . . . *oo* in *food* [FOOD] and *u* in *rule* [ROOL]
ow . . . . . *ou* in *out* [OWT]
oy . . . . . *oi* in *voice* [VOYS]
s . . . . . *s* in *say* [SAY]

sh . . . . . *sh* in *she* [SHEE]
u . . . . . *u* in *put* [PUT] and *oo* in *foot* [FUT]
uh . . . . . *u* in *cup* [KUHP]
ur . . . . . *er* in *term* [TURM] and *ir* in *sir* [SUR]
y . . . . . *i* in *nice* [NYS]
z . . . . . *s* in *atoms* [AT-uhmz]
zh . . . . . *s* in *treasure* [TREHZH-ur]

A

Accelerate [ihk-SEHL-uh-RAYT]: to move faster and faster during each second of motion

Acid [AS-uhd]: a compound which turns blue litmus paper red, which tastes sour, and which has molecules containing one or more hydrogen atoms joined to one or more other kinds of atoms

Acoustics [uh-KOO-stihks]: the science of sound

Aileron [AY-luh-RAHN]: a movable part located on the back edge of an airplane wing and used to control roll

Air pressure [PREHSH-ur]: the force with which air pushes on a given area of the surface of matter

Air resistance [rih-ZIHS-tuhn(t)s]: the force caused by air pushing on an object that tends to slow down the motion of the object as it moves through the air

Airfoil [A(UH)R-foyl]: the shape of an airplane wing, which helps to cause an upward force as air flows past the wing

Algae [AL-jee]: tiny plants which grow in large numbers in water that contains many nutrients

Alloy [AL-oy]: a solid solution, usually of different metals

Alpha [AL-fuh] **particle**: a particle given off by radioactive matter and made up of two protons and two neutrons

Alternating current: an electric current in which the negative charges move first in one direction and then in the other

Ampere [AM-PIH(UH)R]: the unit used in measuring electric currents

Amplitude [AM-pluh-T(Y)OOD]: (of a transverse wave) half the distance from the bottom of a trough to the top of a crest

Angle of attack: the angle at which the flow of air hits the airfoil, or wing, of an airplane

Angle of incidence [IHN(T)-suhd-uhn(t)s]: the angle at which light rays hit a surface

Angle of reflection: the angle at which light rays leave a surface

Angstrom [ANG-struhm]: a unit of length equal to one ten-millionth of a millimetre that is used for describing very short distances, such as the wave length of light

Artificial radioactivity: the radioactivity caused by placing matter that is not usually radioactive inside a nuclear reactor so that it will soak up neutrons and become radioactive

Atom [AT-uhm]: the tiniest particle of an element that has all the properties of that element

Atomic mass: the mass of an atom in atomic mass units (amu), numerically equal to the number of protons plus the number of neutrons in the atom

Atomic mass unit: a unit used in describing the mass of molecules, atoms, and subatomic particles, abbreviated as amu

Atomic number: the number of protons in an atom

Atomic theory [uh-TAHM-ihk THEE-uh-ree]: the theory that all matter is made up of atoms

B

Base: a compound which turns blue litmus paper red, which tastes bitter, and which contains an oxygen atom joined to a hydrogen atom in a certain way

Battery: a combination of electric cells connected to one another

Bernoulli's principle: the faster a fluid moves along a surface, the less pressure the fluid will exert on that surface

Beta [BAYT-uh] **particle:** a particle that is given off by radioactive matter and that is the same as an electron

Binary [BY-nuh-ree] **numeral:** a numeral that is written with only the digits 0 and 1

Biodegradable [BY-oh-dih-GRAYD-uh-buhl]: easily broken down by natural processes, usually by bacteria or molds

Blue litmus [LIHT-muhs] **paper:** an acid indicator that turns red when touched by an acid

British thermal [THUR-muhl] **unit:** a unit for measuring heat, equal to the amount of heat that will raise the temperature of one pound of water one degree Fahrenheit

Buoyancy [BOY-uhn-see]: an upward push on any matter that is put into a liquid

C

Calorie [KAL-(uh-)ree]: a unit for measuring heat, equal to the amount of heat that will raise the temperature of one gram of water one degree Celsius

Calorimeter [KAL-uh-RIHM-uht-ur]: an instrument for measuring heat

Catalytic [KAT-uhl-IHT-ihk] **cracking unit:** a part of a petroleum refinery where molecules of little-used substances are broken apart, or cracked, to make more-useful substances

Celsius [SEHL-see-uhs] **temperature scale:** the temperature scale in which, at sea level, the freezing point of water is 0° and the boiling point of water is 100°

Chain reaction: a nuclear reaction in which neutrons given off during the fission of one atom cause the fission of other atoms

Character [KAR-ihk-tur]: (in computer coding) a digit, a letter, or a symbol

Charge collector: the metal ball on the top of a leaf electroscope

Charged object: an object that has electric properties because of a shortage or an excess of electrons

Chemical [KEHM-ih-kuhl] **change:** a change in matter in which the kinds of molecules present, but not the kinds of atoms present, are changed

Chemical electricity: the electricity made as a result of a chemical change

Chemical energy: a form of stored energy that is released, often as heat and light, during a chemical change

Chemical engineering: a branch of engineering which involves taking chemists' discoveries and using them in a practical way

Chlorophyll [KLOHR-uh-FIHL]: a material found in the green parts of plants which enables the plants to carry on photosynthesis

Circuit [SUR-kuht]: the wire, or the path, an electric current follows

Circuit breaker: a safety device which acts like a switch to open a circuit if too much current is in the circuit

Civil [SIHV-uhl] **engineering:** a branch of engineering which has to do with the construction of highways, bridges, buildings, dams, and waterways

Cloud chamber: an instrument consisting of a container filled with very cold alcohol vapor in which the passage of alpha and beta particles appear as "vapor trails"

Cohesion [koh-HEE-zhuhn]: a force that holds molecules of the same substance together

Complementary [KAHM-pluh-MEHNT-uh-ree] **colors:** the pairs of colors which, when mixed in equal amounts, make white light

Compound [KAHM-POWND]: a substance in which the molecules are made up of two or more different kinds of atoms

Compression [kuhm-PREHSH-uhn]: (in a longitudinal wave) a part of the wave in which particles of the medium are closer together than they normally are

Computer [kuhm-PYOOT-ur]: an electronic device that does things people design it to do, including the handling of many kinds of data, the storing of data, and the printing out of data

Computer programmer [PROH-GRAM-ur]: a person who writes programs for computers

Concave [kahn-KAYV] **lens:** a lens which is thinner in the middle than at its edges (also called a diverging lens because of its effect on parallel rays of light)

Concave mirror: a mirror which curves inward at its center

Condense [kuhn-DEHN(T)S]: to change from a gas to a liquid

Conductor: a material in which negative electric charges, or electrons, move about easily

Conservation [KAHN(T)-sur-VAY-shuhn] **of energy:** a principle of science stating that energy can be changed from one form to another, but cannot be created or destroyed by ordinary chemical reactions

Conservation of mass: a principle of science stating that matter can be changed into other kinds of matter, but cannot be created or destroyed by ordinary chemical reactions

Conservation of mass-energy: a principle of science stating that matter can be changed into energy and energy can be changed into matter, but the total amount of energy and matter in the universe stays the same

Control jet: a jet of compressed gas used in controlling the movement of a spacecraft and keeping the spacecraft in its proper position

Converging [kuhn-VURJ-ihng] **lens:** a convex lens, or a lens which causes parallel rays of light to converge

Convex [kahn-VEHKS] **lens:** a lens which is thinner at its edges than it is in the middle (also called a converging lens)

Convex mirror: a mirror which is curved outward at its center

Crest: (of a transverse wave) the high point of a transverse wave

Cryolite [KRY-uh-LYT]: a mineral used in the electrolysis of aluminum ore

Cycle [SY-kuhl]: (of an internal combustion engine) the number of strokes needed to let fuel into a cylinder, burn the fuel, and remove the used gases

Cylinder [SIHL-uhn-dur]: (of an engine) the metal, pipelike part of an engine and inside which a piston moves

D

Data [DAYT-uh]: any information obtained by observing and/or measuring; also, the numbers, words, charts, or symbols that computers work with

Data processing: the many different ways a computer can quickly handle numbers, complicated ideas, and great amounts of information

Decibel [DEHS-uh-BEHL]: a unit of measure for comparing the loudness of sounds

Decimal [DEHS(-uh)-muhl] **numeral:** a numeral that is written with the ten digits—0, 1, 2, 3, 4, 5, 6, 7, 8, and 9

Degree [dih-GREE]: a unit used to measure temperature

Density [DEHN(T)-suht-ee]: the mass/volume ratio of a piece of matter

Diesel [DEE-zuhl] **engine:** a piston engine that uses a light oil for fuel, and uses the heat from air compressed by the piston in order to start the fuel burning

Direct current: the current in which negative charges always go in the same direction; abbreviated as d. c.

Direct output: the output that comes from equipment connected directly to the computer which handled the input

Displacement [dihs-PLAY-smuhnt]: a way of determining the volume of an odd-shaped piece of matter

Dissolve [dihz-AHLV]: to cause the molecules of one substance to become separated from each other and become scattered in between the molecules of another substance

Distance-time graph [DIHS-tuhn(t)s TYM GRAF]: a graph in which distance (marked along the side) is plotted against time (marked along the bottom)

Diverging [duh-VURJ-ihng] **lens:** a concave lens, or lens which causes light rays to spread apart

Drag: the force of air resistance on an airplane that tends to slow the plane down

E

Effort [EHF-urt]: the force acting on a machine

Elastic [ih-LAS-tihk] **material:** a material that will return to its usual shape after being pushed or pulled out of shape

Electric current [KUR-uhnt]: the movement of negative charges in a wire

Electric energy: a form of energy, similar to magnetic energy, that causes forces to act on objects; also, the energy that causes electricity to flow through electric wires

Electric meter: a meter attached to the outside of a home to measure the number of kilowatt-hours of electric energy used in the home

Electric service: the electricity that comes to your home

Electrical [ih-LEHK-trih-kuhl] **engineering:** a branch of engineering which has to do with the making and sending of electricity and also the planning and making of the many devices that use electricity

Electrochemistry [ih-LEHK-troh-KEHM-uh-stree]: the study of the relationship between electricity and chemical change

Electrode [ih-LEHK-TROHD]: in a chemical cell, each of the two different metals placed in an electrolyte; in a dry cell, the zinc container and the carbon rod

Electrolysis [ih-LEHK-TRAHL-uh-suhs]: the breakdown or separation of a compound into its elements by using a direct current; for example, water to hydrogen and oxygen

Electrolyte [ih-LEHK-truh-LYT]: the liquid or paste which conducts electricity between the electrodes in a chemical cell

Electromagnet [ih-LEHK-troh-MAG-nuht]: a magnet made by passing electric current through loops of a wire wound around an iron core

Electromagnetic spectrum [ih-LEHK-troh-mag-NEHT-ihk SPEHK-truhm]: the whole range of radiant energy

Electromagnetic waves: the waves of all forms of radiant energy

Electron [ih-LEHK-TRAHN]: a part of an atom having a negative electric charge

Electron cloud: the space around the nucleus of an atom through which the electron or electrons of the atom move

Electronic [ih-LEHK-TRAHN-ihk] **device:** a device or piece of machinery, such as a radio or a computer, that uses electron tubes and/or transistors

Electronic engineering: a branch of engineering which has to do with electronic devices

Electroplating [ih-LEHK-truh-PLAYT-ihng]: the process in which a material, most often a metal, is covered with another kind of metal

Electrostatic generator [ih-LEHK-truh-STAT-ihk JEHN-uh-RAYT-ur]: a machine that can produce high voltages and large sparks

Electrostatic precipitator [prih-SIHP-uh-TAYT-ur]: a device which removes particulates from smoke by attracting them to a metal plate which has been charged with electricity

Element [EHL-uh-muhnt]: a substance in which every molecule is made up of a single kind of atom

Elevator [EHL-uh-VAYT-ur]: the parts of the tail of an airplane which control the pitch of the plane

Energy [EHN-ur-jee]: the ability to do work or to cause activity

Energy conversion [kun-VUR-zhuhn]: the changing of one form of energy into another form of energy

Energy level: any of the places within the structure of an atom where electrons are believed likely to be

Engineering [EHN-juh-NIH(UH)R-ihng]: the changing of scientific discoveries into technology

Equal-arm balance [BAL-uhn(t)s]: a device used to make careful measurements of mass

Eutrophication [yu-TROH-fuh-KAY-shuhn]: a change in water in which the amount of oxygen becomes much less, causing many fish and other animals in the water to die and algae to grow in great numbers

Evaporate [ih-VAP-uh-RAYT]: a term used by scientists to mean a liquid dries up, or changes to a gas, as molecules move from the surface of the liquid into the air

Experimentalist [ihk-SPEHR-uh-MEHNT-uhl-uhst]: a scientist who makes many observations and gathers and records information about a particular subject

Experimenting [ihk-SPEHR-uh-muhnt-ihng]: the process of setting up a situation and making observations of that situation

External-combustion [ehk-STURN-uhl kuhm-BUHS-chuhn] **engine:** the kind of engine in which the fuel is burned outside the engine

F

Fahrenheit [FAR-uhn-HYT] **temperature scale:** the temperature scale in which, at sea level, the freezing point of water is 32° and the boiling point of water is 212°

Fission [FIHSH-uhn]: a nuclear change in which an atom splits into two or more parts

Flowchart: a diagram of the series of steps a computer follows in carrying out a task

Focal [FOH-kuhl] **length:** the distance from the lens to the focal point

Focal point: the point to which light is focused by using a concave mirror or convex lens

Focused [FOH-kuhst]: a word which means that parallel rays of light are made to pass through one point

Force [FOH(UH)RS]: a push or a pull that acts on an object

Freezing point: the temperature at which a liquid changes to a solid

Frequency [FREE-kwuhn-see]: the number of waves made in one second

Friction [FRIHK-shuhn]: a force that exists wherever two objects rub together, tending to keep the objects from moving

Fuel cell: a device which uses a chemical reaction between hydrogen and oxygen gases to make electricity

Fulcrum [FUL-kruhm]: the fixed point around which a lever moves

Fundamental [FUHN-duh-MEHNT-uhl] **tone:** the lowest sound that can be made when a certain length of string vibrates

Fuse: a safety device which keeps too much electricity from flowing through an electric circuit

G

Galvanometer [GAL-vuh-NAHM-uht-ur]: a device used for detecting and measuring small amounts of electric current

Gas: a phase of matter in which the matter has neither a definite shape nor a definite volume

Geiger-Müller counter: an instrument for detecting and measuring radioactivity

Gravitational attraction [GRAV-uh-TAY-shnuhl uh-TRAK-shuhn]: a force of attraction between all pieces of matter

Ground: an object large enough to remain almost neutral when negative charges are added or taken away

Grounded circuit: a circuit that is connected to the earth by being connected to a water pipe or to a copper rod that has been put in the earth

Grounded object: an object that is connected to the earth by means of a conductor

H

Heat: a form of energy that can be used to do work, but which is only given off when another form of energy is also present; also, the heat energy present in an object (the total of all the kinetic energy of its molecules)

Hertz [HURTS]: a term used to describe frequency, equal to one wave a second

Horsepower: a unit of power defined by James Watt as being equal to 550 foot-pounds of work per second and equal to 746 watts

Hydrocarbon [HY-druh-KAHR-buhn]: a substance made up of molecules which only contain atoms of hydrogen and carbon

Hydrogen [HY-druh-juhn]: the element with atomic number 1, which is found in nature as a very lightweight gas

Hypothesis [hy-PAHTH-uh-suhs]: a possible explanation for something that happens

I

Image [IHM-ihj]: a likeness of an object viewed in a mirror or through a lens

Indicator [IHN-duh-KAYT-ur]: a substance which indicates by changing color that either an acid or a base is present

Indirect evidence [IHN-duh-REHKT EHV-uhd-uhn(t)s]: any observations of things that can be seen, felt, or heard to learn about things that cannot be seen, felt, or heard

Indirect output: the output from a computer in some form that cannot be seen or read directly, such as output on a punched card

Induction [ihn-DUHK-shuhn]: the causing of an electric current in a wire, even though the wire is not connected to a source of electricity

Inertia [ihn-UR-shuh]: the tendency of matter not to change its state of motion unless unbalanced forces act on it

Inference [IHN-f(uh-)ruhn(t)s]: a conclusion reached by making observations

Infrared [IHN-fruh-REHD] **rays:** a form of radiant energy having wave lengths longer than those of visible light but shorter than most radio waves; also, heat energy

Input: the data that is put into the computer

Insulator [IN(T)-suh-LAYT-ur]: a material in which negative charges do not move about easily

Integrated [IHNT-uh-GRAYT-uhd] **circuit:** a tiny circuit that takes up much less space than an ordinary circuit

Interference [IHNT-uh(r)-FIHR-uhn(t)s]: the coming together of two or more series of sound waves

Internal-combustion [ihn-TURN-uhl kuhm-BUHS-chuhn] **engine:** the kind of engine in which fuel is burned inside the engine

International System of Units: a system of units, sometimes called the metric system, that is used by scientists everywhere; abbreviated SI

Inversion [ihn-VUR-zhuhn]: a weather condition in which a layer of cool air is trapped near the surface of the earth

Ion [EYE-uhn]: a charged particle formed when an atom either gains or loses one or more electrons

Ionosphere [eye-AHN-uh-SFIH(UH)R]: a layer of the atmosphere which ranges from about 50 kilometres to 500 kilometres above the surface of the earth

Iris [EYE-ruhs]: a structure in the eye which acts like the diaphragm of a camera to change the amount of light coming into the eye

J

Jet propulsion [pruh-PUHL-shuhn]: a way of moving a plane forward by causing expanding gases to rush out the rear of jet engines

K

Kilogram [KEE-luh-GRAM]: the basic SI unit of mass

Kilowatt [KIHL-uh-WAHT]: a unit of power equal to 1 000 watts

Kilowatt-hour: the amount of electric energy used when one kilowatt of power is used for one hour

Kinetic [kuh-NEHT-ihk] **energy:** the kind of energy a moving object has because of its motion

Kinetic-molecular [kuh-NEHT-ihk muh-LEHK-yuh-lur] **theory:** an explanation of what matter is like, based on a model in which matter is believed to be made of tiny, fast-moving particles (also known as the kinetic theory of matter)

L

Leaf electroscope [ih-LEHK-truh-SKOHP]: a device used to find out if an object is charged with electricity

Lens: an object made of glass or some other transparent material, often circular in shape, which refracts the light which passes through it; also, a part of the eye in which light is refracted

Lift: the upward force on an airplane

Liquid [LIHK-wuhd]: a phase of matter in which the matter has a definite volume but not a definite shape

Litre [LEET-ur]: the basic SI unit of volume

Lodestone [LOHD-STOHN]: a kind of naturally magnetic rock that always lines up in a certain direction when suspended by a string

Longitudinal wave: a wave in which matter moves back and forth in a direction parallel to the direction in which the wave moves

Luminous [LOO-muh-nuhs] **object:** a thing which gives off its own light

M

Machine: a device which is used to (1) change the direction of a force, (2) change the amount of force, or (3) change the distance and speed through which a force acts

Magnetic [mag-NEHT-ihk] **energy:** a form of energy found in magnets that causes a force to act on certain kinds of objects

Magnetic field: the space all around a magnet, in which magnetic materials would be affected

Magnetic lines of force: the lines that are used to form a kind of picture of a magnetic field

Magnetic property: a property that any magnetic object would have, such as attracting iron and facing toward a certain direction when suspended on a string

Mass [MAS]: the amount of matter present in an object

Matter: anything which has mass and takes up space

Measuring [MEHZH-(uh-)rihng]: comparing unknown amounts with known amounts

Mechanical advantage [mih-KAN-ih-kuhl uhd-VANT-ihj]: the number of times a machine multiplies the force acting on the machine

Mechanical energy: the kind of energy an object has because it is moving (kinetic mechanical energy) or because it can move (potential mechanical energy)

Mechanical engineering: a branch of engineering which has to do with producing and using mechanical energy

Melting point: the temperature at which a solid changes to a liquid

Metre [MEET-ur]: the basic SI unit of length

Mixture [MIHKS-chur]: two or more different kinds of matter mixed together

Molecule [MAHL-ih-KYOO(UH)L]: the smallest particle of a substance that has all the properties of that substance

Motion [MOH-shuhn]: a change in position

N

Neutral [N(Y)OO-truhl] **object:** (in electricity) an object that has an equal number of positive and negative charges

Neutron [N(Y)OO-TRAHN]: a neutral part of the nucleus of an atom

Newton [N(Y)OOT-uhn]: a unit of force in SI

Nitrogen [NY-truh-juhn] **fixing:** the changing of nitrogen gas in the air into nitrogen compounds that green plants can use

Nonluminous [NAHN-LOO-muh-nuhs] **object:** an object which does not give off its own light

Nonspontaneous energy conversion: an energy conversion that begins only after some energy is added to start the conversion

Nuclear [N(Y)OO-klee-ur] **change:** a change in matter resulting from a change in the nucleus of an atom

Nuclear energy: a form of energy given off when one kind of atom splits into two or more parts

Nuclear reaction [ree-AK-shuhn]: a process in which the nucleus of an atom changes; also, a nuclear change

Nuclear reactor: a place in which a controlled nuclear chain reaction is allowed to take place

Nucleus [N(Y)OO-klee-uhs]: the central part of an atom (made up of protons and neutrons)

O

Observing [uhb-ZURV-ihng]: using the senses to find out about the environment

Ohm [OHM]: a unit used in measuring the amount of resistance in a circuit

Opaque [oh-PAYK]: a term used to describe a material through which a form of energy, such as light, will not pass

Optical illusion [AHP-tih-kuhl ihl-OO-zhuhn]: a diagram or image that can fool your sense of seeing

Orbit [AWR-buht]: the path a satellite follows

Organic [awr-GAN-ihk] **pollutant:** a pollutant which is living or has come from living things

Output: the data that comes out of a computer

Overtone: a higher pitched tone than the fundamental tone, having a frequency that is a multiple of the frequency of the fundamental tone

Oxide [AHK-SYD]: a compound formed by the combining of oxygen and one other element

Oxygen [AHK-sih-juhn]: a gaseous element found in air that is necessary for any fuel to burn

P

Parallel circuit: a circuit in which there is more than one path for the current to follow

Pendulum [PEHN-juh-luhm]: a mass suspended by a cord that is attached to a fixed point in such a way that the mass is free to swing

Permanent [PURM(-uh)-nuhnt] **magnet:** a magnet that keeps most of its magnetic properties over a long period of time

Phase [FAYZ]: a form, or state, in which matter occurs —solid, liquid, or gas

Photosynthesis [FOHT-oh-SIHN(T)-thuh-suhs]: a process occurring in green plants in which light energy is used to change molecules of carbon dioxide and water into molecules of sugar

Physical [FIHZ-ih-kuhl] **change:** a change in which the appearance of matter, but not the kind of matter present, is changed

Piston [PIHS-tuhn]: a thick metal plate pushed back and forth by expanding gases inside the cylinder of an engine

Pitch: (kind of motion) the motion about the horizontal axis of an airplane, a satellite, or any other vehicle

Pitch: (of sound) the characteristic of a sound that is determined by the frequency of the sound; sometimes referred to as high or low

Plane mirror: a flat mirror, like those found on medicine cabinets

Poles [POHLZ]: (of a magnet) the parts of a magnet where the magnetic properties are most noticeable

Pollutant [puh-LOOT-uhnt]: something in the environment that should not be there

Pollution: the fouling of the environment

Potential [puh-TEHN-chuhl] **energy:** stored energy

Power: the rate of doing work

Predict [prih-DIHKT]: to make a statement in advance about some future occurrence

Primary [PRY-MEHR-ee] **color:** any of a set of colors—red, green, or blue—from which all other colors may be obtained

Program [PROH-GRAM]: a set of instructions given to a computer

Programmed: a term which means that a computer has been given its set of instructions

Property [PRAHP-urt-ee]: something special about a material that makes the material what it is and that can be used in identifying it

Protein [PROH-TEEN]: a nitrogen-containing substance found in all living things

Proton [PROH-TAHN]: a positively charged part of the nucleus of an atom

Pupil: (of the eye) an opening through which light enters the eye

Q

Quality [KWAHL-uht-ee]: (of sound) the number and loudness of overtones

R

Radar: radio detecting and ranging, or the detecting of radio wave "echoes"

Radiant [RAYD-ee-uhnt] **energy:** the forms of energy that are given off by radiation

Radiation [RAYD-ee-AY-shuhn]: the moving outward of energy from an object in the form of rays, waves, or particles

Radio transmitter [tran(t)s-MIHT-ur]: a device which sends out radio waves in all directions

Radio waves: a form of radiant energy having a range of wave lengths from about 1 millimetre to 100 000 kilometres and which are used for radio broadcasting, television broadcasting, and radar

Radioactive [RAYD-ee-oh-AK-tihv] **matter:** any matter that gives off X rays and other forms of radiant energy

Radium [RAYD-ee-uhm]: a radioactive element discovered in pitchblende by Marie Curie

Rarefaction [RAR-uh-FAK-shuhn]: the part of a longitudinal wave in which the particles of the medium are farther apart than they normally are

Reaction engine: an engine which operates by using the principle of the third law of motion (action equals reaction)

Real image: an image which is really at the place where you see it because the light rays that form the image are at that place

Reciprocating [rih-SIHP-ruh-KAYT-ihng] **motion:** a back-and-forth motion

Recycle [ree-SY-kuhl]: to change used materials into a form that can again be useful

Red litmus paper: a base indicator that turns blue when touched to a base

Reflection [rih-FLEHK-shuhn]: the bouncing back of a wave or ray

Reforming [rih-FAW(UH)RM-ihng] **unit:** the part of a petroleum refinery where molecules of little-used substances are joined together to make more-useful kinds of molecules

Refraction [rih-FRAK-shuhn]: a change in the direction of moving waves that is caused by a change in the speed of the waves

Resistance [rih-ZIHS-tuhn(t)s]: the force a machine overcomes to do work; also, in electricity, the property of a conductor that determines the amount of current in the conductor

Retina [REHT-uhn-uh]: the surface on which light is focused at the back of the eye

Reverberation [rih-VUR-buh-RAY-shuhn]: the repeated reflection of sound waves from smooth surfaces in a large, unsoundproofed area, such as a gymnasium

Rhythm [RIHTH-uhm]: (of sound) the regular pattern of tones in a series or in groups

Ripple tank: a tank in which ripples, or small water waves, can be made for the purpose of studying the way water waves behave

Roll: the motion about the longitudinal axis of an airplane, a satellite, or any other vehicle

Rotor [ROHT-ur]: (in a Wankel engine) the triangular-shaped part that acts like a rotating piston

Rudder [RUHD-ur]: the part of the tail of an airplane which controls the yaw, or turning, of the airplane

S

Salt: a compound formed, along with water, when an acid and a base are mixed

Sanitary [SAN-uh-TEHR-ee] **landfill**: a place set aside for disposing of garbage by spreading out the garbage each day and covering it with a layer of soil

Satellite [SAT-uhl-YT]: an object that travels all the way around another object

Scientific [SY-uhn-TIHF-ihk] **law**: a statement about the way things happen in the world; sometimes called a law of nature

Scientific method [MEHTH-uhd]: an orderly way of solving problems that involves observing, measuring, explaining, and testing

Scrubber [SKRUHB-ur]: a device which cleans smoke by using steam and chemicals

Series [SIH(UH)R-eez] **circuit**: a circuit in which there is only one path for current to follow

Service panel: the place where the electricity coming into a home is separated into different circuits and where the fuses or circuit breakers are located; sometimes called a fuse box or circuit-breaker box

Sewage [SOO-ihj]: the waste material carried away by sewers

Sewage treatment [TREET-muhnt]: the changing of sewage into less harmful kinds of matter

Short circuit: a defect in a circuit which lowers the resistance of the circuit, increasing the current and

producing very hot wires and/or sparks which could start a fire

Slope [SLOHP]: the slant of a line or surface

Sludge [SLUHJ]: the solid matter which is allowed to settle out during secondary treatment of sewage after bacteria have been allowed to eat most of the organic matter in the sewage

Solar [SOH-lur] **cell**: a thin disk of silicon and other chemicals which produces a small amount of electricity when sunlight strikes the disk

Solid [SAHL-uhd]: a phase of matter in which the matter has a definite shape and a definite volume

Solution [suh-LOO-shuhn]: a mixture in which the different kinds of matter are not separately visible

Sound wave: a longitudinal wave that can produce the sensation of hearing

Soundproofing [SOWN(D)-PROOF-ihng]: a process of stopping sound waves that are not wanted

Speed: the rate of motion

Spontaneous [spahn-TAY-nee-uhs] **energy conversion**: an energy conversion which starts without another form of energy being used to start the conversion

Standing wave: a kind of wave in which certain parts of matter move rapidly while other parts do not move at all; a wave often formed when reflected waves interact with incoming waves

Starch [STAHRCH]: a substance made by green plants and stored in various parts of the plant

Stroke [STROHK]: (in a piston engine) each movement of a piston from one end of the cylinder to the other end

Substance [SUHB-stuhn(t)s]: a kind of matter in which every molecule in that matter is the same

T

Technology [tehk-NAHL-uh-jee]: the using of scientific discoveries to meet the needs of people

Temperature [TEHM-puh(r)-CHU(UH)R]: a measure of the average speed of the molecules in matter, characterized by the degree of hotness or coldness of the matter

Terminal [TURM-nuhl] **speed**: the maximum speed of a falling object due to the effect of air resistance

Theorist [THEE-uh-ruhst]: a scientist who works with facts, data, and ideas, as opposed to an experimentalist who collects data through observation and experimentation

Theory [THEE-uh-ree]: a principle or set of principles offered as an explanation of some observation or occurrence

Thermocouple [THUR-muh-KUHP-uhl]: a device consisting of two unlike metals that uses a difference in temperature to make electricity

Thrust: a force which moves an airplane forward

Transformer [tran(t)s-FAWR-mur]: a device that changes the voltage of alternating-current electricity

Transistor [tranz-IHS-tur]: an electronic device that can do the same job as an electron tube but is much smaller and uses only a small amount of power

Transparent [tran(t)s-PAR-uhnt]: a term used to describe a material through which a form of energy, such as light, will pass

Transverse [tran(t)s-VURS] **wave**: a wave in which particles of the medium move at right angles to, or across, the direction in which the wave moves

Trough [TRAWF]: the lowest point of a transverse wave

Turbine [TUR-buhn]: an engine in which gases or liquids push on sets of movable blades fastened to a shaft, causing the shaft to turn

U

Ultraviolet [UHL-truh-VY-uh-luht] **rays**: a form of radiant energy having shorter wave lengths than visible light and which may cause sunburn

Updraft [UHP-DRAFT]: an upward-moving current of air

V

Van de Graaff generator: a kind of electrostatic generator that can produce sparks that look like lightning

Vibrate [VY-BRAYT]: move back and forth

Virtual [VURCH-(uh-)wuhl] **image**: an image which appears to be behind a mirror or lens

Visible [VIHZ-uh-buhl] **light**: a form of radiant energy that you can see

Visible spectrum: all the colors of light, taken together, that make up white light

Voltage [VOHL-tihj]: the push that can cause negative charges to move from one object to another

Volume [VAHL-yuhm]: the amount of space a piece of matter takes up

W

Wankel [WAHNG-kuhl] **engine**: an internal-combustion engine that has a turning rotor instead of reciprocating pistons

Watt [WAHT]: a unit of power equal to a rate of one newton-metre of work done per second; often used to describe the rate at which electric energy is used by an appliance

Watt-hour: the amount of energy used when an appliance uses one watt of power for one hour

Wave length: the distance between any place on one wave and the same place on the next wave

Weight: the force of attraction (pull) between the earth and another object on or near the earth; also, the measure of the pull of gravity on an object

Weightlessness [WAYT-luhs-nuhs]: a term used to describe a condition in which an object in orbit seems to have no weight

Wimshurst machine: a kind of electrostatic generator used in some schools

Wing flap: a movable part on the rear of a wing which can be lowered to help increase the lift of the wing at low speeds

Work: a transfer of energy that occurs when a force acts on an object, causing the object to move while the force is acting on it

X

X rays: a form of radiant energy having shorter wave lengths than visible light and which penetrate many materials that visible light will not penetrate

Y

Yaw: the motion about the vertical axis of an airplane, a satellite, or any other vehicle

INDEX

A

Acceleration: definition of, 241; of falling objects, 241–242

Acid, 157

Acoustical engineer, 421, *ill.* 421

Acoustics, 418–420

"Action equals reaction," 237

Air pollution: causes of, 522–524, *ill.* 523; controlling, 526–527, 537, *ill.* 526, 537; definition of, 521–522; weather and, 524–526, *ill.* 524

Air pressure, effect on boiling point, 142

Air resistance: definition of, 242; effect on falling objects, 242–243

Airfoil, 508–510, *ill.* 508, 509

Airplane: control of, 510–512, *ill.* 511–512; engines, 505–506; first, 504–505; motions of, 511, *ill.* 511; pilots, 517; and science of flight, 506–512

Airship, 502, *ill.* 502

Algae, 529, *ill.* 529

Alloy, 112

Alpha particle, 162

Alpha ray, 161

Aluminum: and electrolysis, 354; uses of, 354

Ammeter, 313

Ampere, 312

Amplitude. *See* Wave amplitude.

Angle of attack, 509–510, *ill.* 509

Angle of incidence, 445

Angle of reflection, 445

Angstrom, 438

Animal electricity, 349–350

Aristotle, 77

Artificial light, 432

Artificial radioactivity: how caused, 182–183; used to study plants, 183–184; used to treat disease, 477

B

Atom: 107–108, 118–128, 160; energy levels of, 125–128, *ill.* 125–126; how they combine, 126–128; models of, 121–122, *ill.* 122; parts of, 120–121

Atomic mass, 123–124

Atomic mass unit, 124

Atomic number, 123

Atomic theory, 107

Attraction: between ions, 128; electric, 214, 291–292; gravitational, 46, 239; magnetic, 214, 329–331

B

Babbage, Charles, 542

Bacon, Francis, 14, *ill.* 14

Base, 157

Battery, 316, 353, 361, *ill.* 350

Bernoulli, Daniel, 508

Bernoulli's principle, 508–512, *ill.* 508

Beta particle, 162

Beta ray, 161

Binary numeral, 549–551, *ill.* 550

Biodegradable material, 534–535, *ill.* 534

Black, Joseph, 20

Blue litmus paper, 157

Boiling point, 142

British thermal unit (Btu), 135–136

Brownian movement, 144

Brownout, 380

Building inspector, 377

Buoyancy, 51–52, *ill.* 51

C

Calculator, 541–542, *ill.* 541

Calorie: 135–137; measure of food energy, 137; unit of heat, 135

Calorimeter: 136–137; bomb, *ill.* 137; water, *ill.* 136

Capacity: definition of, 40; in English-system units, 40; in SI units, 42, *ill.* 42

Carpenter, 53

Catalytic cracking unit, 173

Chain reaction: description of, 180; uncontrolled, 181, *ill.* 181; used to make electricity, 182

Charge collector, 295

Charging, 291, 296–297

Chemical cell, 350, *ill.* 350

Chemical change, 152, 155–157, 348, 350–351, 353

Chemical electricity, 351

Chemical energy, 213–215

Chemical engineering, 495, *ill.* 495

Chemicals: problems caused by use of, 189–190; used in farming, 188; used in making synthetic materials, 189

Chemist, 129

Chlorophyll: and green parts of plants, 175; and photosynthesis, 176

Circuit, 308

Circuit breaker, 375

Circuit breaker box. *See* Service panel.

Civil engineering, 492, *ill.* 492

Cloud chamber, 163, *ill.* 163

Cohesion, 145

Color: 436–440; complementary, 440; primary, 440; seeing, 440; as seen through colored objects, 437–438; visible spectrum, 436–437; wave lengths of, 438

Complementary colors, 440, *ill.* 440

Compound: 108, 110; kinds of, 157–159

Computer: arithmetic of, 549–551, *ill.* 550; codes, 551–552, *ill.* 552; history of, 541–543; how they work, 544–548; program for, 543, 545–548; programming, 553, *ill.* 553; uses of, 556–558

Computer programmer, 546, 548, 553, *ill.* 548
Concave lens, 453, 456, *ill.* 453
Concave mirror, 447, 449, *ill.* 449
Condensing, 147
Conductor, of electricity, 292, 310
Conservation of energy, 221
Conservation of mass, 221
Conservation of mass-energy, 223
Contact electricity, 350
Converging lens. *See* Convex lens.
Convex lens, 450–453, 456, *ill.* 451
Convex mirror, 449–450, *ill.* 450
Cosmic ray, 426, 461–462
Crest, of a wave, 388–389, 391, *ill.* 388–389
Cryolite, 354
Curie, Marie, 222, *ill.* 222
Current: alternating, 323–324; direct, 321–322; electric, 308
Cylinder, of an engine, 272

D

Dalton, John, *ill.* 107
Data processing, 541
Decibel, 413
Decimal numeral, 549–551, *ill.* 550
Density: definition of, 47, 140; determining, 48–49; effects of temperature on, 140; explaining, 46–47
Diesel engine, 278
Displacement, 49
Dissolve, 154
Distance-time graph: description of, 232, *ill.* 232, 241
Diverging lens. *See* Concave lens.
Drag, 507, *ill.* 506
Dry cell, 311, 352, *ill.* 352

E

Earthquake, 401
Echo, 420

Edison, Thomas, 483, *ill.* 483
Effort, definition of, 251
Einstein, Albert, 223
Electric appliance, 365, 370, *ill.* 370
Electric charge, 292, 296, 349
Electric energy: and attraction of matter, 214; and magnetism, 214, 337–344; measuring, 369–370; used in the home, 370; and voltage, 299
Electric meter, 371, *ill.* 371
Electric outlet, 368, *ill.* 368
Electric plug, 368, *ill.* 368
Electric service, 365–366
Electric shock, 372–373
Electrical engineer, 345
Electrical engineering, 496
Electrician, 377
Electricity: 289–377; alternating current, 323–324; animal, 349–350; charging with, 291–299; chemical, 348, 350–352; contact, 350; direct current, 321–323; generating plants, 380; lightning and, 301–304; and magnetism, 337–344; measuring, 312–314, 369–371; producing, 381–382; rules of safety, 376
Electrochemistry, 353
Electrode, 350, 351, 352, 354
Electrolysis, 353–354, 355, *ill.* 353
Electrolyte, 350, 352
Electromagnet, 339, 345
Electromagnetic spectrum, 426, 460–473, 476–478, *ill.* 426, 461. *See also* Radiant energy.
Electromagnetic wave, 426, 460, 461–462. *See also* Radiant energy.
Electron: description of, 120; sharing of, 127; transfer of, 127–128
Electron cloud, 123
Electron tube, 542–543, *ill.* 543
Electronic device, 496, 541–543
Electroplating, 355, 357, *ill.* 355
Electroscope, 295–297
Electrostatic generator, 300
Electrostatic precipitator, 527
Element, 108–110

Energy: 204–208, 213–224; changing kinetic to potential, 219; changing potential to kinetic, 207, 218–219; chemical, 213–215; conservation of, 221, 223; conversion of, 212, 217–220; definition of, 204; electric, 213–214; heat, 133, 213, 216–217; kinetic, 148, 205–208; magnetic, 213–214; mechanical, 213–214; nuclear, 213, 215; potential, 205–208; radiant, 213, 216, 424–440, 460–472; sound, 408; transfer by waves, 387; and voltage, 299
Energy conversion: definition of, 212; nonspontaneous, 218; spontaneous, 218
Energy levels: and electrons, 125, *ill.* 125, 126; used to explain how atoms combine, 126–128, *ill.* 127, 128
Engine: 268–285; airplane, 505–506; definition of, 269; diesel, 278; external-combustion, 269, 272–275; four-stroke cycle, 277–278, *ill.* 277; internal-combustion, 269, 275–280; problems caused by, 285–286; reaction, 279–280; reciprocating steam, 272–274, *ill.* 203, 272; steam turbine, 274–275, *ill.* 274; two-stroke cycle, 276–277, *ill,* 276; used in factories, 284; used in farming, 284; used in making electricity, 274–275, 284; Wankel, 278–279, *ill.* 279
Engineering: 488–496; branches of, 491–496; chemical, 495, *ill.* 495; civil, 492, *ill.* 492; definition of, 488; early wonders of, 491–492; electrical, 496; and flight of *Mariner 10,* 488–490; mechanical, 494; and technology, 482–496; today, 490–491
English system of units, 38–40
Equal-arm balance, 44–45, *ill.* 45
Eutrophication, 529, *ill.* 529
Evaporate, 57, 147–154
Exhaust, 276

Music: 414–418; compared to noise, 414, *ill.* 414; and percussion instruments, 417–418; and stringed instruments, 415–416, *ill.* 415; and wind instruments, 416, *ill.* 416

N

Natural light, 432
Natural magnet. *See* Lodestone.
Nearsightedness, 456, *ill.* 456
Negative charge: in charged objects, 292–294; and electric currents, 309–310; of electrons, 120
Neutral, 292
Neutron, 121
Newton, Sir Isaac, 234, 239, 436
Newton, unit of force, 197
Nitrogen, 178
Nitrogen fixing: 178–179; by bacteria, 178–179; by lightning, 178
Noise, 414
Nonluminous object, 432–433
Nuclear change: causing fission, 180; definition of, 160; types of radiation given off, 160–162, *ill.* 161
Nuclear energy, 213, 215
Nuclear power plant, 165, 181–182, 381, *ill.* 165, 215
Nuclear reaction, 180
Nuclear reactor, 165, 182–183, 477
Nucleus, 122

O

Observing: 10–29; air, 59–60; the scientific method as a guide to, 13–15; using instruments, 27–28; using the senses, 11–12; water, 57–59
Oersted, Hans Christian, 337
Ohm, 312, 313

Oil: from animals and plants, 169–170; from petroleum, 170–172
Opaque, 430–431, *ill.* 430
Optical illusion, 17, *ill.* 16, 17
Organic pollutants, 528–531
Overtone, 415–416, *ill.* 415
Output, 545–548
Oxide, 159

P

Parallel circuit: of bulbs, 318–319, *ill.* 318; of dry cells, 319–321, *ill.* 321
Particulates, 522–524, *ill.* 523
Pascal, Blaise, 542
Pendulum: conversion of kinetic energy to potential energy, 219–220; conversion of potential energy to kinetic energy, 219; description of, 219, *ill.* 219
Percussion instrument, 417–418, *ill.* 417
Permanent magnet. *See* Magnet.
Petroleum: formation of, 171; meaning of word, 169; refining of, 171–173; separating the substances of, 171–172; substances in, 171
Phase: definition of, 103; gas, 104–105; heat and changes in, 141–142; liquid, 104; solid, 103–104
Philosopher, 9, 77
Phlogiston, 88
Photosynthesis, 176
Physical change, 152–154
Piston, 272
Piston engine: diesel, 278; four-stroke cycle, 277–278, *ill.* 277; reciprocating steam, 272–274, *ill.* 272; two-stroke cycle, 276–277, *ill.* 276
Pitch: and frequency, 411; and hearing, 413; and music, 414–416
Pitchblende, 222
Plane mirror, 447

"Plum-pudding" model, 121–122, *ill.* 122
Pole, magnetic, 330
Pollution: air, 521–527; land, 533–536; and technology, 485–487; water, 527–532
Pollution-control device, 526–527, *ill.* 526
Positive charge: in charged objects, 292–294; of protons, 120
Potential energy, 205
Power: definition of, 199; of electric circuits, 314; measuring, 199–200; of people, 203; units of, 200–203
Predict: from observations, 76, 80; from theories, 84–85
Primary colors, 440, *ill.* 440
Properties: electric, 291; of gases, 104–105; general, 100; of liquids, 104; magnetic, 328–331, 336; of solids, 104; special, 99; and uses of matter, 102–103; using to identify matter, 100–102, 113
Protein: and nitrogen, 178; uses for, 178
Proton, 120
Pulley: description of, 249; fixed, 259–260; as a lever, 259–260, *ill.* 259; movable, 259–260
Pupil, of the eye, 454, *ill.* 454

Q

Quality, of sound, 414

R

Radar, 470–471, *ill.* 470
Radiant energy: effect on materials, 429–431; forms of, 216, 425–428; speed of, 428–429
Radiation: alpha, 161–162; beta, 161–162; cosmic, 426, 461;